A. Fidgett, M. Clauss, U. Gansloßer,
J.-M. Hatt, J. Nijboer
(eds.)

# Zoo Animal Nutrition

## Vol. 2



Filander Verlag
Fürth

Zoo Animal Nutrion, Vol. II / A. Fidgett, M. Clauss, U. Gansloßer, J.-M. Hatt, J. Nijboer (eds.). - Fürth: Filander Verlag, 2003
ISBN 3-930831-51-1

# Introduction

Keen to follow the success of the First European Zoo Nutrition Conference held in the Netherlands in 1999, plans for a second conference in the United Kingdom in 2001 were sadly curtailed by an outbreak of Foot and Mouth Disease in parts of the country that year.

The programme intended for the Second Conference promised to be diverse and stimulating. The volume and range of topics submitted for inclusion indicated that the subject of zoo animal nutrition required a forum within Europe. A dedicated group has now been established under the auspices of the European Association of Zoo and Aquaria (EAZA) to advance the study of nutrition within European zoos.

Proceedings from the First Conference were successfully published as Zoo Animal Nutrition, providing an accessible means of sharing information, and demonstrating the breadth of research being conducted, across Europe and beyond. Despite having to cancel the Second Conference, it was important not to lose the momentum generated, or the research that would have been presented. This second volume of Zoo Animal Nutrition represents a selection of the material that would have been presented and the editors extend their gratitude to all the authors who contributed papers.

The editors were largely responsible for reviewing the manuscripts published in this book but would like to thank several additional anonymous referees who assisted in the process. Organising a conference and publishing the proceedings requires the help of many individuals and organizations. We would particularly like to express our gratitude to Cologne Zoo, Rotterdam Zoo, Marwell Preservation Trust, Sparsholt College and the University of Southampton for their hospitality during planning meetings held there, and the EAZA Research Committee for their endorsement of the conference. Special mention must go to Peter Bircher (Marwell Preservation Trust) for his tireless efforts preparing for the Second Conference. Credit must also go to several additional institutions for their support in the production of this volume: North of England Zoological Society; Institute of Animal Physiology, Physiological Chemistry and Animal Nutrition, Veterinary Faculty of the LM-University Munich; Division of Zoo Animals and Exotic Pets, University of Zurich; Institute of Zoology, University of Erlangen-Nurnberg; Rotterdam Zoo.

It is the editors' sincere hope that readers find this second volume of papers useful as a reference and as a resource for improving the understanding of both free-ranging and captive wild animal nutrition. We look forward to future conferences with an aim to producing more volumes in this series, helping generate a reference library for this fascinating topic.

Dr. Andrea Fidgett

# Contents

*A. Bond*[1]

# A review of diets fed to two Columbiforme species at Bristol Zoo Gardens

***Abstract***

*When presented with a mixed diet, birds will preferentially select certain food items. It is therefore inappropriate to assess the nutritional content of diets offered to birds with the assumption that all of the nutrients are ingested in the proportions offered. This study used the nutrition software Zootrition (Zootrition™ 1999, Wildlife Conservation Society) to compare the nutritional content of diets offered and diets eaten by Mindanao bleeding heart doves (Gallicolumba criniger) and superb fruit doves (Ptilinopus superbus) at Bristol Zoo Gardens. The nutrients present in both the offered diet and the eaten diet were compared to recommended nutrient requirements for domestic pigeons (Brue 1994), the closest species for which nutrient requirements have been suggested.*

*For both species, large differences in composition between the diet offered and the diet eaten were identified. These differences were more marked in P. superbus suggesting that these birds are more selective in their food consumption. The change in composition of the diet as a result of selection caused the proportion of nutrients eaten to differ from the proportion offered. The more selective behaviour of P. superbus lowered the proportions of crude protein and crude fat in the diet by approximately 20 %. Conversely, the proportion of crude protein in the diet eaten by G. criniger was increased by 19 %, and the proportion of crude fat was increased by approximately 30 %.*

*Neither the nutrients offered to, nor the nutrients eaten by either species matched recommended nutrient levels for domestic pigeons. The health of both species and in particular, the breeding success of the G. criniger, suggests that nutrient recommendations for domestic pigeons are not an accurate representation of the nutrient requirements of these two species.*

## 1 Introduction

The Mindanao bleeding heart dove, *Gallicolumba criniger* (Pucheran 1853), is also referred to as Bartlett's dove or Hair-breasted pigeon (Birdlife International 2000). *G. criniger* lives in primary and secondary forest in the Philippines. There are three subspecies. *G. c. leytensis* (Hartert 1918) on Samar, Leyte and

[1] Department of Bioscience, Cardiff University & Bristol Zoo Gardens,

Bohol; *G. c. criniger* (Pucheran 1853) on Mindanao and Dinagat; and *G. c. bartletti* (P. L. Sclater 1863) on Basilan (Birdlife International, 2000). There is no available data on the wild diet of *G. criniger* but it is presumed to be similar to that of *G. luzonica,* which feeds on seeds, fallen berries, insects, worms and other invertebrates on the forest floor (Birdlife International, 2000). *G. criniger* has an IUCN (World Conservation Union) status of 'Endangered' because the global population is both small and declining (Birdlife International, 2000).

The distribution of the superb fruit dove, *Ptilinopus superbus* (Temminck, 1810), stretches from Sulawesi, through New Guinea and the surrounding islands, extending to coastal east Australia (Birdlife International, 2000). Two subspecies have been described. *P. s. temminckii* (Des Murs and Prévost 1849) is restricted to Sulawesi and Sulu Island whilst *P. s. supurbus* (Temminck 1810) occurs from the Island of Moluccas, through Papuan Island, New Guinea, the Solomon Islands to the east coast of Australia (Birdlife International 2000). It lives in a variety of forest habitats including mangroves and agro-forest (Birdlife International 2000). The diet of *P. superbus* is better studied than that of *G. criniger.* It is frugivorous, taking a variety of small to medium-sized fruits from families such as Lauraceae and Arecaceae. *P. superbus* most often feeds in the canopy and outer foliage, but also feeds in low trees, in understory and at the forest edge (Birdlife International 2000). *P. superbus* is listed as 'Not globally threatened' by IUCN (Birdlife International, 2000) but its' situation is more serious if we acknowledge the sub-species.

In captivity, birds are never left without food, since they have very high metabolic rates and this means that in practice they are fed an excess of food. By feeding a mixed diet of various fruits, grains and pulses in excess it is possible that the birds may select only one or two of the food items offered in order to satisfy their hunger. It is also possible that such selection could go unnoticed due to the high proportions of leftover food. If the items being selected by the birds do not create a balanced diet then the diet consumed by the birds will be poor, regardless of the quality of the diet that is offered to them. It is therefore inappropriate to assess the nutritional content of the diets offered to the birds, with the assumption that all of the nutrients are ingested in those proportions.

The aim of this study was to establish whether the two pigeon species are selective in their captive feeding habits, and to analyse how this selectivity affects the nutritional content of the diet consumed.

## 2 Method

Feeding trials were conducted during December. Four individuals were available for the study and these were housed in two off-show enclosures at the zoo, approximately 4 m long × 1.5 m wide × 2.5 m high. A pair of *G. criniger* were housed in one enclosure and a pair of *P. superbus* were housed in the other. Feeding trials took place over three consecutive days as part of a preliminary study into the diets consumed by a wide selection of species in the Zoo. A longer time frame could not be accommodated by this initial study.

Both species receive the same diet in the zoo (see table 1) since they are both pigeon species (family Collumbiformes). The Luzon bleeding heart dove (*G. luzonica*) also receives this diet.

**Table 1.** Pigeon diet at Bristol Zoo Gardens.

| **Product** | **Suppliers/ manufacturers** | **Description** |
|---|---|---|
| Apple | N/A | Chopped into 0.5mm² pieces (with peel) |
| Dried Mixed Fruit | 3663 | A mix of raisins, currants, sultanas and mixed peel. |
| Egg | N/A | Hardboiled then crushed (with shell) |
| Insectivorous mix | Witte-Molen | A 1:1 combination of two powdery mixes for insectivorous birds, one containing dried fruit, the other containing dried shrimp |
| Mazuri Diet A | Mazuri Zoo Foods | A diet supplement in crumb form |
| Mixed Corn | Farmcare feeds | 50% Wheat, 40% Maize, 10% Oats |
| Mixed Pulses | Versele-Laga | Junior O, Mixed feed for pigeons. Includes; Wheat, Dari, Maple Peas, Green Peas and Safflower. |
| Rice | N/A | White, cooked |
| Standard Budgie | Harrisons | One part canary seed, four parts white millet |
| Nutrobal | VetArk Professional | Vitamin and mineral powder supplement. (Ca:P ratio = 46:1) |

In order to establish what was eaten by the two pigeon species, individual food items of each feed were weighed before being placed into the enclosure in the morning, and the leftover feed was weighed the following morning when it was removed from the enclosure. The left over feed was then allowed to dry overnight in a warm room (20 °C) before the individual food items were separated. This drying period enabled a more accurate separation of the individual food items. Once separated, each food item was weighed, and by accounting for the water loss that had occurred during the drying process, an estimation of how much of each food item had been eaten was possible.

The powder supplement, Nutrobal, could not be separated from the left-over feed and weighed. Nutrobal was therefore weighed before being sprinkled onto the offered feed, and the amount of Nutrobal eaten was estimated using the total percentage of the offered feed that was eaten.

The estimated mass of each food item offered and the mass of each food item eaten were entered into Zootrition (Zootrition™ 1999). Zootrition is a software package developed by the Wildlife Conservation Society that can calculate the nutritional content of a diet, based on nutrient data contained within its database, if its constituents are known. The nutritional content of both the diet offered and the diet eaten by *P. superbus* and *G. criniger* were established using the software and changes in both the individual components of the diets as well as the nutritional content of the diets were analysed.

The occurrence of individual food items within each diet was summarised using the graphical format illustrated in figure 1, which shows theoretical data for species 'a' and species 'b'. Species 'a' has eaten 100 % of each food item offered. Species 'b' has eaten half of each food item offered. Neither animal has shown any preference for the different components of the feed.

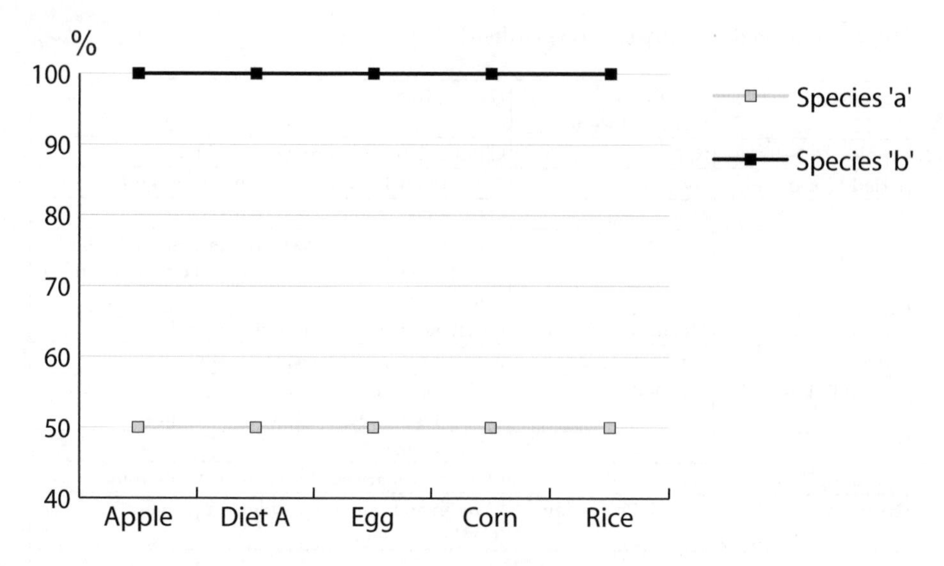


**Figure 1**. % feed consumed by species 'a' and species 'b'.

The nutrient data was presented as the percentage change in nutrient quantity from the offered diet to the eaten diet, so that a lower proportion of any nutrient in the eaten diet than the offered diet is indicated by a negative change.

## 3 Results

### *3.1 The selection of food items*

Figure 2 shows the average proportion of each food item that was eaten per day by the pair of *G. criniger* and the pair of *P. superbus*. The *G. criniger* were found to have eaten 80 % of the mixed corn and mixed pulse offered to them, but only 15 % of the dried mixed fruit that was offered to them. No food item was completely excluded from the diet, nor was any one food item entirely devoured. This suggests that *G. criniger* were not highly selective, yet they appear to show mild preferences for certain food items.

*P. superbus* were clearly much more selective. They ate 98 % of the mixed fruit that was offered to them and 86 % of the apple. They did not eat any of the mixed corn offered to them, and only 9 % of the insectivorous mix.

### *3.2 Effects of selectivity on the nutritional composition of the feed.*

By selecting more of one food item than another, the composition of the diet is altered. This alters the nutritional content of the diet. *G. crinigers'* selection of food increased the already high level of crude fat in the diet by over 25 %

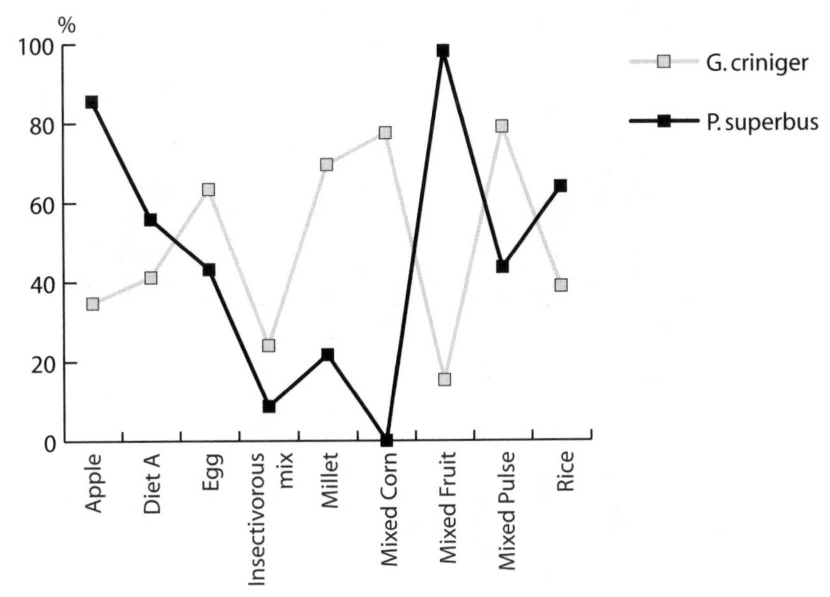


**Figure 2**. Average % of each food item eaten by the two pigeon species.

(from 6.09 $g^{-100g}$ to 7.69$g^{-100g}$) (see figure 3). This is because less low fat food items were eaten, such as apple and dried mixed fruit and more high fat food items, such as egg, millet, mixed corn and mixed pulse were eaten (see figure 3). These food items are also relatively high in fat and this is reflected in the crude protein content of the consumed diet, which was 19 % higher than in the offered diet.

Potassium levels were actually lower in the consumed diet than in the offered diet, because the biggest source of potassium in the diet was from the fruit items, much of which were left uneaten.

It is interesting that with the exception of potassium all of the nutrients occured in higher proportions in the eaten diet that in the offered diet. In contrast, the same graph for *P. superbus* (figure 4) shows that there was a decrease in the proportion of many of the nutrients, especially crude fat and crude protein. The exception is the very large increase in the potassium level, which was 35 % higher in the consumed diet than in the offered diet.

The change in nutrient levels can be explained by examining the food selection of *P. superbus*. The bulk of the consumed diet consisted of only one food group, fruit. In fact, 60 % of the eaten diet consisted of dried mixed fruit and apple. Both of these food items are very low in protein and fat, and very high in potassium. So it is *P. superbus'* selection for fruit items that dramatically decreased the proportions of crude fat and crude protein in the diet and increased the potassium level.

A comparison of figure 3 and figure 4 clearly shows that the more selective feeding of *P. superbus* has resulted in a general decrease in the proportions

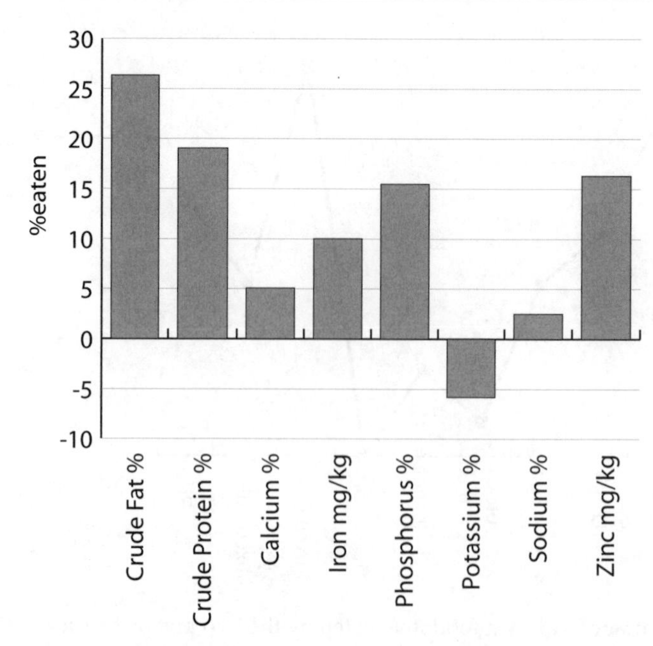


**Figure 3.** Nutrients present in the eaten diet of G.criniger expressed as a % change from the offered diet.

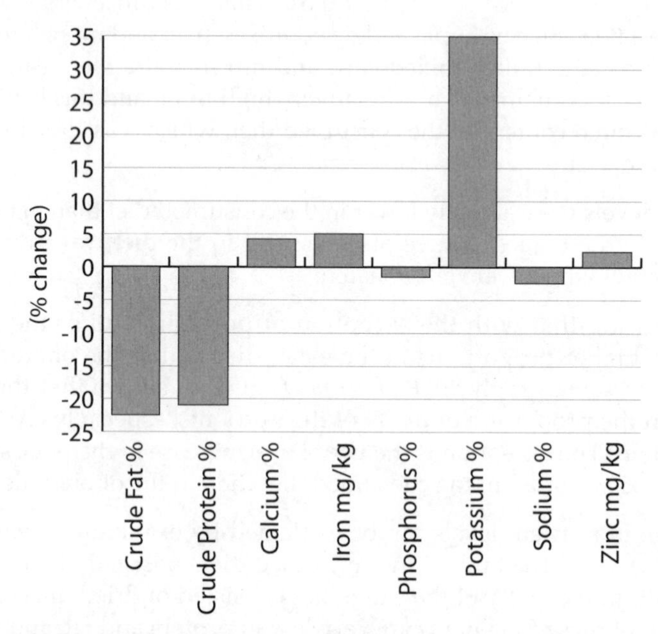


**Figure 4.** Nutrients present in the eaten diet of *P. superbus* expressed as a % change from the offered diet.

of certain nutrients in the diet, particularly crude fat and crude protein. Interestingly, Bristol Zoo is much more successful with *G. criniger* than with

*P. superbus*. The *P. superbus* are not as healthy as the *G. criniger*, nor do they breed. The more extreme selectivity of *P. superbus*, and resulting lower intake of protein and fat might play a part in this.

### 3.3 Analysing the quality of the diet.

Since there are no recommended diets available at present for *G. criniger* or *P. superbus*, the nutritional content of the diets consumed have been compared to the nutritional requirements of a domestic pigeon (figure 5). This is not ideal as domestic species have different nutritional requirements to wild species. In the case of racing pigeons, the nutritional requirements are likely to be higher than those of wild species, due to the high physiological demands of racing. Furthermore, domestic pigeons are granivorous, whilst the diet of *G. criniger* and *P. superbus* is somewhere between frugivorous and omnivorous. Hence efforts to match the zoo diets to the domestic pigeon nutrient recommendations would be inappropriate. However, until nutritional data becomes available for a wild and more frugivorous pigeon species, domestic pigeons provide the best available reference species and comparisons between the bird diets and the nutritional requirements of domestic pigeons may aid the analysis of the bird diets by a nutritionist.

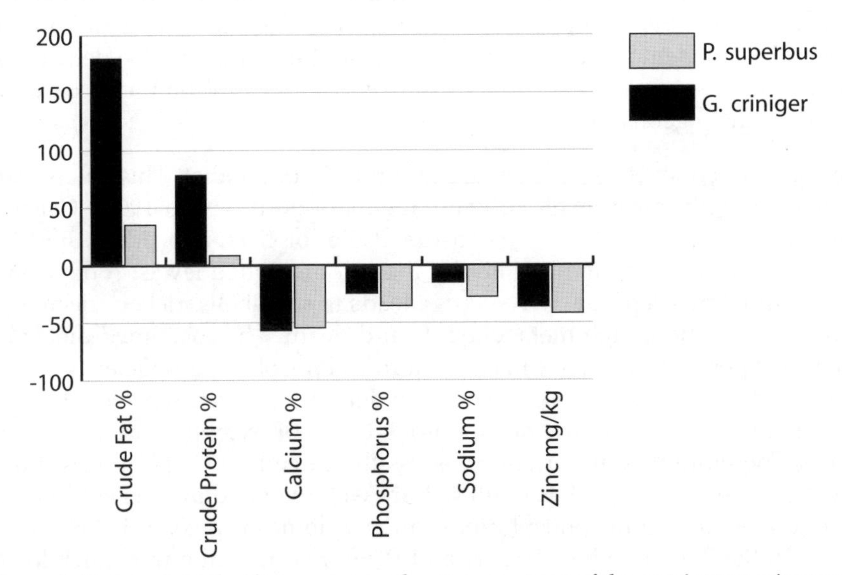


**Figure 5.** Nutrients in the diets consumed as a percentage of the nutrient requirements of a domestic pigeon.

## 4 Discussion

Accurately measuring the consumed diet of bird species is particularly problematic since a) they do not eat all of the food items they are offered, and b) their diet consists of very small food items such as pulses and grains, making the separation and identification of leftover food difficult. Presenting different components of the diet in separate dishes was found to affect the feeding behaviour of the birds, causing food to be eaten more selectively. Furthermore, the large number of dishes needed to feed all of the food items separately increased the events of dishes being knocked over or tipped into the water bowl, thus preventing data collection. Hence feeds were offered as a mixture and leftover food was dried out to enable the components to be separated sufficiently.

Despite the dearth of good comparative nutritional data, the nutritional content of the consumed diets of *G. criniger* and *P. superbus* were analysed in relation to their health by considering possible toxicities or deficiencies in the diet when compared to the recommended nutrient intake of a domestic pigeon.

Crude fat and crude protein both appeared at higher levels in the diet of the study species than the recommended levels for domestic pigeons. This was much more marked in the diet of *G. criniger* which consumed over 175 % of the recommended value of crude fat, and over 75 % of the recommended value of crude protein. The levels of crude fat and crude protein in the diet of *P. superbus* were much lower, at 35 % and 9 % of the recommended values respectively. Excess crude fat or crude protein in the diet may lead to obesity. More importantly it may alter the birds intake of the diet by lowering the total mass consumed. The fact the *G. criniger* are healthier and breed more successfully than *P. superbus* at Bristol Zoo Gardens may suggest that fat and protein levels are sufficient in the diet of *G. criniger* and may possibly be deficient in the diet of *P. superbus*, despite being above that of the recommended values for domestic pigeons.

Recommended levels of calcium are around 1 % of the diet. This level is controversial, with lower levels proving adequate (Roudybush 1996). Calcium formed only 0.43–0.45 % of the consumed diet of *G. criniger* and *P. superbus*, therefore occurring in the diet at half the recommended levels. A deficiency in calcium limits reproductive success, leads to soft shells, rickets, decreased food consumption, high metabolic rate and death. The consumed diets also showed a possible deficiency in phosphorous. Phosphorous deficiency results in similar symptoms to those of a calcium deficiency. A deficiency in phosphorous may occur due to low phosphorous levels or excess calcium, and vice versa. Therefore it is important to assess the calcium: phosphorous ratio of the diet. Ratios between 1.4 : 1 and 4 : 1 are well tolerated in chickens and the recommended calcium: phosphorous ratio for domestic pigeons is 1.6 : 1(Brue, 1994). In the diet of both *G. criniger* and *P. superbus* the ratio was much lower than recommended and an increase in calcium may be required as opposed to a decrease in phosphorous. This could be provided through supplementation with ground cuttlebone.

Sodium and zinc were also present in the consumed diets at levels lower than those recommended for domestic pigeons and this may be a possible cause for concern. Decreased egg production and slow growth are symptoms of a dietary sodium deficiency, whilst even moderate deficiencies in zinc can lead to retarded growth, frayed feathers, lower egg production and hatchability and a decreased appetite. Both these minerals could be increased in the diet since excess sodium is readily excreted and excess zinc can be tolerated due to efficient regulation of zinc absorption. It would be advisable to consider supplementing zinc in particular since the consumed diets contained approximately 28mg/kg of zinc yet the recommended amount for domestic pigeons is 50mg/kg and adult chickens can usually tolerate zinc at levels up to 2g/Kg (Klasing, 1998).

Comparative data for recommended iron values were not found. Iron was present in the consumed diet of both *G. criniger* and *P. superbus* at a level of 55 mg/kg of feed. There is no record of iron storage disease in either of the pigeon species and this level of iron is comparable to iron levels in the diets of softbills at the zoo such as toucans (45 mg Fe/Kg feed), who are fed a low iron diet as they are known to be susceptible to iron storage disease.

The nutrients present in the diet eaten are not necessarily absorbed and utilised by the animal in the same proportions as they present. Therefore, it is important to consider the complex interrelationships between vitamins and minerals when assessing the nutritional content of diets. For example, the calcium: phosphorous ratio that is absorbed by a bird depends on the availability of Vitamin D since this vitamin regulates calcium: phosphorous homeostasis in birds (Shafey 1993).

Finally, the nutritional analysis of the diets offered to and eaten by *G. criniger* and *P. superbus* have been based on data contained within Zootrition™, with the exception of 'Diet A' for which nutritional data was supplied by the manufacturers. The nutritional data provided above is therefore only the potential nutrient composition of the diet. Independent chemical analysis of food items, to compare values found within Zootrition to actual values, would be required to ascertain the actual nutrient composition of the diet and thereby verifying the actual contribution of a particular food item to a particular nutrient. Such an analysis may be advisable before any major alterations to a diet are made.

## 5 Conclusion

There is not at present sufficient data with which to compare these bird diets in order to establish whether they are 'good' diets or 'bad' diets since information of nutrient requirements or recommendations is currently limited to a few, mostly domestic species. Further research into the nutritional needs of non-domestic animals is therefore much needed. Research into the actual diets consumed by species such as *P. superbus* and *G. criniger* will be more feasible in captive birds as their environment can be more easily controlled and manipulated and may therefore be the immediate focus of nutritional studies. However, knowledge of wild diets is extremely limited and require further research attention if a naturalistic diet is to be developed for these pigeon species.

The absolute nutritional requirements for rare species are not known, and are not likely to be discovered since individuals are too valuable to be sacrificed for such experiments. However, the pooling of nutritional details of diets consumed both in captivity and in the wild, alongside the corresponding health of the individuals, will enable the nutritional requirement of a species to be derived. Analysis of both successful diets and of diets which have caused specific health problems will be equally valuable to the process.

Despite the very limited time frame of this study, and the use of only published composition values as opposed to direct chemical analyses, a great variety in the dietary habits of two pigeon species has been recognized. In most captive situations these two species would be grouped together for diet formulation purposes and yet it is clear that the more frugivorous nature of *P. superbus* has led to a greater degree of selectivity, resulting in a reduced intake of crude fat and crude protein in the consumed diet than the offered diet. This may have serious health implications for both the longevity and breeding success of *P. superbus*. The results of this study suggest a possible need for an even more species-specific approach to diet formulation, and recognition that selective feeding can significantly alter the nutritional composition of an offered diet.

## Acknowledgements

I would like to thank Duncan Bolton (Curator, Bristol Zoo Gardens), Dr. John Young (Project supervisor, Cardiff University), Sharon Redrobe (Hons) BVetMed CertLAS MRCVS (Veterinary officer, Bristol Zoo Gardens) and all the keeping staff at Bristol Zoo Gardens for their guidance and support during the course of this study.

## References

BirdLife International (2000): *Threatened birds of the world*. Lynx Edicions and BirdLife International, Barcelona and Cambridge, UK.

Brue, R. (1994): Chapter 3: Nutrition. In: *Avian Medicine, Principles and Applications*. (B. Ritchie, G. Harrison, L. Harrison, eds.). Wingers Publishing Inc., pp. 63–95.

Roudybush, T. (1996): Chapter 15: Nutrition. In: *Diseases of Cage and Aviary Birds*, 3rd Edition. (W. Rosskopf, R. Woerpel, eds.). Williams and Wilkins, pp. 218–234.

Shafey, T. M. (1993): Calcium tolerance of growing chickens – effect of ratio of dietary calcium to available phosphorous. *World's Poultry Science Journal* 49: 5–18.

Zootrition © (1999) Wildlife Conservation Society. Written by Island Business Group Inc.

M. Clauss[1], E. Kienzle[1], H. Wiesner[2]

# Feeding browse to large zoo herbivores: how much is "a lot", how much is "sufficient"?

*Abstract*

*Diet evaluations in captive browsers are often confounded by the fact that the amount of browse offered is difficult to quantify, especially if whole branches are fed. For a diet survey in captive moose (Alces alces), we established correlations between the diameter at point of cutting of a branch and the amount of foliage and edible twigs on it. Nine different species of trees were investigated. The correlations were allometric, and highly significant. For all tree species combined, e.g., the correlations of the total weight of a branch ($y_1$) and the weight of its leaves ($y_2$) with the diameter at point of cutting (x) were $y_1 = 0.84\ x^{1.94}$ and $y_2 = 0.48\ x^{2.48}$, respectively. Given the according equations, it was only necessary to measure the diameter of the branches fed in the institutions that participated in the diet survey. Examples are given for diet evaluations based on the estimation of edible browse derived from the equations.*

*Keywords*

*foliage, twigs, bark, moose (Alces alces), weight-diameter correlation*

## 1 Introduction

Large zoo herbivores are fed a diet that consists of a ration of trough feeds, i.e. pellets, fruits, vegetables etc., the quantity of which is generally more or less accurately known, of hay, and of additional browse (Oftedal et al. 1996). While hay is generally given *ad libitum*, the amount of browse offered is mostly limited, due to logistic reasons, or because it is not regarded as important. For many zoos, especially those situated in a city environment, browse is hard to come by. Additionally, browse takes time to cut, and is difficult to transport and store (Oftedal et al. 1996).

[1] Institute of Animal Physiology, Physiological Chemistry and Animal Nutrition, Ludwig-Maximilians-University, Munich, Germany. Corresponding author: Marcus Clauss, Institute of Animal Physiology, Physiological Chemistry and Animal Nutrition, Veterinaerstr. 13, 80539 Muenchen, Germany, FAX ++49 89 2180 3208, clauss@tiph.vetmed.uni-muenchen.de

[2] Zoological Garden »Hellabrunn«, Munich, Germany

While the opportunistic provision of browse is, for most zoo herbivores, mostly a question of behavioral enrichment (Oftedal et al. 1996), there are some species for which the provision of sufficient amounts of browse is regarded as a crucial factor for a successful captive management. For example, it has been repeatedly postulated that moose (*Alces alces*) cannot be kept successfully without fair amounts of browse (Crandall 1964, Schwarz 1992, Shochat et al. 1997). Other examples of animals who benefit decisively from browse feeding are eland (*Taurotragus oryx*) (Edwards 1999) or even the grazer muskoxen (*Ovibos moschatus*) (Boyd et al. 1996). For a more detailed discussion about the importance of browse for browsing ruminants, see Clauss et al. (this volume).

The obvious question is, how much browse is enough, and how do you measure that amount? In the literature, the occasional recommendation can be found that is mostly not particularly helpful: "2–4 branches, each 2 meters long" (Kuehme 1974); "20 pounds of twigs" (Patenaude 1978); "at least 3 kg browse material per moose and day" (Sperlich 1980); "at least 4 kg edible browse material, i. e. 12 kg total branch weight" (Ritscher 1990). The last recommendation hints at the common problem in describing the amount of browse fed: most of the material offered cannot be used by the animals.

While preparing a survey on the feeding practice in moose husbandry (Clauss et al. 1999), preliminary interviews with moose keepers from different facilities revealed that, while many were convinced that they fed a "sufficient amount" of browse, the actual amounts observed seemed to differ enormously. In order to evaluate the influence of the feeding regime on the body score and health parameters, the proportion of browse in the actual diet ration had to be quantified, and therefore a method to measure offered browse was warranted.

First attempts revealed that neither the length of a branch nor its weight were reliably correlated to the amount of foliage and edible twigs it carried. Thus, we finally chose to adapt a method that had been used in studies of free-ranging beaver (*Castor canadensis*) (Fryxell and Doucet 1991), where the amount of foliage, edible twigs, and bark was related to the diameter of the branch at the point of cutting. The results allowed us to estimate the amount of browse fed to moose at different facilities and calculate recommendations for the quantity of browse that should be offered to this species.

## 2 Materials and methods

Branches from different tree species were cut by hand with a saw in the forests around Munich, Bavaria, Germany, in July 1997. Branches were cut late in the evening, mostly after sunset, transported by car for about one hour, and stored erect over night outside with the cut ends in buckets filled with water.

Only branches that were cut once were investigated, i.e. from the point of cutting onwards the branches were intact. To our experiences, this simulated the feeding practice of moose facilities quite well.

We investigated two species of willow (*Salix caprea, Salix alba*), beech (*Fagus sylvatica*), ash (*Fraxinus excelsior*), birch (*Betula pubescens*), maple (*Acer pseudoplatanus*), hazel (*Corylus cornuta*), and two species of oak (*Quercus rubra, Quercus robur*). These tree species were selected according to the interviews led previously with moose keepers from different facilities.

All branches were processed within 12 hours after cutting. The diameter at the point of cutting was determined to the nearest millimeter using calipers. Most branches were not exactly circular; therefore, an average diameter was calculated from the lowest and the highest diameter measurement taken on a branch. The foliage was removed by hand, including the stems, and weighed on an electronic scale to the nearest gram. The edible portion of the twigs was removed and weighed. The "edibility" of a twig had been determined by measuring the diameter of twigs that a group of captive moose at the Tierpark Hellabrunn, Munich, had plucked off branches. For the willow species, the bark was peeled off the branch and weighed. Other tree species were not peeled, as previous experience had shown that moose engage in bark peeling mostly on willow branches. The remaining rest of the branch was weighed as well; the total weight of the whole branch "as cut" was calculated by adding the weights of the individual items. Subsamples of foliage, twigs and willow bark were taken to determine dry matter (DM) by drying in an oven at 103 °C for 12 hours, and to determine crude fiber content according to Naumann and Bassler (1988). It was logistically not possible to determine the dry matter content of the whole branches themselves.

The data were correlated using Excel software. An allometric function was expected to provide the closest correlation. The significance of the results was controlled by the Pearson's correlation coefficient.

In order to control for the delay between cutting and processing, the dry matter content in the leaves of two maple branches after 12, 24 and 48 hours after cutting was compared. Both branches (diameters app. 30 mm) were stored in the shade; one was standing in a bucket of water, the other was standing on the ground. On the two days of this experiment, midday temperatures were between 25–28 °C in the shade.

## 3 Results

The results of the regression analyses of branch diameter and the according fresh and dry matter weights of leaves, twigs and bark are presented in table 1. All correlations were statistically significant ($p \leq 0.0001$). A comparison of total and foliage weight, as shown for *Salix alba* in figure 1, demonstrates that, with increasing diameter, the total weight of the branch increases much faster than the weight of its leaves.

The comparison of the maple leaves from a watered and a dryly stored branch show that after 12 hours, there was no difference in water content of the leaves; after 2 days, however, the leaves of the branch stored without water had lost about half of their water content (figure 2).

**Table 1.** Allometric functions of the correlation of diameter at point of cutting (mm; x) of a branch and the fresh weight (*fw*) and dry matter (DM) in *g* (y) of its leaves, twigs, bark and total weight for several tree species. All correlations are significant at $p \leq 0.0001$.

| Species | Material | *n* | **$fw(g) = a\ (mm)^b$** | $DM(g) = a\ (mm)^b$ | $r^2$ |
|---|---|---|---|---|---|
| **Willow** | Leaves | 19 | $y = 2.52 * x^{1.68}$ | $y = 0.800 * x^{1.68}$ | 0.84 |
| (*Salix caprea*) | Twigs | 19 | $y = 1.19 * x^{1.69}$ | $y = 0.577 * x^{1.69}$ | 0.75 |
| | Bark | 19 | $y = 0.08 * x^{2.47}$ | $y = 0.037 * x^{2.47}$ | 0.96 |
| | Whole branch | 19 | $y = 0.89 * x^{2.33}$ | | 0.96 |
| **Willow** | Leaves | 23 | $y = 0.59 * x^{2.05}$ | $y = 0.199 * x^{2.05}$ | 0.88 |
| (*Salix alba*) | Twigs | 23 | $y = 0.30 * x^{2.07}$ | $y = 0.137 * x^{2.07}$ | 0.86 |
| | Bark | 23 | $y = 0.12 * x^{2.35}$ | $y = 0.052 * x^{2.35}$ | 0.95 |
| | Whole branch | 23 | $y = 1.08 * x^{2.26}$ | | 0.97 |
| **Beech** | Leaves | 25 | $y = 4.12 * x^{1.33}$ | $y = 1.524 * x^{1.33}$ | 0.58 |
| (*Fagus sylvatica*) | Twigs | 25 | $y = 0.61 * x^{1.69}$ | $y = 0.259 * x^{1.69}$ | 0.86 |
| | Whole branch | 14 | $y = 0.64 * x^{2.37}$ | | 0.88 |
| **Birch** | Leaves | 8 | $y = 1.02 * x^{1.83}$ | $y = 0.428 * x^{1.83}$ | 0.95 |
| (*Betula* | Twigs | 8 | $y = 0.15 * x^{2.25}$ | $y = 0.071 * x^{2.25}$ | 0.97 |
| *pubescens*) | Whole branch | 8 | $y = 0.63 * x^{2.33}$ | | 0.99 |
| **Maple** | Leaves | 25 | $y = 0.22 * x^{2.47}$ | $y = 0.093 * x^{2.47}$ | 0.89 |
| (*Acer pseudo-* | Twigs | 25 | $y = 0.22 * x^{1.82}$ | $y = 0.111 * x^{1.82}$ | 0.49 |
| *platanus*) | Whole branch | 10 | $y = 0.22 * x^{2.73}$ | | 0.92 |
| **Ash** | Leaves | 20 | $y = 0.53 * x^{2.09}$ | $y = 0.178 * x^{2.09}$ | 0.69 |
| (*Fraxinus* | Twigs | 20 | $y = 0.03 * x^{2.05}$ | $y = 0.014 * x^{2.05}$ | 0.81 |
| *excelsior*) | Whole branch | 20 | $y = 0.49 * x^{2.43}$ | | 0.93 |
| **Oak** | Leaves | 17 | $y = 1.06 * x^{1.80}$ | $y = 0.430 * x^{1.80}$ | 0.81 |
| (*Quercus robur*) | Twigs | 17 | $y = 0.47 * x^{1.84}$ | $y = 0.212 * x^{1.84}$ | 0.91 |
| | Whole branch | 17 | $y = 0.71 * x^{2.33}$ | | 0.90 |
| **Oak** | Leaves | 20 | $y = 0.87 * x^{1.95}$ | $y = 0.350 * x^{1.95}$ | 0.77 |
| (*Quercus rubra*) | Whole branch | 20 | $y = 0.23 * x^{2.73}$ | | 0.95 |
| **Hazel** | Leaves | 39 | $y = 0.54 * x^{2.10}$ | $y = 0.196 * x^{2.10}$ | 0.94 |
| (*Corylus* | Twigs | 39 | $y = 0.21 * x^{2.09}$ | $y = 0.097 * x^{2.09}$ | 0.97 |
| *cornuta*) | Whole branch | 39 | $y = 0.45 * x^{2.51}$ | | 0.98 |
| All species | Leaves | | *$y = 0.84 * x^{1.94}$* | *$y = 0.315 * x^{1.94}$* | *0.82* |
| | Whole branch | | *$y = 0.48 * x^{2.48}$* | *$y = 0.224 * x^{2.48}$* | *0.95* |

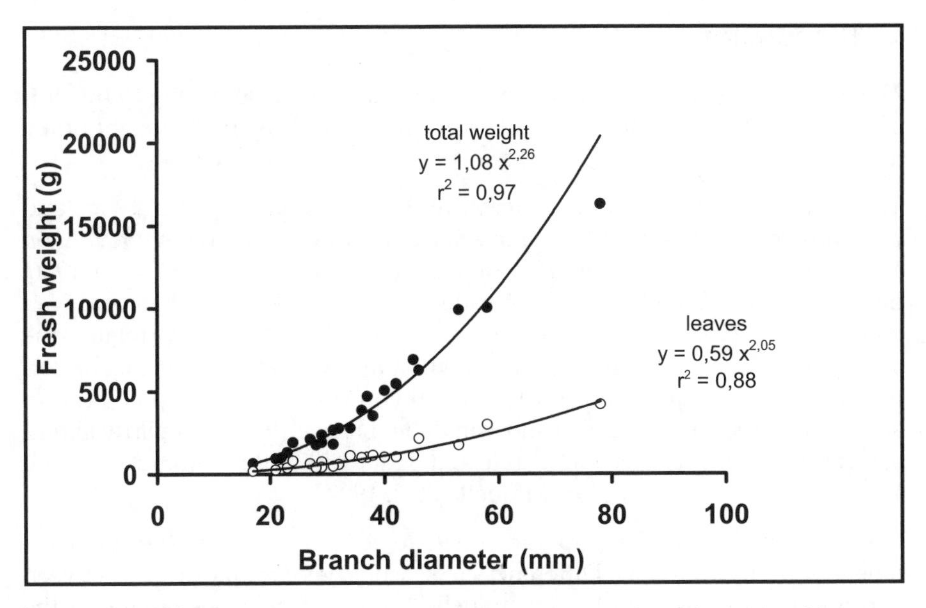


**Figure 1.** Comparison of the increase of total branch weight and weight of leaves in relation to the diameter of the branch at point of cutting. Data for *Salix alba* branches.

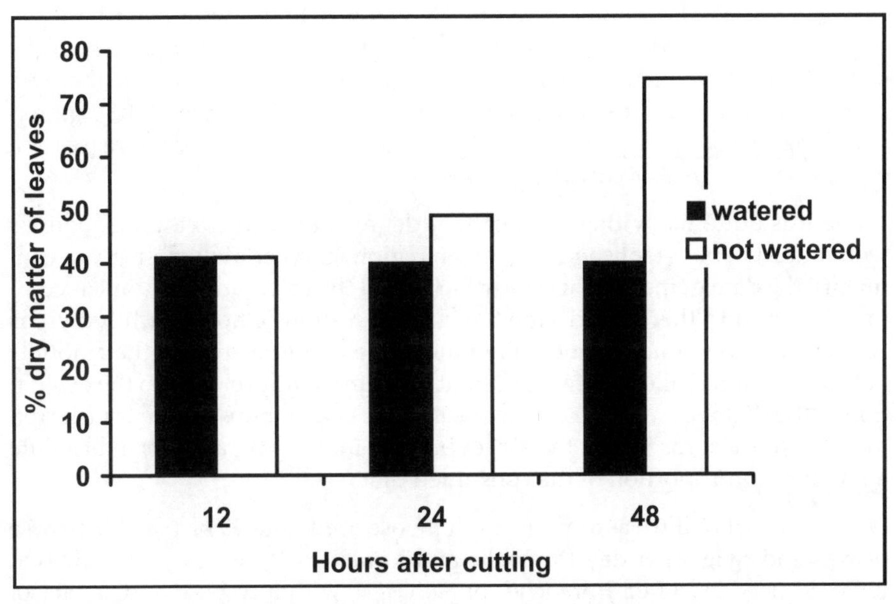


**Figure 2.** Dry matter content of leaves from maple branches stored in and without water.

## 4 Discussion

The overnight delay in working on the cut branches is, according to the outcome of the storage trial, unlikely to have influenced the fresh weight of the leaves.

There are many reports in the literature that the total weight of twigs and branches correlates with the diameter at point of cutting (Telfer 1969, Lyon 1970, Peek et al. 1971, Crete and Bedard 1975, Schewe and Stewart 1986, Bergström and Danell 1987, Miquelle et al. 1992, MacCracken and Van Ballenberghe 1993). However, we found no publication that correlated the amount of foliage and twigs separately with the diameter of a branch. The correlations demonstrated were partly linear (Lyon 1970, Peek et al. 1971, Schewe and Stewart 1986, MacCracken and Van Ballenberghe 1993), and partly allometric, as in our data (Telfer 1969, Crete and Bedard 1975, Bergström and Danell 1987, Fryxell and Doucet 1991, Miquelle et al. 1992 ).

MacCracken and Van Ballenberghe (1993) extensively discuss the problems inherent in this approach. Differences in seasons, geographic origin, between current year's growth and older branches, and differing positioning of the branch on a tree (top or side) are recognized as sources of deviation from an established equation. While Peek et al. (1971) claim that for some tree species, geographical differences can be too distinct to allow transfer between regions, Schewe and Stewart (1986) and MacCracken and Van Ballenberghe (1993) found that such a transfer is valid. In our data, it is obvious that tree phenotype influences the outcome of the regression analysis. Ash, e. g., has very long leaf stems and only few thin twigs, and the slope of the regression equation for twigs is accordingly low.

While it is quite likely that for a certain degree of exactness these equations would need to be established for a given region (and certainly for a given continent), the data gained in this study facilitated the calculation of some recommendations and therefore decide the initial question of how much browse is "a lot", and how much is not really much. The quantification of the amounts of browse offered allowed two different conceptual approaches to the evaluation of the diets presented to the moose. These calculations can be transferred to other species, for which the target browse intake might differ in absolute amount or in proportion of the consumed diet.

On the one hand, if we assume an adult moose to require 25 kg of fresh browse (leaves and twigs) per day (Miquelle and Jordan 1979), we can calculate that it would need 26, 14 or 9 branches of *Salix alba*, with a respective diameter of 30, 40 or 50 mm (Table 2). The total weight of branches offered would differ between 60 and 67 kg. Although one would need fewer branches of larger diameter, their total weight would be higher than that of the more numerous and smaller branches. The weight, and the number, of branches therefore are no good indicators of the amount of edible browse offered. As this calculation does not account for any additional trough feeds, this amount of browse would surely be "a lot". If one would aim at providing the 25 kg of fresh material from leaves only, the necessary quantity would be even higher.

**Table 2.** Calculation of the number and weight of branches needed to meet the food requirement of a moose entirely from browse (total daily browse consumption according to Miquelle and Jordan 1979; browse regression equations for leaves and twigs for all tree species from Table 1).

| Target amount fresh weight (kg) | branches Ø 30 mm number/total weight (kg) | branches Ø 40 mm number/total weight (kg) | branches Ø 50 mm number/total weight (kg) |
|---|---|---|---|
| 25 (leaves and twigs) | 26/60.5 | 14/64.2 | 9/67.1 |
| 25 (leaves only) | 40/93.5 | 22/99.3 | 14/104.1 |

On the other hand, we can take trough feeds into account. For captive ruminants (Elze et al. 1978), as for domestic ruminants (Kamphues et al. 1999), a crude fiber content of 18–20 % DM is recommended, of which two thirds should consist of coarse material of typical "fiber structure". Transferring this to a browsing ruminant, and one that is additionally known to thrive poorly on hay and not consume significant amounts of it (Bo and Hjeljord 1991), we can evaluate the diet by checking whether a) it contains crude fiber at about 20 % DM and b) whether two thirds of this fiber are derived from leaves. An according calculation is presented in Table 3, assuming a target dry matter intake of a 300 kg moose to be 2 % of body weight in dry matter (6 kg). An amount of 7 branches of 50 mm diameter would be "sufficient" to meet these recommendations, if leaves only are calculated. If one keeps 3 moose, this means a total weight of about 160 kg of branches per day.

While it cannot be expected that keepers check the diameters of the branches they cut every day, we suggest that the method of establishing diameter-foliage weight correlations is a useful tool in zoo animal dietary management, and that intermittent checks by this method of the amount of browse offered can help control a feeding regime and develop estimating abilities as to how much should be fed. For example, our calculations demonstrate that a "sufficient" amount of browse for 3 moose is more than can be carried by one person in one go.

**Table 3.** Calculation of a "sufficient" amount of browse for moose. Assumed crude fiber content of leaves 20 % DM; assumed DM content of leaves 35 % of OS. Browse regression equations used from Table 1 for leaves only. See text for further explanations.

| Target DM intake (kg) | of which 20 % crude fiber (kg) | of which 2/3 (kg) | corresponds to DM of leaves (kg) | corresponds to OS of leaves (kg) | branches Ø 30 mm number/ total weight (kg) | branches Ø 40 mm number/ total weight (kg) | branches Ø 50 mm number/ total weight (kg) |
|---|---|---|---|---|---|---|---|
| 6 | 1.2 | 0.8 | 4.0 | 11.4 | 19/41.0 | 11/47.9 | 7/54.0 |

## Conclusions

1. It was demonstrated with 9 tree species that is is possible to reliably correlate the diameter at the point of cutting of a branch with the amount of foliage and edible twigs on it.

2. We suggest that the most feasible way to measure the amount of browse offered is to measure the diameter of a branch and calculate the amount of foliage and twigs with the according equation. Such equations for different browse species could be a useful tool in diet design, evaluation and in developing estimating skills for keeping personnell.

## References

Bergström, R.; Danell, K. (1987): Moose winter feeding in relation to morphology and chemistry of six tree species. *Alces* 22: 91–112.

Bo, S.; Hjeljord, O. (1991): Do continenntal moose ranges improve during cloudy summers? *Can. J. Zool.* 69: 1875–1879.

Boyd, C. S.; Collins, W. B.; Urness, P. J. (1996): Relationship of dietary browse to intake in captive muskoxen. *J. Range Manage.* 49: 2–7.

Clauss, M.; Kienzle, E.; Wiesner, H. (1999): A survey on health and nutrition of captive moose in Europe. *Nutrition Advisory Group Conf. Proc.* 3: 64–77.

Clauss, M.; Kienzle, E.; Hatt, J.-M. (2003): Feeding practice in captive wild ruminants: peculiarities in the nutrition of browsers/concentrate selectors and intermediate feeders. A review. (this volume)

Crandall, S. L. (1964): *Management of Wild Animals in Captivity*. Chicago: University of Chicago Press.

Crête, M.; Bédard, J. (1975): Daily browse consumption by moose in the Gaspé peninsula, Quebec. *J. Wildl. Manage.* 39: 368–373.

Edwards, M. (1999): Nutritional management of acute and chronic bloat in Eastern giant eland. *Nutrition Advisory Group Conf. Proc.* 3: 25–29.

Elze, K.; Krische, G.; Eulenberger, K.; Schüppel, K. F. (1978): Pansenazidose und Pansenalkalose bei Zoowiederkäuern. *Verh. Ber. Erkr. Zootiere* 20: 101–107.

Fryxell, J. M.; Doucet, C. M. (1991): Provisioning time and central-place foraging in beavers. *Can. J. Zool.* 69: 1308–1313.

Kamphues, H.; Schneider, D.; Leibetseder, J. (1999): *Supplemente zu Vorlesungen und Übungen in der Tierernährung*. Alfeld-Hannover, Germany: M. & H. Schaper.

Kuehme, W. (1974): Klauenpflege beim Nord-Elch. *Zschrft. Kölner Zoo* 17: 23–28.

Lyon, L. J. (1970): Length- and weight-daimeter relations of serviceberry twigs. *J. Wildl. Manage.* 34: 456–460.

MacCracken, J. G.; Van Ballenberghe, V. (1993): Mass-diameter regressions for moose browse on the Copper River Delta, Alaska. *J. Range Manage.* 46: 302–308.

Miquelle, D. G ; Jordan, P. A. (1979) : The importance of diversity in the diet of moose. *Alces* 15: 54–79.

Miquelle, D. G.; Peek, J. M.; Van Ballenberghe, V. (1992): Sexual segregation in Alaskan moose. *Wildl. Monogr.* 122: 1–57.

Naumann, C.; Bassler, R. (1988): *Die chemische Untersuchung von Futtermitteln.* Vol. III. Darmstadt, Germany: J. Naumann-Neudamm.

Oftedal, O. T.; Baer, D. J.; Allen, M. E. (1996): The feeding and nutrition of herbivores. In: *Wild Mammals in Captivity: Principles and Techniques* (D. G. Kleimann, M. E. Allen, K. V. Thompson, S. Lumpkin, eds.). Chicago: University of Chicago Press, pp. 129–138.

Patenaude, R. (1978): Medical care of captive moose. *AAZV Ann. Conf. Proc.*, pp. 143–149.

Peek, J. M.; Krefting, L. W.; Tappeiner, J. C. (1971): Variation in twig diameter-weight relationships in northern Minnesota. *J. Wildl. Manage.* 35: 501–507.

Ritscher, D. (1990): Erkrankungen und Todesfälle bei Elchen im Zoologischen Garten Rostock. *Verh. Ber. Erkr. Zootiere* 32: 297–213.

Schewe, A. M.; Stewart, J. M. (1986): Twig weight-diameter relatinships for selected browse species on the Duck Mountain Forest Reserve, Manitoba. *Can. J. For. Res.* 16: 675–680.

Schwartz, C. C. (1992): Techniques of moose husbandry in North America. *Alces* Suppl. 1: 177–192.

Shochat, E.; Robbins, C. T.; Parish, S. M.; Young, P. B.; Stephenson, T. R.; Tamayo, A. (1997): Nutritional investigations and management of captive moose. *Zoo. Biol.* 16: 479–494.

Sperlich, W. (1980): Elche im Zoo – ein Rückblick aus der Sicht ihrer Ernährung. *Jahresbericht des Zoologischen Garten Rostock*, pp. 19–24.

Telfer, E. S. (1969): Twig weight-diameter relationships for browse species. *J. Wildl. Manage.* 33: 917–921.

*M. Clauss[1], E. Kienzle[1], J.-M. Hatt[2]*

# Feeding practice in captive wild ruminants: peculiarities in the nutrition of browsers/ concentrate selectors and intermediate feeders. A review.

### *Abstract*

*We present a review on the feeding practice, the nutritional pathology and the documented nutritional peculiarities of zoo ruminants. The difference in chemical composition between browse and grass historically led to the conclusion that browsers need a diet lower in fibre and higher in protein than grazing ruminants. The term "concentrate selectors", coined to describe browsing ruminants, additionally focused the attention on the chemical nature of a browser's diet assumed high in easily fermentable, soluble nutrients; the choice of the term "concentrate" therefore has been criticized in the scientific literature (e.g. Owen-Smith 1996). In comparative nutritional surveys, browsing ruminants in zoos tend to consume less fibre, more protein and more nitrogen-free extracts than grazers. While this could be interpreted as a reflection of their nutritional needs, this feeding type displays, in comparative pathological surveys, a higher incidence of acidotic changes in the ruminal mucosa, indicating that this group does not ingest sufficient amounts of fibrous material. Additionally, data from controlled balance trials does not support the notion that browsing ruminants have higher protein requirements. We suspect that the lesser fibre intake in browsers is due to their reluctance to ingest hay, which is usually offered ad libitum. Reluctance to ingest hay and digestive problems after hay ingestion have been reported for different captive browsing ruminant species and is reflected by a similar reluctance of free-ranging browsers to ingest grasses. There is reason to believe that it is the physical rather than the chemical difference between grass and browse that affected the evolution of different ruminant*

[1] Institute of Animal Physiology, Physiological Chemistry and Animal Nutrition, Ludwig-Maximilians-University, Munich, Germany. *Corresponding author:* Marcus Clauss, Institute of Animal Physiology, Physiological Chemistry and Animal Nutrition, Veterinaerstr. 13, 80539 Muenchen, Germany, Tel. ++49 89 2180 2554, FAX ++49 89 2180 3208, clauss@tiph.vetmed.uni-muenchen.de

[2] Division of Zoo Animals and Exotic Pets, University of Zurich, Switzerland.

*feeding types. Attention within the zoo community should focus on providing browsers with a fibre source that corresponds to the physical characteristics of their natural forage.*

***Keywords***

*Grass, browse, hay, lucerne, rumen acidosis, physical structure, ruminant diversification*

## 1 Introduction

Forty years ago, when the first complete rations were designed for zoo animals, all ruminants were thought to thrive well on one formula (Ratcliffe 1966, Wackernagel 1966, Abrams 1968), and this approach to ruminant husbandry has had followers ever since (e.g. Ullrey 1973, Brambell 1977, Skinner 1977, Baker et al. 1998).

On the other hand, the distinction according to the natural forage – grazers and browsers –, and most notably, the classification by Hofmann (1973, 1989) of three feeding types (grass and roughage eaters, GR; intermediate feeders, IM; "concentrate selectors", CS) according to morphophysiological characterristics, have not gone unnoticed in the zoo community.

A difference in formula design for wild ruminants often follows observed differences in the main forage types, grass and browse. Commercially available herbivore pellets often are labelled as either a "browser" or a "grazer diet". In general, browse contains more protein and less fibre than grasses (Van Soest 1994), and the rumen contents of free-ranging browsers contain higher concentrations of nitrogen than those of grazers (Giesecke and Van Gylswyk 1975, Maloiy et al. 1982). Therefore, Sedgewick and Fowler (1973) remain the one odd exception who postulate a diet of high fibre/low protein for captive browsers and low fibre/high protein for captive grazers (and one is tempted to interpret this as a misprint). Other recommendations (e.g. Blankenship 1977, Topps 1977, Fowler 1978, Hofmann and Matern 1988, Lintzenich and Ward 1997) or feeding practices (e.g. Fundova 1974, Trusk et al. 1991) follow the trend of the natural forages, i.e. provide browsers with more protein and less fibre than grazers.

While a high protein/low fibre recommendation can be deducted from the difference in natural forage alone, Hofmann's theory implies that browsers/CS are adapted to a food with higher contents of soluble, readily fermentable nutrients like sugars and starches, measured as nitrogen-free extracts (NfE) in classic proximate nutrient analysis. This nutrient group tends to trigger acidotic changes in the forestomach pH in domestic ruminants, which interestingly are all classified as grazers or intermediate feeders; yet it is postulated that browsers/CS produce more buffering saliva and have faster rumen clearance rates that prevent sugars/starches from being completely fermented in the forestomach.[3] Although there have not been recommendations to increase the proportion of starches or sugars in the diet of browsers (and interestingly, when Fowler 1978 suspected that giraffe[4] did not receive enough energy from captive diets, he suggested an increase in protein, not NfE), there has at least been one investigation that showed that roe deer, a browser/CS, can be kept on a diet that consisted mainly of oat flakes, waste cookies, beet pulp and hay without clinical problems or measurable physiological deteriorations (Treichler 1972). Additionally, it was observed in a zoological garden that the browsing ruminants seemed to consume diets higher in NfE and lower in fibre than the grazers (Dinglreiter 2000), and that captive moose, a browser/ CS, received very high NfE contents with their diets in a survey of different facilities (Clauss et al. 2001a). Furthermore, the analysis of the recorded feeding practice within one facility (Grisham and Savage 1990) showed that grazing ruminants received a higher hay:concentrate ratio than did browsing ruminants (figure 1). The question arose whether the observed and recorded feeding patterns indicate a better adaptation of browsers to NfE, and whether according recommendations can be formulated.

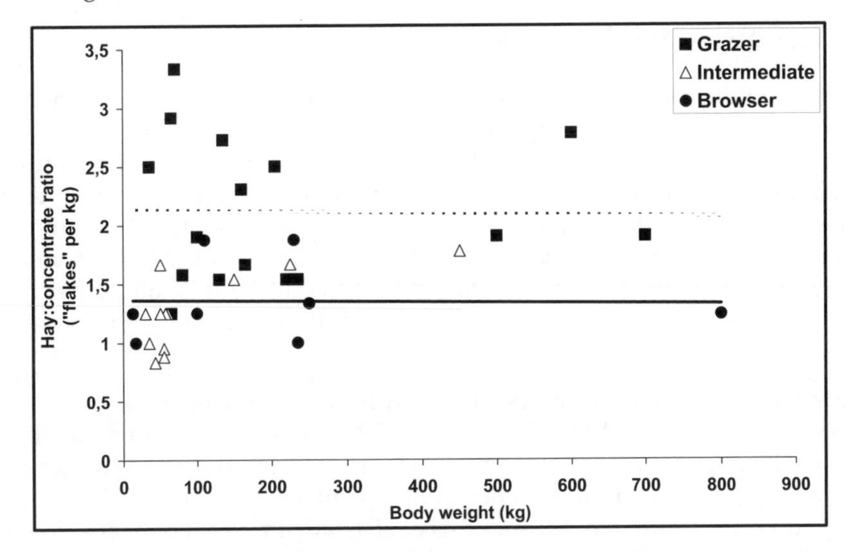


**Figure 1.** The feeding ratios of hay (measured in "flakes") and concentrates (in kg) for captive wild ruminants of different feeding types and body weight at the Oklahoma City Zoo (data from Grisham and Savage 1990). Regression lines (solid = browsers, dotted = grazers) fitted to emphasize trends.

In order to substantiate a necessary difference in the feeding regime of ruminant feeding types, we followed a four-step protocol:

---

[3] This necessitates the presence of special musocal transporters in the small intestine for the absorption of glucose, which are absent in grazers (Rowell et al. 1996) because in grazers, due to their longer rumen retention times, soluble nutrients are fermented completely in the forestomach.

[4] Latin names of all species mentioned in the text are summarized in Table 5.

1. Search for detectable influences of feeding type on the recorded feeding practices in the available literature.
2. Search for differences in reports of pathological findings (necropsy protocols) linked to nutrition between the feeding types.
3. Check recorded experiences with fibre supplementation to wild and zoo ruminants.
4. Compare established nutrient requirements for ruminants of different feeding types.

Investigations on the influence of feeding type are generally confounded by the fact that the ruminant feeding types are not equally distributed over the ruminant body weight range: Most browsers are small, and most grazers are big, with notable exceptions on both ends (Van Wieren 1996a). We therefore plotted ration parameters against body weights, either those given in the according studies themselves, or average values from Grzimek (1988).

## 2 Recorded feeding practice

Records of the diets actually consumed by the animals could be obtained for several zoological institutions. We considered only studies that offered at least one diet ingredient (i.e. hay) *ad libitum*, and that investigated several ruminant species within one facility; differences between the feeding regimes of different feeding types should manifest themselves most distinctively within the same facility, whereas a comparison between facilities would be confounded by fundamental differences in feeding management. Additionally, differences in analytical approaches to nutrient analysis make most inter-study comparisons difficult.

Data were gathered for one facility each from Fundova (1974), Gutzwiller (1984), Kozaki et al. (1991), Hatt (1994), Dinglreiter (2000), for four different facilties from Prins et al. (1983), and summarized in table 1. In general, GR always consumed diets higher in fibre content than IM or CS. The only exception was facility no. 4 from Prins et al. (1983) that kept only one IM species, the European bison, that received the same diet as other buffalo species. Differences between IM and CS were not as consistent, with the lowest fibre consumption by IM in 5 and by CS in 4 facilities. GR consumed generally diets lower in crude protein and NfE than IM or CS.

When plotted against (assumed) body weight (figure 2–3), it becomes obvious that larger animals generally consume diets higher in fibre and lower in crude protein and NfE content, and that grazers seem to consume, on average, a diet of higher fibre content and lesser protein content than browsers.

While correlations between body size and fibre content of diet might reflect the tendency for browsers to be smaller and grazers to be bigger, and could also underline the fact that larger animals are, in general, better adapted to a more fibrous diet due to their digestive capacity (Demment and Van Soest 1985), the data points for the largest giraffe, however, deviate conspicuously from the

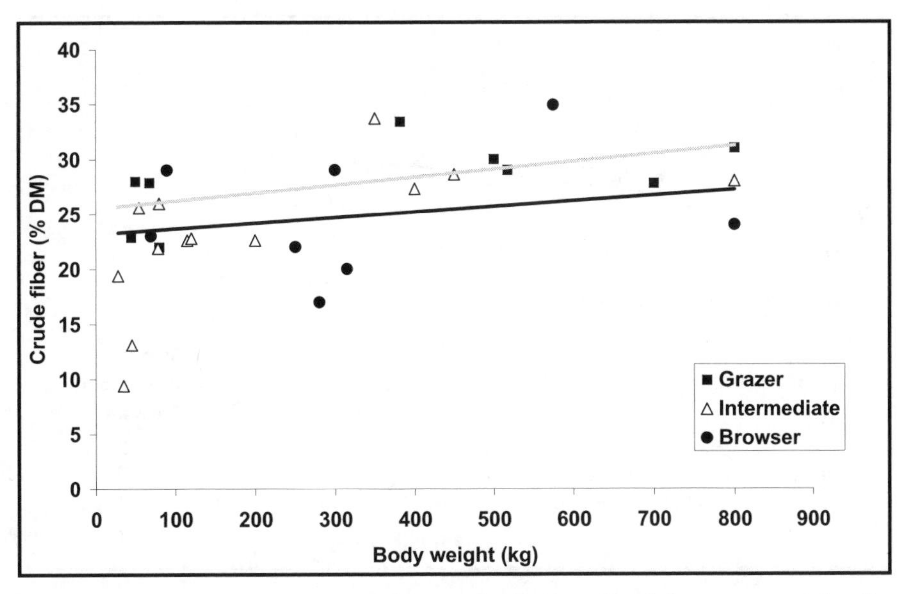


**Figure 2a.** Fibre content (measured as crude fibre) in % of dry matter of the diet consumed plotted against body weight for zoo ruminants of different feeding types. Data from Dinglreiter (2000), Hatt (1994) and Gutzwiller (1984). Regression lines (solid = browsers, weak = grazers) fitted to emphasize trends.

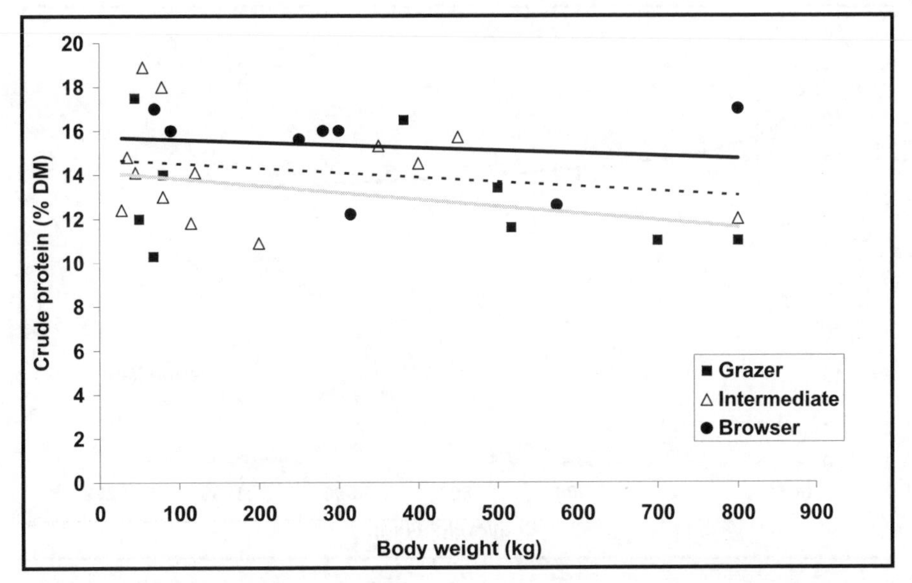


**Figure 2b.** Protein content (measured as crude protein) in % of dry matter of the diet consumed plotted against body weight for zoo ruminants of different feeding types. Data from Dinglreiter (2000), Hatt (1994) and Gutzwiller (1984). Regression lines (solid = browsers, dotted = intermediate, weak = grazers) fitted to emphasize trends.

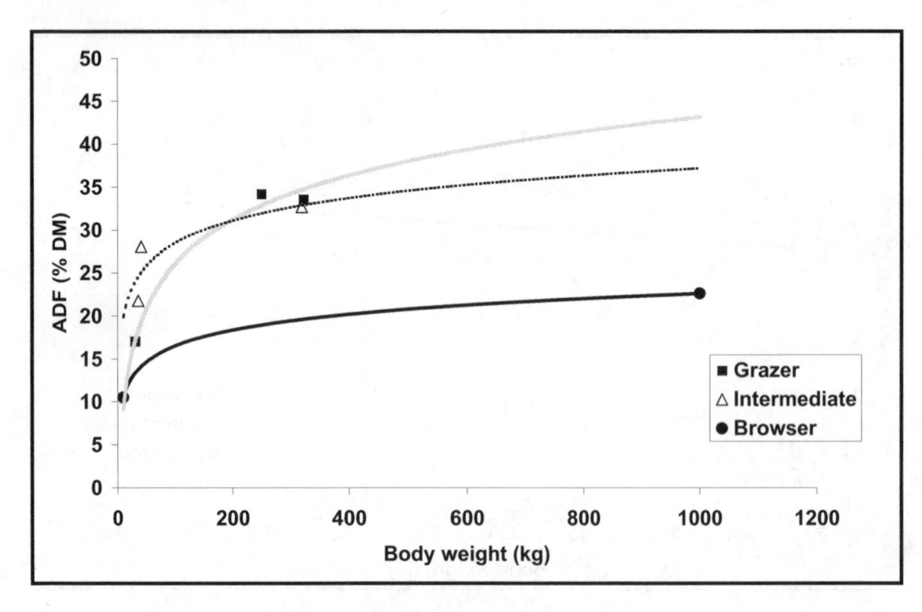


**Figure 3a.** Fibre content (measured as acid detergent fibre) in % of dry matter of the diet consumed plotted against body weight for zoo ruminants of different feeding types. Data from Kozaki et al. (1991). Regression lines (solid = browsers, dotted = intermediate, weak = grazers) fitted to emphasize trends.

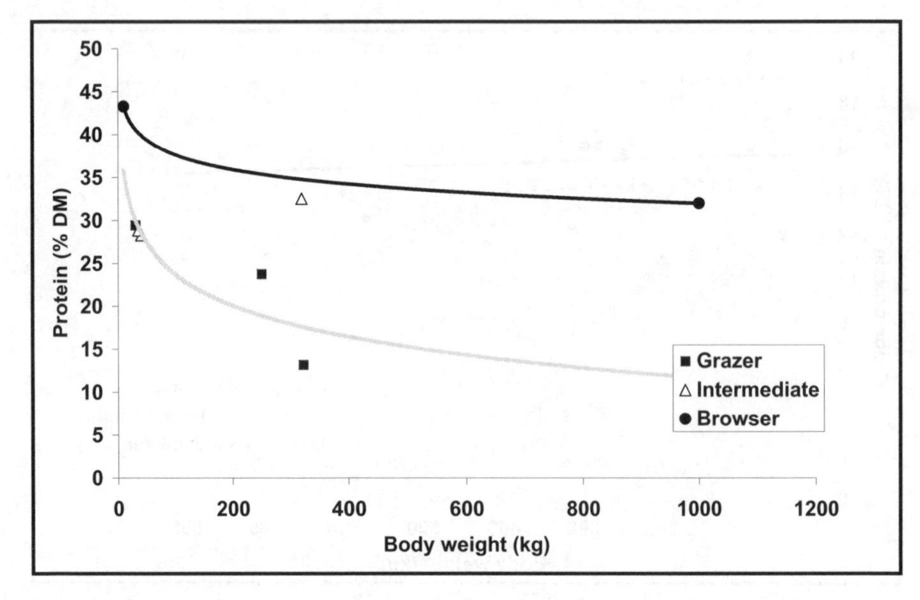


**Figure 3b.** Protein content (measured as crude protein) in % of dry matter of the diet consumed plotted against body weight for zoo ruminants of different feeding types. Data from Kozaki et al. (1991). Regression lines (solid = browsers, weak = grazers) fitted to emphasize trends.

common scheme in figure 2a, 2b, 3a and 3b, and in the data from Prins et al. (1983), indicating that this biggest browser/CS consumes a diet lower in fibre and higher in protein than would be expected from its size alone.

The correlations can be intepreted in three ways:

a) Grazers/larger herbivores are deliberately fed a diet higher in fibre and lower in protein and NfE than browsers/CS and IM or smaller animals.

b) Browsers/CS and IM or smaller animals actively select for a diet higher in protein and NfE than grazers or bigger animals.

c) Browsers/CS and IM or smaller animals refuse to eat much hay fibre and therefore their diet consist of a higher proportion of trough feeds, which are generally lower in fibre and higher in protein and NfE. In this case, the nutrient composition would not be the result of an active selection *for* the nutrients, but of a *rejection* of a certain food type.

If a) were true, and the rationale behind this feeding regime was reasonable, we would expect a low incidence of gastrointestinal disease, and no difference between the feeding types.

If b) were true, and we ascribe the same (low) degree of nutritional wisdom to all feeding types, we would expect an even distribution of digestive disorders, whether their incidence be high or low.

If c) were true, we would assume that the rejection of hay fibre indicates a dietary inadequacy for many zoo ruminants, and expect gastrointestinal disorders mainly in those ruminants that do not ingest hay fibre.

## 3 Necropsy reports

Numerous reports document the high incidence of gastrointestinal (GIT) disorders in zoo ruminants. GIT disorders were responsible for a high proportion of cases in Lindau (1966), Ippen (1967), Kronberger et al. (1974), Dollinger (1973), Steger (1973), Herceg et al. (1973), Mikulica et al. (1984), Ippen and Henne (1985), Eulenberger et al. (1985), Ippen and Henne (1988), Kiupel (1988), Zwart et al. (1988), Hatt et al. (1995). Elze et al. (1978) report several cases of acidosis in their collection, in sheep, muskoxen, giraffe, okapi and Père David's deer. Hofmann and Nygren (1992) found acidotic changes of the ruminal mucosa in all seven captive moose they investigated, and there are many reports on digestive disorders in single ruminant species that are too numerous to list here. In contrast, digestive disturbances played only a minor role in the pathology of the collections surveyed by Montali et al. (1985) and Steger and Lackermeier (1985).

The data are generally not presented in a way that allows quantitative comparisons between ruminant feeding types, and therefore the number of articles just emphasizes the importance of GIT – and thus probably nutritional – disorders. From this background alone, we would suspect the feeding regimes of many zoo ruminants to be inadequate.

**Table 1.** Average (SD, range) fibre and nutrient compositions consumed by different feeding types at different zoological facilities. Rfa = crude fibre; Rp = crude protein; NfE = nitrogen-free extracts; ADF = acid detergent fibre; NDF = neutral detergent fibre.

| Source | Feeding type | *n* | Fibre type % DM | SD | range | Rp % DM | SD | range | NfE % DM | SD | range |
|---|---|---|---|---|---|---|---|---|---|---|---|
| | | | Rfa | | | | | | | | |
| Dinglreiter (2000) | GR | 4 | 28.8 | 4.4 | (22.9–33.4) | 14.8 | 2.7 | (11.6–17.5) | 48.4 | 2.1 | (45.4–50.0) |
| | IM | 7 | 22.8 | 8.7 | (9.4–33.7) | 15.9 | 1.8 | (14.1–18.9) | 53.1 | 6.7 | (47.5–63.1) |
| | CS | 2 | 25.5 | 10.5 | (20.0–34.9) | 12.4 | 0.3 | (12.2–12.6) | 52.2 | 10.9 | (44.4–59.9) |
| Hatt (1994) | GR | 2 | 27.9 | 0.1 | (27.8–27.9) | 10.7 | 0.5 | (10.3–11.0) | 53.0 | 0.4 | (52.7–53.2) |
| | IM | 4 | 21.9 | 1.6 | (19.4–22.8) | 12.3 | 1.3 | (10.9–14.1) | 55.3 | 3.0 | (51.1–57.9) |
| | CS | 1 | 22.0 | – | – | 15.6 | – | – | 52.2 | – | – |
| Gutzwiller (1984) | GR | 3 | 27.0 | 4.6 | (22–31) | 12.3 | 1.5 | (11–14) | | | |
| | IM | 2 | 27.0 | 1.4 | (26–28) | 12.5 | 0.7 | (12–13) | | | |
| | CS | 5 | 24.4 | 5.0 | (17–29) | 16.4 | 0.5 | (16–17) | | | |
| | | | ADF | | | | | | | | |
| Kozaki (1991) | GR | 3 | 28.3 | 9.7 | (17.1–34.2) | 22.1 | 8.2 | (13.2–29.5) | | | |
| | IM | 3 | 27.5 | 5.5 | (21.8–32.7) | 29.9 | 2.3 | (28.3–32.5) | | | |
| | CS | 2 | 16.5 | 8.6 | (10.5–22.6) | 37.6 | 8.0 | (32.0–43.3) | | | |
| Fundova (1974) | GR | 3 | | | | 9.0 | 0.8 | (8.2–9.8) | | | |
| | IM | 2 | | | | 8.3 | 0.3 | (8.1–8.5) | | | |
| | CS | 4 | | | | 11.9 | 1.3 | (11.0–13.8) | | | |
| | | | NDF | | | | | | | | |
| Prins et al. (1983) 1 | GR | 7 | 66.5 | 5.4 | (61.3–76.9) | | | | | | |
| | IM | 5 | 51.3 | 7.9 | (40.2–61.5) | | | | | | |
| | CS | 2 | 55.5 | 2.8 | (53.5–57.4) | | | | | | |
| Prins et al. (1983) 2 | GR | 7 | 58.5 | 9.9 | (49.3–78.4) | | | | | | |
| | IM | 7 | 55.5 | 7.5 | (48.9–67.5) | | | | | | |
| | CS | 5 | 57.3 | 5.5 | (51.9–66.1) | | | | | | |
| Prins et al. (1983) 3a | GR | 5 | 50.1 | 3.6 | (47.4–55.6) | | | | | | |
| | IM | 3 | 50.6 | 2.4 | (48.4–53.1) | | | | | | |
| | CS | 1 | 47.6 | – | – | | | | | | |
| Prins et al. (1983) 3b | GR | 5 | 57.8 | 7.4 | (48.4–65.1) | | | | | | |
| | IM | 2 | 48.4 | 4.5 | (45.2–51.5) | | | | | | |
| | CS | 1 | 50.5 | – | – | | | | | | |
| Prins et al. (1983) 4 | GR | 11 | 52.9 | 2.4 | (48.1–54.0) | | | | | | |
| | IM | 1 | 54.0 | – | – | | | | | | |
| | CS | 1 | 49.7 | – | – | | | | | | |

The data from Kiupel (1988), and from the study of Marholdt (1991) who focused solely on pathological changes of the ruminal mucosa, can be ordered according to feeding types and weight classes (table 2 and 3). The tables show that GR have a lower incidence of GIT disorders in general and of acidotic changes of the ruminal mucosa in particular. Accordingly, it can be observed in table 2 that the bigger ruminants have less GIT disturbances, while the limited number of cases in table 3 prevents any conclusive result. Yet, the absence of large ruminants from the study of Marholdt (1991) underlines the notion that grazers, regardless of their size, are seemingly better adapted to the conventional zoo diet, i.e. hay fibre. The extremely high incidence of acidotic changes in the ruminal mucosa of browsers/CS indicates a fact of semantic irony, namely that the so-called "concentrate selectors" seem to have digestive problems when selecting too much concentrate feeds.

**Table 2.** Occurence of gastrointestinal disorders among different feeding types and weight classes of zoo ruminants. Data from Kiupel (1988).

| Feeding type | *n* | Proportion of GIT pathology | Weight class | *n* | Proportion of GIT pathology |
|---|---|---|---|---|---|
| | | % | kg | | % |
| GR | 9 | 11 | < 100 | 120 | 20 |
| IM | 141 | 31 | 100–200 | 48 | 54 |
| (IM/GR | 38 | 37) | 200–300 | 30 | 30 |
| (IM/CS | 103 | 28) | 400–500 | 5 | 20 |
| CS | 61 | 26 | 600–700 | 8 | 0 |

**Table 3.** Occurence of acidotic changes of the ruminal mucosa among different feeding types and weight classes of zoo ruminants. Data from Marholdt (1991).

| Feeding type | *n* | Proportion of acidotic changes of rumen mucosa | Weight classes | *n* | Proportion of acidotic changes of rumen mucosa |
|---|---|---|---|---|---|
| | | % | kg | | % |
| GR | 13 | 23 | < 100 | 37 | 35 |
| IM | 30 | 27 | 100–200 | 13 | 54 |
| (IM/GR | 25 | 16) | 200–300 | 13 | 62 |
| (IM/CS | 5 | 80) | 300–400 | 3 | 67 |
| CS | 24 | 83 | 600–700 | 1 | 100 |

**Table 4.** Reports of problems in browsing ruminants/CS and one IM with hay or grass fibre.

| Feeding type/ Species | Problem reported | Source |
|---|---|---|
| **CS** | | |
| Giraffe | refuse to eat hay or live on hay alone | Foose (1982), Gutzwiller (1984) |
| | changed rumen mucosa due to high hay/grass fibre intake | Hofmann and Matern (1988); c.f. Fox (1938) |
| | phytobezoars (and abomasal irritation) due to ingestion of hay or grass | Fox (1938), Gradwell (1976), Klöppel (1976), Altmann (1978), Gorgas et al. (1978), Brancker (1980), Franz et al. (1984), Matern and Klöppel (1995) |
| Moose | refuse to eat hay | Baines (1965), Landowski (1969), Heptner and Nasimowitsch (1974), Bo and Hjeljord (1991), Schwartz and Hundertmark (1993) |
| | weight loss on alfalfa hay-only diet | Schwartz and Hundertmark (1993) |
| | hay/grass consumption suspected to be responsible for chronic wasting and diarrhea | Schwartz (1992), Shochat et al. (1997) |
| Mule deer | refuse to eat hay or live on hay alone | Doman and Rasmussen (1944) |
| | alfalfa hay does not work as emergency feed | Carhart (1943), Doman and Rasmussen (1944), Nagy et al. (1969) |
| | omasal impaction and abomasal inflammation due to phytobezoars after alfalfa feeding | Schoonveld et al. (1974) |
| Roe deer | refuse to eat hay or live on hay alone | Dissen (1983) |
| Chinese water deer | changed rumen mucosa due to high grass fibre intake | Hofmann et al. (1988) |
| Blue duiker | mortalities when fed coarse forages | Cowan 1982 |
| Small ruminants (Pudu, Brocket, Duiker spp.) | high refusal rates for ad libitum-offered hays | Van Soest et al. (1995) |
| **IM** | | |
| Reindeer | do not thrive on hay diets, refuse hay diets | Eriksson and Schmekel (1962), Kurkela (1976), Luick (1977), Valtonen et al. (1983) |
| Eland | changed rumen mucosa due to high grass fibre intake | Hofmann (1973, p. 40) |

## 4 Experiences with fibre (hay or grass) supplementation in zoo ruminants

There are numerous reports that underline the inadequacy, and the low acceptance, of hay or grass fibre for browsers/CS of all body sizes (table 4). Accordingly, browsers/CS are likely to avoid grass fibre when possible, and consequently will consume relatively more trough feeds, which leads to a higher incidence in GIT disorders. The limited data available from the seminal thesis of Foose (1982, figures 4a and b) indicates that on hay-only diets IM have comparatively lower intakes on grass hay than GR (figure 4a), a difference that seems to vanish when lucerne hay is used (figure 4b). The only browser used in this study, the giraffe, however, has alarmingly low intakes on either hay type.

## 5 Comparison with established nutrient requirements

While many studies describe the nutritional content of the forage of browsing and grazing ruminants, very few studies investigated and compared the actual nutrient requirements. The higher protein content of browse need not necessarily imply a higher protein requirement in browsers, but might just mean that browsers consume a natural diet high in protein, their actual requirements notwithstanding. A browse diet induces increased faecal and urinary nitrogen losses (Robbins 1993) due to secondary plant compounds, but this does not necessarily imply that browsers have these higher faecal and urinary nitrogen losses on *any* kind of diet. In order to establish higher protein requirements for browsing ruminants, they have to be compared on the same diet as grazers, and therefore, data from different studies are difficult to compare.

Ruminants are able to recycle nitrogen into the rumen as ammonia via the blood or as urea via the saliva (Van Soest 1994). For the browser white-tailed deer, it has been shown that this nitrogen recycling occurs to the same extent as in the grazer cattle (Robbins et al. 1974). Klein and Schonheyder (1970) showed that recycling must be functional in black-tailed deer, roe deer and reindeer, and Choshniak et al. (1984) demonstrated functional recycling in the nubian ibex. High protein requirements in a particular sub-group, therefore, would be principally surprising, and have been questioned already (Baer et al. 1985).

Arman et al. (1975) found no difference in the metabolic faecal nitrogen losses of sheep, goat, buffalo, hartebeest, reedbuck, Uganda kob, and topi, and relatively lower nitrogen losses in eland and wildebeest. In the same study, the metabolic faecal nitrogen losses of sheep and duiker were comparable as well. In comparative feeding trials with roe deer and domestic ruminants, both Eisfeld (1982) and Dissen (1983) found no significant difference in nitrogen balance between the species. McEwan and Whitehead (1970) observed requirements of digestible nitrogen in reindeer comparable to those of sheep and cattle. Protein maintenance requirements of only 5.8 and 6.8 % of dietary

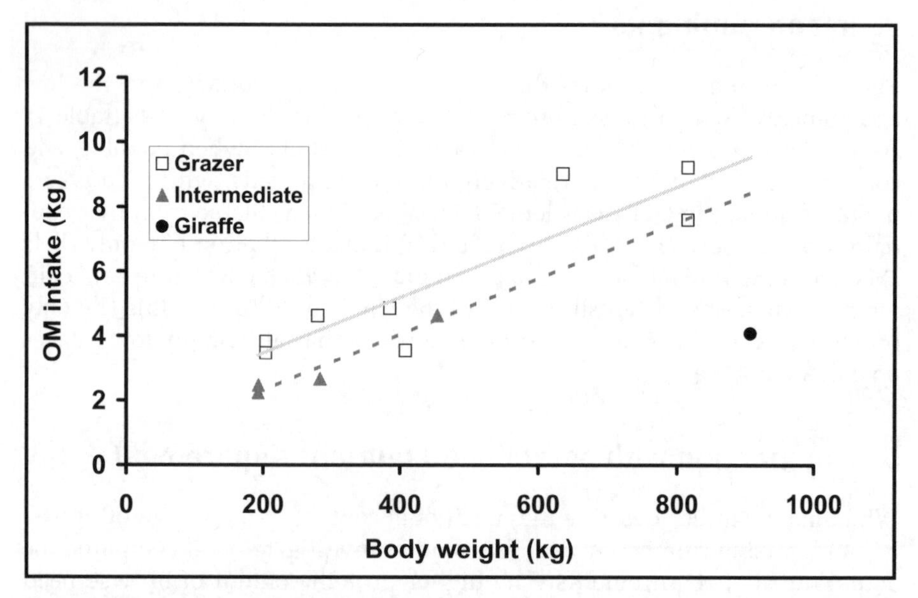


**Figure 4a.** Organic matter (OM) intake from a diet consisting of grass hay (*ad libitum*) plotted against body weight for zoo ruminants of different feeding types. Data from Foose (1982). Regression lines (dotted = intermediate, weak = grazers) fitted to emphasize trends.

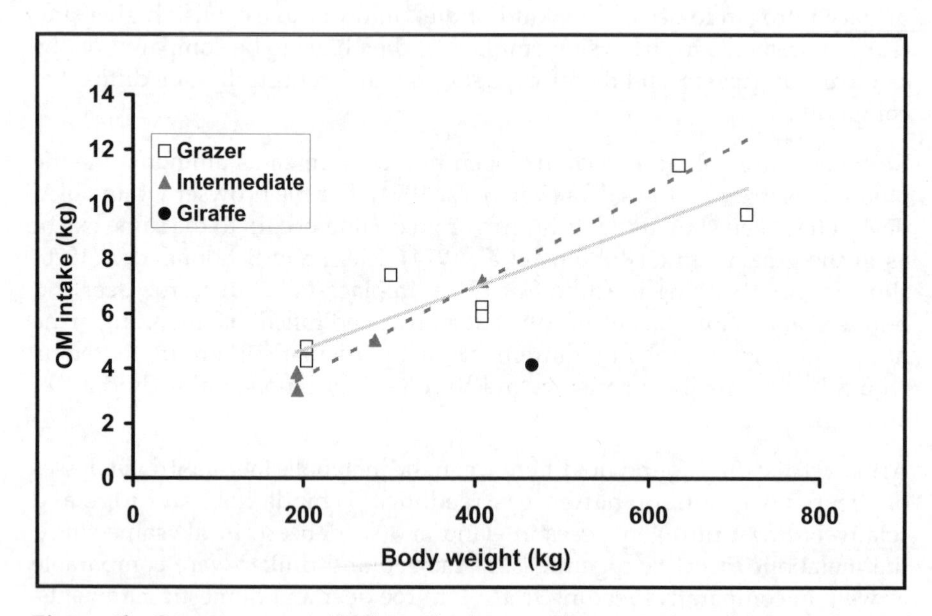


**Figure 4b.** Organic matter (OM) intake from a diet consisting of lucerne hay (*ad libitum*) plotted against body weight for zoo ruminants of different feeding types. Data from Foose (1982). Regression lines (dotted = intermediate, weak = grazers) fitted to emphasize trends.

dry matter (DM) were determined for the browsers white-tailed deer (Holter et al. 1979) and moose (Schwartz et al. 1987a), respectively. Similarly, Mould and Robbins (1981) found maintenance protein requirements for elk of about 6–8 %, and Priebe and Brown (1987) for nilgai antelope of 4.9–7.0 % of dietary DM.

Thus, the experimental evidence does not support the notion that browsers/CS have higher protein requirements than grazing ruminants. In fact, it was shown that white-tailed deer, when given the opportunity to choose between feeds of high or low energy content with adequate or high protein concentrations, selected for a diet high in energy but not high in protein (Berteaux et al. 1998).

## 6 Summary: the present state

Summarizing, there is a group of zoo ruminants, the browsers/CS and IM, who ingest disproportionately low fibre and high protein and NfE levels in their diet, although according requirements have not been demonstrated. On the contrary, this same group has a high incidence of GIT disorders, which leads to the suspicion that the actual feeding practice is in many cases not adequate.

The acidotic damage triggered by diets high in NfE was demonstrated by Marholdt (1991). High protein levels, on the other hand, have been associated with hoof overgrowth (although the only evidence that can be found in the literature speaks against this – Sikarskie et al. 1988). High protein and carbohydrate diets have also been associated with digestive upsets due to overgrowth of certain bacteria in the small and large intestine in domestic ruminants – e.g. *Clostridium*-induced enterotoxemia in sheep and goats (Radostis et al. 1999). A constant provision with high protein and NfE levels without appropriate fibre structure might be the underlaying cause for the high number of not only ruminal but also intestinal disorders in cervids and other small captive wild ruminants. As most facilities are likely to offer hay *ad libitum* to all of their ungulates, this situation is probably, at least partially, due to a refusal of the ruminant species in question to ingest hay in larger amounts.

The classic conceptualization of ruminant nutrition thus comes to a dead end, which might be the reason for the problems of this group in captivity: If the usual fibre source is rejected, but protein and NfE levels should not be elevated, what other ingredient could be put in the formula? One should compose a pelleted feed with a high fibre content, and possibly include carbohydrates, like pectins from beet pulp, that do not trigger acidosis when fermented in the rumen (Van Soest 1996). Yet pelleted feeds, even if they consist of ground hay only, reduce rumination (Kick et al. 1937) and decrease the pH of the rumen contents markedly (Hinders et al. 1961), and the more so if they contain proportions of concentrates. The ruminal pH can only be corrected by the ingestion of a fibre source whose structure induces rumination (Cullison 1961). This is the rationale behind the usual feeding scheme for ruminants that consists of a pelleted or concentrate feed plus hay *ad libitum*. But why do browsers/CS and

IM refuse, in varying degrees, to ingest grass hay? To answer this question, we must take a closer look at the natural forages.

## 7 Browse and grass

Carhart (1943) observed that mule deer on poor winter ranges died from malnutrition with their forestomachs filled with the alfalfa pellets that were fed as an emergency ration (c.f. table 4); however, if the range still provided sufficient amounts of browse that could be ingested in addition to the alfalfa, most animals survived. Giving a typical example of an ingredient-orientated approach, the author concluded that it had to be a chemical component of the browse, namely the tannins, that enhanced the digestion of the alfalfa. Yet, if anything, tannins have been shown to impede forage digestion in ruminants (e.g. Kumar and Singh 1984). In contrast, Smith (1952) and Schoonveld et al. (1974) realized that "the inadequacy of alfalfa as a supplemental winter food for deer must be attributed to causes other than nutrient values", as many browse species commonly used by deer have similar or even higher amounts of fibre and lignin. So why, as Nagy et al. (1969) ask, "do deer which have been feeding on natural browse starve when fed [...] hay?"

A chemical "ingredient" that has not yet been investigated in zoo animal diets is, admittedly, lignin. While browse contains generally less fibre, its fibre fraction contains a significantly larger amount of lignin than the fibre fraction of grasses (Van Soest 1994). To our knowledge, no controlled long-term feeding trials have been done to test the health effects of a diet for browsers/CS with a high lignin proportion in the fibre fraction. A high proportion of lignin in the diet of browsing ruminants has been theoretically linked to a faster passage rate (Schwartz 1980, Renecker 2001), and a high lignin content of the fibre fraction has therefore been postulated to be appropriate for browsing ruminants. However, experiments by Hjeljord et al. (1982), Spalinger et al. (1986) and Baker and Hobbs (1987) demonstrated that forage of increasing lignin content is retained in the rumen for a longer time. Finally, Schwartz et al. (1987b) summarized data that resulted in the same correlation. This does not devalidate the original theoretical background, namely that browse ("lignified forage") breaks down into particles whose shape allows a faster rumen clearance – it simply shows that the chemical component "lignin" is not an appropriate measurement of this physical property.

One of the main differences between browse and grass is not related to their respective chemical compositions, but to their physical structure. While grass and grass hay is broken down into thin, longish "fibre-like" particles, browse is broken down into cubical, polygonal ones (Troelsen and Campbell 1969, Van Wieren 1996b, c.f. figure 5). In carefully designed feeding trials, Spalinger et al. (1986) demonstrated that the physical rather than the chemical structure of forages determined their behavior in the rumen. The authors used electron microscopy to determine the cell wall thickness of forages, which was correlated to their respective particle breakdown rates, and postulated that ruminants should select forages according to physical characteristics like cell wall thickness. Several other investigators have tried to isolate a mechanical forage property that correlates with intake and digestibility: Lees et al. (1982) correlated morphological and mechanical characterstics of different legume leaves, as measured by microscope and a glass-bead disruption technique, to their respective digestibilities. Chai et al. (1984) and McLeod et al. (1990) measured the resistance to breakdown of different forages by correlating the number of chews necessary for defined size reductions. Inoué et al. (1994) investigated the effects of ryegrass of different leaf shear breaking loads. Troelsen and Bigsby (1964) constructed a device for artificial mastication and found that particle breakdown characteristics of different forages were correlated to the voluntary intake of these forages observed in sheep. Such parameters cannot be measured by nutrient analyses, and therefore probably have neither been investigated nor accounted for in greater scope. Yet it might be that many of the morphological characterstics described by Hofmann (1989) are adaptations to forages of different *physical structure,* and that the choice of the terms "concentrate selectors" and "roughage eaters" unfortunately and unduely emphasized the *chemical composition* of the diet.

## 8 Browsers and grazers

On an evolutionary scale, browsing ruminants are the more original ruminant form (Hofmann 1989). They are adapted to a diet that does not induce a stratification of ingesta in the forestomach (Hofmann 1989, Clauss et al. 2001b, figure 5). Their rumen therefore is evenly papillated, and only moderately equipped with muscle layers (Hofmann 1989, Clauss et al. 2003). With the appearance of grasslands, some ruminants could use a diet that displays a strong tendency to induce stratification of forestomach contents (Hofmann 1989, figure 5); they developped the equipment necessary to handle these contents – a differentiated ruminal papillation, stronger muscle layers, and in many species an adhesion of the dorsal rumen region to the inner abdominal wall (as an additional lever point) – and to reinforce the stratification effects (e.g. different openings between the forestomach compartments). The stratification of rumen contents is the prerogative for the selective retention of ingesta particles in the rumen as it is obvious in grazing ruminants today (Lechner-Doll et al. 1991). Accordingly, grazing ruminants achieve a much more prominent selective particle retention than browsing ruminants (Clauss and Lechner-Doll 2001) and a more thorough ingesta particle size reduction via retention and rumination (Clauss et al. 2002a). This leads to an overall increased ability to digest fibrous material in grazers (Iason and Van Wieren 1998). The important consequence is that browsing ruminants, with their anatomical equipment to process non-stratified ingesta, cannot handle loads of stratification-inducing, blocking ingesta (Clauss et al. 2002b, 2003) and therefore consume it in smaller proportions or avoid it altogether. This pattern can also be found in free-ranging ruminants: Van Wieren (1996a) and Clauss et al. (2003) showed that while free-ranging grazers often consume a certain amount of browse in their natural diet, browsers avoid grasses much more exclusively. The latter authors contributed this selective grass avoidance to the mechanical characteristics of grass forage and the weak muscle equipment of the rumen of browsers.

## 9 Future challenges

Robbins (1993) states that "the failure of those feeding captive wildlife to recognize that very basic differences in gastrointestinal anatomy and function prevent the feeding of standardized diets to all members of a group, e.g. grass and legume hays to all ruminants, has killed many animals." Notably, Robbins does not speak of differences in nutrient composition, but in forage classes. The notion that differences in forage classes have to be translated into differences in nutrient composition might, in the case of wild ruminants, be a misleading one. Instead, the structural importance of browse forage for browsers/CS and IM should be recognized. The anecdotal reports that moose (Bo and Hjeljord 1991) and roe deer (Dissen 1983) increase their intake of hay

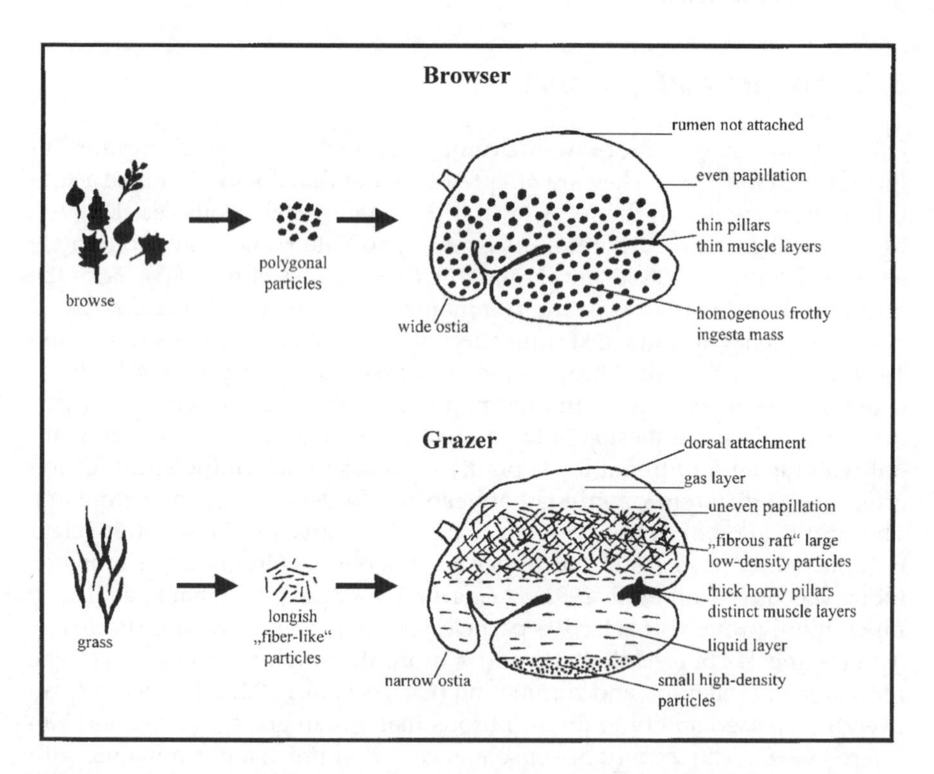


**Figure 5.** Different effect of forages and according ruminant adaptations. Modified from Clauss et al. (2002b, 2003). The structure a forage is broken down into determines its potential behavior in the forestomach. The tendency of grass particles to form a fibrous raft and a stratification of rumen contents is met by particular adaptations of grazing ruminants to handle, exploit and reinforce this tendency. Browsing ruminants are hypothezised to be unable to handle higher proportions of stratification-inducing forage in their forestomach.

if it is chopped into smaller particles underline the importance of the physical structure of the fibre source. Given the fact that browse itself is not available for many zoological institutions, we should attempt to improve the nutrition of browsing ruminants/CS and IM by looking for fibre sources that are acceptable to these species and resembles browse in the way it is processed in the GIT.

For a start, chopped grass, grass-browse mixes (c.f. Baker and Hobbs 1987) or apple pomace could be evaluated, or according silages and mixtures. Carhart (1943) noted that mule deer that received large amounts of apples in addition to alfalfa in an emergency feeding program did not suffer the losses of other groups fed on alfalfa alone. In German forestry practice, silages from a mixture of cabbage, grasses, herbs, fruit pomace, grains and carrots have been used successfully as additional winter food for cervids (Weis 1991). Kim et al. (1996) found that rye and maize silages were appropriate replacements for browse in farmed sika deer. But as long as no alternatives have been established, one should remember that browsers/CS and IM need a fibre source that suits the adaptations of their digestive tract and that they accept readily – browse.

## 10 Conclusions

1. There is a trend that captive browsing ruminants consume diets of lesser fibre and higher protein and NfE content than captive grazing ruminants.
2. This trend is in accord with the historical approach to the nutrition of captive wild ruminants, because browse contains less fibre and more protein than grass.
3. However, captive browsing ruminants have a drastically higher incidence of digestive problems, most notably rumen acidosis, indicating that they do not ingest enough fibre.
4. We propose that the observed intake pattern is not the result of rational feeding regimes, but due to a reluctance of browsers to ingest the staple fibre source – grass or lucerne hay – in similar proportions as grazers.
5. This interpretation is supported by a series of anecdotal reports on browsers refusing to ingest, and having problems after ingesting, hay; by reports on a tendency of free-ranging browsers to avoid grasses; and by feeding experiments that failed to demonstrate higher protein requirements in browsing ruminants.
6. It is proposed that the mechanical characteristics of grass and browse are much more important than their chemical characteristics, and that these mechanical properties were the main driving force behind the ruminant feeding type diversification.
7. In the feeding of captive ruminants, attention should focus on the provision of an adequate, i.e. readily accepted, fibre source for each feeding

type. Until other alternatives have been identified, this means that browsers should recieve higher proportions of browse than they currently do.

## Acknowledgements

We thank B. Peters and C. Witte for help in literature acuisition and W. Loehlein for help in graphic design.

**Table 5.** names of ruminant species mentioned in the text.

| English name | Latin name |
|---|---|
| Black-tailed deer | *Odocoileus hemionus sitkensis* |
| Blue duiker | *Cephalophus monticola* |
| Brocket | *Mazama americana* |
| Buffalo | *Syncerus caffer* |
| Chinese water deer | *Hydropotes inermis* |
| Duiker | *Cephalophus spp. and Sylvicapra grimmia* |
| Eland | *Taurotragus oryx* |
| Elk | *Cervus elaphus* |
| European bison | *Bison bonasus* |
| Giraffe | *Giraffa camelopardalis* |
| Hartebeest | *Alcelaphus buselaphus cokei* |
| Moose | *Alces alces* |
| Mule deer | *Odocoileus hemionus* |
| Muskoxen | *Ovibos moschatus* |
| Nilgai | *Buselaphus tragocamelus* |
| Nubian ibex | *Capra ibex nubiana* |
| Okapi | *Okapia johnstoni* |
| Père David's deer | *Elaphurus davidianus* |
| Pudu | *Pudu Pudu* |
| Reedbuck | *Redunca redunca* |
| Reindeer | *Rangifer tarandus* |
| Roe deer | *Capreolus capreolus* |
| Sika deer | *Cervus nippon* |
| Topi | *Damaliscus korrigum* |
| Uganda kob | *Adenota kob thomasi* |
| White-tailed deer | *Odocoileus virginianus* |
| Wildebeest | *Connochaetus taurinus* |

## Literature

Abrams, J. T. (1968): Fundamental approach to the nutrition of the captive wild herbivore. *Symp. Zool. Soc. Lond.* 21: 41–62.

Altmann, D. (1978): Giraffenerkrankungen und -verluste im Thueringer Zoopark Erfurt. *Verh. Ber. Erkr. Zootiere* 20: 77–82.

Arman, P.; Hopcraft, D.; McDonald, I. (1975): Nutritional studies on East African herbivores. II. Losses of nitrogen in the faeces. *Br. J. Nutr.* 33: 265–276.

Baer, D. J.; Oftedal, O. T.; Fahey, G. C. (1985): Feed selection and digestibility by captive giraffe. *Zoo Biol.* 4: 57–64.

Baines, T. H. (1965): Notes on the breeding of the Rocky Mountain goat and the care of other ungulates at Calgary zoo. *Int. Zoo Yb.* 5: 66–69.

Baker, D. L.; Hobbs, N. T. (1987): Strategies of digestion: digestive efficiency and retention time of forage diets in montane ungulates. *Can. J. Zool.* 65: 1978–1984.

Baker, D. L.; Stout, G. W.; Miller, M. W. (1998): A diet supplement for captive wild ruminants. *J. Zoo Wildl. Med.* 29: 150–156.

Berteaux, D.; Crête, M.; Huot, J.; Maltais, J.; Ouellet, J. P. (1998): Food choice by white-tailed deer in relation to protein and energy content of the diet: a field experiment. *Oecologia* 115: 84–92.

Blankenship, L. H. (1977): Diets (natural and synthetic): Gazelle. In: *CRC Handbook Series in Nutrition and Food* (M. Rechcigl, ed.). Section G: Diets, Culture Media, Food Supplements, Vol. I: Diets for Mammals. Cleveland: CRC Press Inc., pp. 381–418.

Bo, S.; Hjeljord, O. (1991): Do continental moose ranges improve during cloudy summers? *Can. J. Zool.* 69: 1875–1879.

Brambell, M. R. (1977): Diets of mammals at the London Zoo. In: *CRC Handbook Series in Nutrition and Food* (M. Rechcigl, ed.). Section G: Diets, Culture Media, Food Supplements, Vol. II: Food Habits of, and Diets for Invertebrates and Vertebrates – Zoo Diets. Cleveland: CRC Press Inc., pp. 381–387.

Brancker, W. M. (1980): Two cases of idiopathic ileus in giraffes. *Br. Vet. Zool. Soc. Newsl.* 10: 3.

Carhart, A. H. (1943): Fallacies in winter feeding of deer. *Trans. North Am. Wildl. Conf.* 8: 333–338.

Chai, K.; Kennedy, P. M.; Milligan, L. P. (1984): Reduction in particle size during rumination in cattle. *Can. J. Anim. Sci.* 64 (Suppl.): 339–340.

Choshniak, I.; Arnon, H.; Shkolnik, A. (1984): Digestive efficiency in a wild goat: the Nubian ibex. *Can. J. Anim. Sci.* 64 (Suppl.): 160–162.

Clauss, M.; Lechner-Doll, M. (2001): Differences in selective reticulo-ruminal particle retention as a key factor in ruminant diversification. *Oecologia* 129: 321–327.

Clauss, M.; Kienzle, E.; Wiesner, H. (2001a): A survey of the nutrition of captive moose in Europe. *Proc. Soc. Nutr. Physiol.* 10: 34.

Clauss, M.; Lechner-Doll, M.; Behrend, A.; Lason, K.; Lang, D.; Streich, W. J. (2001b): Particle retention in the forestomach of a browsing ruminant, the roe deer. *Acta Theriol.* 46: 103–107.

Clauss, M.; Lechner-Doll, M.; Streich, W. J. (2002a): Faecal particle size distribution in captive wild ruminants: an approach to the browser/grazer-dichotomy from the other end. *Oecologia* 131: 343–349.

Clauss, M.; Lechner-Doll, M.; Flach, E. J.; Wisser, J.; Hatt, J. M. (2002b): Digestive tract pathology in captive giraffe – a unifying hypothesis. *Proc. EAZWV Conf.* 4: 99–107.

Clauss, M.; Lechner-Doll, M.; Streich, W. J. (2003): Ruminant diversification as an adaptation to the physicomechanical characteristics of forage. A reevaluation of an old debate and a new hypothesis. *Oikos* 102: 253–262.

Cowan, R. L. (1982): Application of fundamental principles of nutrition in feeding captive wild animals. *Proc. Ann. Dr. Scholl Conf. Nutr. Captive Wild Anim.* 2: 17–24.

Cullison, A. E. (1961): Effect of physical form of the ration on steer performance and certain rumen phenomena. *J. Anim. Sci.* 20: 478–483.

Demment, M. W.; Van Soest, P. J. (1985) : A nutritional explanation for body-size patterns of ruminant and nonruminant herbivores. *Am. Nat.* 125: 641–672.

Dinglreiter, S. (2000): *Eine Feldstudie über die Fütterung ausgewählter Zoowiederkäuer.* [dissertation] University of Munich, Germany.

Dissen, J. (1983): *Untersuchungen über die Verdaulichkeit von Rohnährstoffen verschiedener Futterrationen an Rehwild und Ziegen sowie Beobachtungen über das Äsungsverhalten von Gehege-Rehen.* [dissertation] University of Bonn, Germany.

Dollinger, P. (1973): Analyse der Wiederkäuerverluste des Züricher Zoos von 1954 bis 1972. *Verh. Ber. Erkr. Zootiere* 15: 21–23.

Doman, E. R.; Rasmussen, D. I. (1944): Supplemental winter feeding of mule deer in Northern Utah. *J. Wildl. Manage.* 8: 317–338.

Eisfeld, D. (1982): Stickstoff-Verwertung des Rehes bei Stickstoff-Mangel. *Zbl. Vet. Med.* 29A: 375–386.

Elze, K.; Krische, G.; Eulenberger, K.; Schueppel, K. F. (1978): Pansenazidose und Pansenalkalose bei Zoowiederkäuern. *Verh. Ber. Erkr. Zootiere* 20: 101–107.

Eriksson, S.; Schmekel, J. (1962): A comparison between the ability of reindeer and sheep to digest their feed. *Kungl. Lantbrukshögsk Ann.* 28: 175–180.

Eulenberger, K.; Schueppel, K. F.; Krische, G.; Haupt, W.; Selbitz, H. J.; Schyra, A.; Seifert, S.; Elze, K. (1985): Beitrag zum Krankheitsgeschehen und zur Narkose bei Cerviden. *Verh. Ber. Erkr. Zootiere* 27: 37–54.

Foose, T. J. (1982): *Trophic strategies of ruminant versus nonruminant ungulates.* [PhD disertation] University of Chicago.

Fox, H. (1938): The giraffe. Some notes upon the natural characters of this animals, its care and its misfortune. *Report Penrose Res. Lab.*, pp. 35–67.

Fowler, M. E. (1978): Peracute Mortality in Captive Giraffe. *JAVMA* 173: 1088–1093.

Franz, W.; Ehrlichmann, D.; Kirste, M.; Heymann, H.; Jacob, A. (1984): Zum Tetanus bei Giraffen. *Verh. Ber. Erkr. Zootiere* 26: 399–404.

Fundova, A. (1974): Nutrition and feeding of African ungulates during quarantine at Dvur Kralove Zoo. *Int. Zoo Yb.* 15: 75–78.

Giesecke, D.; van Gylswyk, N. O. (1975): A study of feeding types and certain rumen functions in six species of South African wild ruminants. *J. Agric. Sci.* (Camb) 85: 75–83.

Gorgas, M.; Lindau, K. H.; Marholdt, D. (1978): Geburts- und Aufzucht-Probleme bei Kap-Giraffen im Kölner Zoo. *Tieraerztl. Praxis* 6: 113–118.

Gradwell, D. V. (1976): A case of abomasal impaction in a captive giraffe. *Koedoe* 19: 179–180.

Grisham, J.; Savage, B. (1990): Hoofstock management at Oklahoma City Zoo. *Int. Zoo Yb.* 29: 212–219.

Grzimek, B. (ed.) (1988): *Grzimeks Enzyklopaedie der Säugetiere,* Vol. V. München: Kindler Verlag.

Gutzwiller, A. (1984): *Beitrag zur Ernährung der Zoosäugetiere.* [dissertation] University of Zurich, Switzerland.

Hatt, J. M. (1994): Anwendung des Computer-Fütterungsprogrammes Animal Nutritionist im Zoologischen Garten Zürich unter besonderer Berücksichtigung der Wiederkäuer. [dissertation] University of Zurich, Switzerland.

Hatt, J. M.; Hauser, B.; Baumgartner, R.; Isenbuegel, E. (1995): Sektionsergebnisse bei Wiederkäuern im Zoo Zürich – eine Auswertung unter spezieller Berücksichtigung fütterungsbedingter Erkrankungen. *Verh. Ber. Erkr. Zootiere* 37: 259–265.

Heptner, W. G.; Nasimowitsch, A. A. (1974): *Der Elch.* Neue Brehm-Bücherei, Wittenberg, Germany: A. Ziemsen Verlag.

Herceg, M.; Huber, I.; Maran, B. (1973): Sektionsergebnisse bei Wiederkäuern des Zoologischen Gartens der Stadt Zagreb. *Verh. Ber. Erkr. Zootiere* 15: 15–20.

Hinders, R. C.; Vidacs, G. Y.; Ward, G. M. (1961): Effects of feeding dehydrated alfalfa pellets as the only roughage to dairy cows. *J. Dairy Sci.* 44: 1178.

Hjeljord, O.; Sundstøl, F.; Haagenrud, H. (1982): The nutritional value of browse to moose. *J. Wildl. Manage.* 46: 333–343.

Hofmann, R. R. (1973): The ruminant stomach. *E. Afr. Monogr. Biol.* 2: 1–354.

Hofmann, R. R. (1989): Evolutionary steps of ecophysiological adaptation and diversification of ruminants: a comparative view of their digestive system. *Oecologia* 78: 443–457.

Hofmann, R. R.; Matern, B. (1988): Changes in gastrointestinal morphology related to nutrition in giraffes: a comparison of wild and zoo specimens. *Int. Zoo Yb.* 27: 168–176.

Hofmann, R. R.; Nygren, K. (1992): Ruminal mucosa as indicator of nutritional status in wild and captive moose. *Alces Suppl.* 1: 77–83.

Hofmann, R. R.; Kock, R. A.; Ludwig, J.; Axmacher, H. (1988): Seasonal changes in rumen papillary development and body condition in free ranging Chinese water deer. *J. Zool.* (Lond) 216: 103–117.

Holter, J. B.; Hayes, H. H.; Smith, S. H. (1979): Protein requirement of yearling white-tailed deer. *J. Wildl. Manage.* 43: 872–879.

Iason, G. R.; Van Wieren, S. E. (1998): Adaptations of mammalian herbivores to low quality forage. In: *Herbivores, plants and predators* (H. Olff, V. K. Brown, R. H. Drent, eds.). Oxford: Blackwell Science, pp. 337–369.

Inoué, T.; Brookes, I. M.; Kolver, E. S.; Barry, T. N. (1994): Effects of leaf shear breaking load on the feeding value of perennial ryegrass for sheep. II. Effects on feed intake, particle breakdown, rumen digesta outflow and animal performance. *J. Agric. Sci.* (Camb) 123: 137–147.

Ippen, R. (1967): Auswertung der bei 1400 Zoo- und Wildtieren (Mammalia) erhobenen Zerlegungsbefunde. *Zbl. Vet. Med.* 14B: 293–320.

Ippen, R.; Henne, D. (1985): Ein Beitrag zu den Erkrankungen der Cerviden. *Verh. Ber. Erkr. Zootiere* 27: 7–16.

Ippen, R.; Henne, D. (1988): Auswertung der Obduktionsbefunde bei 2000 Artiodactyla. *Verh. Ber. Erkr. Zootiere* 30: 5–24.

Kick, C. H.; Gerlaugh, P.; Schalk, A. F. (1937): The effect of mechanical processing of feeds on the mastication and rumination of steers. *J. Agr. Res.* 55: 587–592.

Kim, K. H.; Jeon, B. T.; Kim, Y. C.; Kyung, B. H.; Kim, C. W. (1996): A comparison of oak browse and silages of rye and maize with respect to voluntary intake, digestibility, nitrogen balance and rumination time in penned Korean sika deer. *Anim. Feed Sci. Technol.* 61: 351–359.

Kiupel, H. (1988): Sektionsergebnisse bei Paarhufern (Artiodactyla). *Verh. Ber. Erkr. Zootiere* 30: 29–34.

Klein, D. R.; Schonheyder, F. (1970): Variation in ruminal nitrogen levels among some cervidae. *Can. J. Zool.* 48: 1437–1442.

Klöppel, G. (1976): Giraffe und Okapi. In: *Zootierkrankheiten* (H. G. Klös, E. M. Lang, eds.). Berlin, Germany: P. Parey, pp. 206–213.

Kozaki, M.; Oura, R.; Sekine, J. (1991): Studies on digestion physiology of herbivorous feral animals. II. The comparison of intake of total digestible nutrients among diverse sizes of ruminant and monogastric animals. *J. Fac. Agric. Tottori Univ.* 27: 61–68.

Kronberger, H.; Schueppel, K. F.; Altmann, D. (1974): Erfahrungen aus postmortalen Untersuchungen von Tieren des Thüringer Zooparks Erfurt. *Verh. Ber. Erkr. Zootiere* 16: 297–302.

Kumar, R.; Singh, M. (1984): Tannins – their adverse role in ruminant nutrition. *J. Agric. Food Chem.* 32: 447–453.

Kurkela, P. (1976): Prospects for reindeer husbandry based on grass and silage feeding. *Acta Vet. Scand.* Suppl. 60: 1–75.

Landowski, V. J. (1969): Künstliche Aufzucht und Entwicklung junger Elche. *Zool. Garten* NF 36: 327–336.

Lechner-Doll, M.; Kaske, M.; von Engelhardt, W. (1991): Factors affecting the mean retention time of particles in the forestomach of ruminants and camelids.In: *Physiological aspects of digestion and metabolism in ruminants* (T. Tsuda, Y. Saaski, R. Kawashima, eds.). San Diego: Academic Press, pp. 455–482.

Lees, G. L.; Howarth, R. E.; Goplen, B. P. (1982): Morphological characteristics of leaves from some legume forages: relation to digestion and mechanical strength. *Can. J. Bot.* 60: 2126–2132.

Lindau, K. H. (1966): Analyse der Tierverluste des Kölner Zoo in den Jahren 1961 bis 1964. *Verh. Ber. Erkr. Zootiere* 8: 239–247.

Lintzenich, B. A.; Ward, A. M. (1997): *Hay and pellet ratios: considerations in feeding ungulates.* AZA Nutrition Advisory Group Handbook, Fact Sheet 006.

Luick, J. R. (1977): Diets for captive reindeer. In: *CRC Handbook Series in Nutrition and Food. Section G: Diets, Culture Media, Food Supplements. Vol. I. Diets for Mammals* (M. Rechcigl, ed.). Cleveland, Ohio: CRC Press Inc, pp. 279–292.

Maloiy, G. M. O.; Clemens, E. T.; Kamau, J. M. (1982): Aspects of digestion and in vitro rumen fermentation rate in six species of East African wild ruminants. *J. Zool.* (Lond) 197: 345–353.

Marholdt, F. (1991): Fütterungsbedingte, morphologische Veränderungen der Vormagenschleimhaut von 67 Zoo-Wiederkäuern im Vergleich mit wildlebenden Wiederkäuern. [dissertation] University of Giessen, Germany.

Matern, B.; Klöppel, G. (1995): Giraffe und Okapi. In: Krankheiten der Zoo- und Wildtiere (R. Göltenboth, H. G. Klös, eds.). Berlin, Germany: Blackwell Wissenschafts-Verlag, pp. 284–299.

McEwan, E. H.; Whitehead, P. E. (1970): Seasonal changes in the energy and nitrogen intake in reindeer and caribou. *Can. J. Zool.* 48: 905–913.

McLeod, M. N.; Kennedy, P. M.; Minson, D. J. (1990): Resistance of leaf and stem fractions of tropical forage to chewing and passage in cattle. *Br. J. Nutr.* 63: 105–119.

Mikulica, V.; Mikulicova, E.; Moucha, P.; Vahala, J. (1984): Postmortale Untersuchungsergebnisse bei Antilopen im Zoologischen Garten Dvur Kralove. *Verh. Ber. Erkr. Zootiere* 26: 273–278.

Montali, R. J.; Freeman, R. A.; Collins, L.; Wemmer, C.; Bush, M. (1985): Pathology survey of captive cervids at the National Zoological Park. *Verh. Ber. Erkr. Zootiere* 27: 17–28.

Mould, E. D.; Robbins, C. T. (1981): Nitrogen metabolism in elk. *J. Wildl. Manage.* 45: 323–334.

Nagy, J. G.; Hakonson, T.; Knox, K. L. (1969): Effects of quality on food intake in deer. *Proc. N. Am. Wildl. Conf.* 34: 146–154.

Owen-Smith, N. (1996): Distinctive features of the nutritional ecology of browsing versus grazing ruminants. *Proc. Int. Symp. Physiol. Ethol. Wild and Zoo Anim.* 1: 176–191.

Priebe, J. C.; Brown, R. D. (1987): Protein requirements of subadult nilgai antelope. *Comp. Biochem. Physiol.* 88A: 495–501.

Prins, R. A.; Rooymans, T. P.; Veldhuizen, M.; Domhof, M. A.; Cliné-Theil, W. (1983): Extent of plant cell wall digestion in several species of wild ruminants kept in the zoo. *Zool. Garten* NF 53: 393–403.

Radostis, O. M.; Gay, C. C.; Blood, D. C.; Hinchcliff, K. W. (1999): *Veterinary medicine. A textbook of the diseases of cattle, sheep, pigs, goats and horses.* 9th ed. London/New York: WB Saunders.

Ratcliffe, H. L. (1966): Diets for zoological gardens: aids to conservation and disease control. *Int. Zoo Yb.* 6: 4–23.

Renecker, L. A. (2001): Nutrition of the enigmatic browser: comparative bioenergetics, digestion and feeding of northern versus tropical ungulates. *Proc. NAG Conf.* 4: 136–142.

Robbins, C. T. (1993): *Wildlife feeding and nutrition.* San Diego: Academic Press Inc.

Robbins, C. T.; Prior, R. L.; Moen, A. N.; Visek, W. J. (1974): Nitrogen metabolism of white-tailed deer. *J. Anim. Sci.* 38: 186–191.

Rowell, A.; Dyer, J.; Hofmann, R. R.; Lechner-Doll, M.; Meyer, H. H. D.; Shirazi-Beechey, S. P.; Wood, I. S. (1996): The expression of intestinal sodium-glucose cotransporters in cervids. *Proc. Int. Symp. Physiol. Ethol. Wild and Zoo Anim.* 1: 204–208.

Schoonveld, G. G.; Nagy, J. G.; Bailey, J. A. (1974): Capability of mule deer to utilize fibrous alfalfa diets. *J. Wildl. Manage.* 38: 823–829.

Schwartz, C. C. (1980): A formulated ration for captive moose. *Alces* 16: 82–105.

Schwartz, C. C. (1992): Techniques of moose husbandry in North America. *Alces* Suppl. 1: 177–192.

Schwartz, C. C.; Hundertmark, K. J. (1993): Supplemental feeding of moose during winter: Can hay serve as an emergency ration? *Alces* 29: 135–147.

Schwartz, C. C.; Regelin, W. L.; Franzmann, A. W. (1987a): Protein digestion in moose. *J. Wildl. Manage.* 51: 352–357.

Schwartz, C. C.; Regelin, W. L.; Franzmann, A. W. (1987b): Nutritional energetics of moose. *Swedish Wildl. Res.* Suppl 1: 265–280.

Sedgewick, C. J.; Fowler, M. E. (1973): Methods of feeding mammals. *Proc. AAZV*, pp. 177–221.

Shochat, E.; Robbins, C. T.; Parish, S. M.; Young, P. B.; Stephenson, T. R.; Tamayo, A. (1997): Nutritional investigations and management of captive moose. *Zoo Biol.* 16: 479–494.

Sikarskie, J. G.; Brockway, C. R.; Ullrey, D. E.; Schmitt, S. M.; Nellist, J. T.; Cooley, T. M.; Pao, K. K. (1988): Dietary protein and hoof growth in juvenile female white-tailed deer. *J. Zoo Anim. Med.* 19: 18–23.

Skinner, J. D. (1977): Diets (natural and synthetic): antelopes. In: *CRC Handbook Series in Nutrition and Food. Section G: Diets, Culture Media, Food Supplements* (M. Rechcigl, ed.), Vol. I: Diets for Mammals. Cleveland, Ohio: CRC Press Inc, pp. 419–422.

Smith, A. D. (1952): Digestibility of some native forages for mule deer. *J. Wildl. Manage.* 16: 309–312.

Spalinger, D. E.; Robbins, C. T.; Hanley, T. A. (1986): The assessment of handling time in ruminants: the effect of plant chemical and physical structure on the rate of breakdown of plant particles in the rumen of mule deer and elk. *Can. J. Zool.* 64: 312–321.

Steger, G. (1973): Untersuchungsergebnisse an 1500 Objekten aus der Gruppe der wildlebenden Wiederkäuer. *Verh. Ber. Erkr. Zootiere* 15: 25–34.

Steger, G.; Lackermeier, S. (1985): Die Cerviden im Nürnberger Untersuchungsgut. *Verh. Ber. Erkr. Zootiere* 27: 29–35.

Topps, J. H. (1977): Diets for wild ruminants. In: *CRC Handbook Series in Nutrition and Food. Section G: Diets, Culture Media, Food Supplements* (M. Rechcigl, ed.), Vol. I: Diets for Mammals. Cleveland, Ohio: CRC Press Inc., pp. 423–432.

Treichler, J. (1972): Ein Beitrag zur Ernährung des Rehwildes unter besonderer Berücksichtigung der verschiedenen Möglichkeiten der Winterfütterung. [dissertation] TiHo Hannover, Germany.

Troelsen, J. E.; Bigsby, F. W. (1964): Artificial mastication – a new approach for predicting voluntary forage consumption by ruminants. *J. Anim. Sci.* 23: 1139–1142.

Troelsen, J. E.; Campbell, J. B. (1969): Voluntary consumption of forage by sheep and its relation to the size and shape of particles in the digestive tract. *Anim. Prod.* 10: 289–296.

Trusk, A. M.; Murphy, M. R.; Crissey, S.; Petric, A. (1991): Effect of age on digestibility in exotic ruminants. *Proc. Ann. Dr. Scholl Conf. Nutr. Captive Wild Anim.* 8: 115–131.

Ullrey, D. E. (1973): Nutritional management of exotic ruminants and interrelationships with disease. *Verh. Ber. Erkr. Zootiere* 15: 113–116.

Valtonen, M. H.; Uusi-Rauva, A.; Salonen, J. (1983): Rate of digesta passage in reindeer and sheep. *Acta Zool. Fenn.* 175: 65–67.

Van Soest, P. J. (1994): *Nutritional Ecology of the Ruminant.* 2nd ed. Ithaca: Cornell University Press.

Van Soest, P. J. (1996): Allometry and ecology of feeding behavior and digestive capacity in herbivores: a review. *Zoo Biol.* 15: 455–479.

Van Soest, P.J.; Dierenfeld, E. S.; Conklin, N. L. (1995): Digestive strategies and limitations of ruminants. In: *Ruminant physiology: digestion, metabolism, growth and reproduction* (W. von Engelhardt, ed.). Proc. VIII. Int. Symp. on Ruminant Physiol. Berlin/New York: Ferdinand Enke Verlag, pp. 579–597.

Van Wieren, S. E. (1996a): Browsers and grazers: Foraging strategies in ruminants. In: S. E. Van Wieren: *Digestive Strategies in Ruminants and Nonruminants.* [PhD dissertation] Landbouw University of Wageningen, Netherlands, pp. 119–145.

Van Wieren, S. E. (1996b): Nutrient extraction from mixed grass-browse diets by goats and sheep. In: S. E. Van Wieren: *Digestive Strategies in Ruminants and Nonruminants.* [PhD dissertation] Landbouw University of Wageningen, Netherlands, pp. 67–80.

Wackernagel, H. (1966): Feeding wild animals in zoological gardens. *Int. Zoo Yb.* 6: 23–37.

Weis, G. B. (1991): AFS-Silage für das Wild – Schutz für den Wald! *Die Pirsch* 8, 12. April 1991.

Zwart, P.; de Jonge, B; van der Hage, M. H.; Dorrestein, G. M. (1988): Erkrankungen bei einigen Wiederkäuern in den Niederlanden. *Verh. Ber. Erkr. Zootiere* 30: 25–28.

*M. Clauss*[1]

# Tannins in the nutrition of wild animals: a review

***Abstract***

*Many free-ranging wild animals consume significant amounts of tannins and other polyphenolics. Historically, attention has focused on their negative effects: tannins reduce apparent digestibility, impair the use of absorbed nutrients, can be toxic and reduce the palatability of many forages. Thus, tannins act as feeding deterrents. However, recently the antioxidant and cardioprotective potential of tannins / polyphenolics has been emphasized in human nutrition.*

*Wild animals in captivity are fed a diet relatively low in tannins. It has been hypothesized that this might lead to a "lacking" in species that have evolutionarily adapted to and potentially become dependent on tannins. Potentially positive effects of tannins are a reduction in ruminal protein degradation with an increased flow of valuable amino acids into the lower gut, the prevention of bloat, a reduction of gastrointestinal parasites and of pathogenic bacteria, and the chelation of iron. With respect to iron chelation, it could be hypothesized that some species have evolutionarily adapted to a natural diet with low iron availability due to its tannin content, and therefore cannot restrict iron absorption on captive diets high in available iron.*

*Several observations from zoos can be compared to these effects. Especially, but not exclusively during the transition from the wild into captivity, many folivorous animals suffer from gastrointestinal disorders such as bloat, enteritis and helmithic infestations. Long-lived species whose natural diet contains tannins can suffer from cardiovascular disease in captivity. Additionally, some folivorous, hindgut-fermenting species develop excessive iron storage on captive diets. It is tempting to suggest the lack of tannins as an underlying factor.*

*The potentially beneficial effects of a more natural dietary tannin supply should be investigated, especially with respect to the antioxidant properties of polyphenolics in the face of iron storage disease. However, studies on the possibility to prevent the mentioned conditions by other dietary means, most notably a reduction in overall concentrate intake, should also be performed.*

***Keywords***

*polyphenolics, iron storage disease, bloat, antioxidant, enteritis, concentrate feeds*

[1] Institute of Physiology, Physiological Chemistry and Animal Nutrition, Veterinary Faculty of the Ludwigs-Maximilians-University of Munich, Germany; Veterinaerstr. 13, 80539 Munich, Germany; Tel.: ++49 89 2180 2554, Fax: ++49 89 2180 3208, Email: clauss@tiph.vetmed.uni-muenchen.de

## Objective

The natural diet of many wild animals contains significant amounts of tannins and other polyphenolics. In contrast, most dietary items fed as staple diets in zoological collections contain little or no tannins or related polyphenolics. It is this general discrepancy that triggers our recent interest in the role tannins could play in the nutrition of different animal species.

The existing literature on tannins and their interplay with animal organisms is immense. It would be beyond the scope of this contribution to review all existing publications that cover animal species of interest to the zoo community. It is therefore the aim of this review to raise common awareness and hopefully increase the interest in the tannin issue, and to show up directions future research could follow up.

## 1 Introduction

Polyphenolics comprise a vast variety of compounds defined by their chemical nature, i.e. the phenol unit that is the core structure of them all. These compounds can not be produced by animals, who encounter them as an ubiquitous part of plant forage (Hagerman and Butler 1991). Some polyphenolics may be absorbed, while others may not. Polyphenolics contribute to the colour, structure, chemical properties, nutritive value and taste of plant products.

Traditionally, several groups of polyphenolics have been known by a single comprehensive name, like "tannins" or "lignins". Such distinctions have developed according to chemical analyses that could detect a specific group of polyphenolics, or due to functions or effects of certain groups. However, even a seemingly uniform group like the lignins consists of a variety of compounds, and some of the "condensed tannins" are chemically closer to the group of "flavonoids" than to the "hydrolyzable tannins" (Bravo 1998). Readers interested in the biochemical features and structural differences between the different tannins, flavonoids and related polyphenolics are referred to Hagerman and Butler (1991) or Bravo (1998).

Due to the complexity of the chemical analyses, the results of many studies cannot be related to a single component and often not even a certain group, but could as well be due to effects of other polyphenolic substances, that occur in parallel to the ones described, but have not been analyzed for. The "condensed tannins" of one plant may have an effect that cannot be duplicated by the tannins of a related plant species – Clausen et al. (1990) showed that when offered exactly same amounts of condensed tannins of two plant species, snowshoe hares (*Lepus americanus*) rejected one over the other, the difference probably being due to a difference in chemical tannin structure. Complex polyphenolics such as tannins may be broken down into smaller units, which may differ in their effects and may even resemble that of the flavonoids. Therefore, all generalizations have to be treated with caution. Caution is especially necessary when transferring effects attained by the commercially available tannin sources – tannic acid and quebracho, that both consist of a variety of polyphenolic constituents – to the effect of natural forage (Hagerman et al. 1992).

## 2 Negative effects of tannins

For quite a long time, especially the negative effects of tannins and related polyphenolics have been studied, and they have been the main protagonists in the postulated "arms race" between plants and the animals who feed on them. Tannins bind to cell solubles and cell walls (Reed 1995), they reduce the (apparent) nutrient digestibility by interfering with bacterial fermentation processes (Makkar et al. 1995), by binding to digestive enzymes (Oh et al. 1985), by increasing endogenous losses, especially of protein (Shahkhalili et al. 1990), and by impairing the use of absorbed nutrients (Butler and Rogler 1992). They have toxic effects (Kumar and Singh 1984) and reduce the palatability of many plants (Cooper and Owen-Smith 1985). Therefore, they act as feeding deterrents (e.g. Provenza et al. 1990). In recent years, it has been repeatedly stressed that the anti-feeding effect of tannins is not due to potential reduction in nutrient digestibility but mainly due to their toxic effects (Mole and Waterman 1987, Bryant et al. 1991) and the according additional energetic costs they impose for detoxification processes (Illius and Jessop 1995, Foley et al. 1995). These additional costs become evident in feeding experiments where the urinary energy excretion is increased and metabolizable energy (ME) gain accordingly reduced for diets with secondary compounds, although the digestible energy (DE) intake is comparable to that of control diets without these compounds (e.g. moose *Alces alces* – Schwartz et al. 1987, greater glider *Petauroides volans* - Foley 1987, general - Robbins 1993). The most extensive review on the physiological effects of tannins is given by Foley et al. (1999).

## 3 Ecological studies

A large number of studies has documented tannins in the natural forage of wild animals. In particular, ecologists have tried to demonstrate an effect of the tannin content of different potential forages on the food choice of the animals under investigation. A collation of several of these investigations is presented in table 1. Looking at this table, the reader is advised to be careful in making comparisons and deductions – the methods used in the individual studies, both analytical and statistical, are often not comparable. If the table quotes that the animals "avoid tannins", this does not mean that tannins are the only factor determining diet choice. In most cases, tannins are just one determining factor among several. As most herbivores cannot completely avoid the ingestion of tannin-containing material but just minimize the amount of ingested tannins, Foley et al. (1999) emphasize that it is appropriate in only relatively few situations to investigate the scientific hypothesis that a herbivorous mammal avoids secondary plant compounds; rather it would be more informative to ask how the animal controls and limits the intake of these substances. The table can be used to compare general trends among animal species. It does not answer the most interesting comparative question, namely the threshold for maximum tannin intake a species will naturally tolerate, and the maximum tannin levels that occur in its natural diet. Therefore, the fact that e.g. both giraffe (*Giraffa camelopardalis*) and cattle are noted to "avoid tannins" does not reveal the fact that giraffes do tolerate a much higher tannin content in their natural diet than cattle. Both try to minimize their tannin intake, but on very different levels. The question whether any animal actively *selects* a diet that contains tannins has very rarely been adressed. Tixier et al. (1997) found that the natural diet selected by roe deer (*Capreolus capreolus*) contained not only higher amounts of soluble carbohydrates and protein than the average available forage, but also higher amounts of tannins. An active selection for dietary tannins (in a low dose) has, so far, only been reported for

**Table 1.** Examples of ecological studies on free-ranging wild animals that document the influence of tannins on diet choice.

| | **Species** | **Comments** | **Source** |
|---|---|---|---|
| REPTILES | Giant tortoises (*Testudo gigantea*) | avoid tannins | Swain (1976) |
| BIRDS | Canada geese (*Branta canadensis*) | avoid tannin-containing grasses | Volz and Clausen (2001) |
| | Canada geese (*Branta canadensis*) | avoid tannins | Buchsbaum et al. (1984) |
| | Greater snow geese (*Branta spp.*) | do not avoid tannins | Gauthier and Bedard (1990, 1991) |
| | Geese (*Ansa* and *Branta spp.*) | do not avoid tannins | Wink et al. (1993) |
| | Hoatzin (*Opisthocomus hoazin*) | cannot tolerate high tannin levels in forage | Jones et al. (2000) |
| | | | |
| MARSUPIAL | Philander opossum (*Caluromys philander*) | avoids tannins | Simmen et al. (1999) |
| | | | |
| RODENTS | Fox squirrel (*Sciurus niger*) | avoids tannic acid | Schmidt (2000) |
| | Grey squirrel (*Sciurus carolinensis*) | avoids tannins | Barthelmess (2001) |
| | Grey squirrel (*Sciurus carolinensis*) | avoids tannic acid | Smallwood and Peters (1986) |
| | Meadow voles (*Microtus pennsylvanicus*) | avoid phenolics | Bergeron and Jodoin (1987) |
| | Voles (*Microtus agrestis, Clethrionomys glareolus*) | avoid phenolics | Hjältén and Palo (1992) |
| LAGOMORPHS | Pika (*Ochotona princeps*) | consume a summer diet low in tannins and store a winter diet high in tannins | Dearing (1996) |
| | Hares (*Lepus timidus*) | avoid phenolics | Hjältén and Palo (1992) |
| | Mountain hare (*Lepus timidus*) | avoids phenolics | Tahvanainen et al. (1985) |
| ELEPHANT | Elephant (*Loxodonta africana*) | avoids phenolics | Jachmann (1989) |

| | Species | Comments | Source |
|---|---|---|---|
| RUMINANTS | Duiker (*Cephalophus spp.*) | do not seem to avoid tannins | Müller et al. (1998) |
| | Duiker (*Cephalophus spp.*) | do not avoid tannins | Faurie and Perrin (1993) |
| | Roe deer (*Capreolus capreolus*) | do not avoid tannins | Tixier et al. (1997) |
| | Mule deer and black-tailed deer (*Odocoileus hemionus spp.*) | do not avoid tannins | McArthur et al. (1993) |
| | Greater kudu (*Tragelaphus strepsiceros*) | avoids tannins | Cooper and Owen-Smith (1985), Cooper et al. (1988) |
| | Giraffe (*Giraffa camelopardalis*) | avoids tannins | Furstenburg and van Hoven (1994) |
| | Impala (*Aepyceros melampus*) | avoids tannins | Cooper and Owen-Smith (1985) , Cooper et al. (1988) |
| | Goat | avoids tannins | Cooper and Owen-Smith (1985) |
| | Cattle | avoids tannins | Wilkins et al. (1953), Donnelly (1954) |
| | African buffalo (*Syncerus caffer*) | avoids tannins | Field (1976) |
| PRIMATES | Lesser mouse lemur (*Microcebus murinus*) | avoids tannins | Simmen et al. (1999) |
| | Mouse lemur (*Microcebus rufus*) | avoids tannins | Ganzhorn (1988) |
| | Greater dwarf lemur (*Cheirogaleus major*) | does not avoid tannins | Ganzhorn (1988) |
| | Weasel sportive lemur (*Lepilemur m. mustelinus*) | avoids tannins | Ganzhorn (1988) |
| | Milne-Edward's sportive lemur (*Lepilemur m. edwardsi*) | seems to avoid tannins | Ganzhorn (1988) |
| | Lesser bamboo lemur (*Hapalemur griseus*) | avoids tannins | Ganzhorn (1988) |
| | Brown lemur (*Eulemur fulvus*) | does not avoid tannins | Ganzhorn (1988) |
| | Eastern woolly lemur (*Avahi l. laniger*) | does not avoid tannins | Ganzhorn et al. (1985) |
| | Western woolly lemur (*Avahi l. occidentalis*) | does not avoid tannins | Ganzhorn (1988) |
| | Coquerel's Sifaka (*Propithecus verreauxi coquereli*) | does not avoid tannins | Ganzhorn (1989) |
| | Indri (*Indri indri*) | does not avoid tannins | Ganzhorn (1988) |
| | Howler monkey (*Alouatta palliata*) | does not necessarily avoid tannins | Milton (1979) |
| | Howler monkey (*Alouatta palliata*) | avoids tannins | Glander (1981) |
| | Marmosets (*Callithrix jacchus, Callimico goeldii*) | avoid tannins | Simmen (1994) |
| | Vervet monkey (*Cercopithecus aethiops*) | avoids tannins | Wrangham and Waterman (1981) |

| | Species | Comments | Source |
|---|---|---|---|
| PRIMATES | Rhesus monkey (*Macaca mulatta*) | avoids tannins | Marks et al. (1987) |
| | Baboons (*Papio anubis*) | avoid phenolics | Barton and Whiten (1994) |
| | Silver leaf monkey (*Trachypithecus auratus sondaicus*) | seems to avoid tannins in leaves but does not seem to avoid tannins in fruits | Kool (1992) |
| | Banded leaf monkey (*Presbytis melalophos*) | does not avoid tannins | Davies et al. (1988) |
| | Red leaf monkey (*Presbytis rubicunda*) | does not avoid tannins | Davies et al. (1988) |
| | South Indian leaf-monkey (*Presbytis johnii*) | avoids tannins partially | Oates et al. (1980) |
| | Angolan black-and-white colobus (*Colobus angolensis*) | does not seem to avoid tannins | Moreno-Black and Bent (1982) |
| | Guereza (*Colobus guereza*) | avoids tannins | Oates et al. (1977) |
| | Black colobus monkey (*Colobus satanas*) | avoids tannins | McKey et al. (1981) |
| | Red colobus monkey (*Procolobus badius rufomitratus*) | no influence of tannins on food choice | Mowry et al. (1996) |
| | Orangutan (*Pongo pygmaeus*) | avoids tannins | Leighton (1993) |
| | Orangutan (*Pongo pygmaeus*) | avoids tannins | N. Gillis upubl., cited in Ganzhorn (1989) |
| | Gorilla (*Gorilla gorilla*) | does not avoid tannins | Calvert 1985 |
| | Chimpanzees (*Pan troglotydes*) | avoids tannins | Wrangham and Waterman (1983) |
| | Chimpanzees (*Pan troglotydes*) | seems to avoid tannins | Reynolds et al. (1998) |

roe deer (Verheyden-Tixier and Duncan 2000). Some unidentified secondary plant compounds may stimulate food intake in some frugivorous birds, e.g. garden warblers (*Sylvia borin*) and blackcaps (*Sylvia atricapilla*, Bairlein 1996). The consumption of plant parts with secondary compounds, including tannins, for medical reasons (pharmacognosy) has repeatedly been postulated for several vertebrate species (e.g. Janzen 1978, Carrai and Borgognini Tarli 2001), but mainly for chimpanzees (*Pan troglotydes*; e.g. Huffman and Seifu 1989).

## 4 Physiological studies

In order to elucidate the effects of tannins on several animal species, a large number of feeding trials has been performed over the years, a selection of which is summarized in table 2. This table comprises only data on captive wild animals and does not summarize the large number of feeding trials performed with laboratory or domestic animals, especially goats and sheep on tropical forages, and chicken. The reader should note that "digestibility" always refers to apparent digestibility; i.e. a reduction in digestibility, e.g. of protein, can always be due to a reduced true digestibility of the dietary protein or due to an increased loss of endogenous protein.

A true dietary requirement for tannins has never been established.

# 5 Adaptations to dietary tannins

## 5.1 Feeding behaviour

Browsing animals display different adaptations to secondary plant compounds in their natural forage. The most obvious adaptation is diet choice. Even between very closely-related species there can be significant differences in the adaptation to tannin-rich forages (e.g. woodrats *Neotoma spp.*, Atstatt and Ingram 1983). Animals avoid toxic or disadvantageous levels of tannins in their diet as long as they can. Learning – conditioned aversion – is important in avoiding negative effects (e.g. Provenza et al. 1990). Other behavioural adaptations have evolved in some species – e.g. voles (*Microtus pennsylvanicus*) have been observed to cut branches of young trees and leave them for several days before eating them, and it has been shown that levels of tannins decrease during this time period (Roy and Bergeron 1990).[2] Geophagy – the consumption of clays that adsorb tannins – has repeatedly been interpreted as a coping strategy (Hladik and Gueguen 1974, Oates 1978, Kreulen 1985, Davies and Baillie 1988, Johns and Duquette 1991, Mahaney et al. 1995, Setz et al. 1999, Wink et al. 1993, Munn 1994).

The habit of many herbivores to include a large number of plant species in their diet has been interpreted repeatedly as an adaptation to the content of secondary plant compounds in the forage – a wide range of different forage species means a wide range of different secondary plant compounds and avoids the accumulation of any one particular compound to toxic levels (e.g. Westoby 1974). As the rate of detoxification processes is likely to be correlated with the basal metabolic rate, which is generally higher in smaller animals, it could be postulated that smaller animals can afford to ingest higher rates of potentially toxic substances like tannins. In an analysis of the feeding records of 74 animal species, Freeland (1991) demonstrated that the number of plant species included in a natural diet increases with the size of the animal, probably because small animals can detoxify larger amounts of a particular plant toxin and therefore do not need to show the same degree of dietary variety as larger animals.

## 5.2 Morphophysiological adaptations

Another measurement that is possibly correlated with the detoxification capacity of an animal is its relative liver size, as most detoxification processes take place in the liver. It has been stated that browsing ruminants have larger

[2] A similar behaviour has been observed in a captive ringtail lemur (C. Wood, pers. comm.).

**Table 2.** Qualitative effects of tannins in feeding trials. TA = tannic acid; Q = quebracho tannin (condensed tannins); NP = natural phenolics (generally extracted from natural forage); ST = sorghum tannin; dosage as % of food offered; aD = apparent digestibility;

| | Species | Tannin used | Dose |
|---|---|---|---|
| FISH | Carp (*Cyprinus carpio*) | Q | **2%** |
| | Carp (*Cyprinus carpio*) | **TA** | 2% |
| BIRDS | Ruffed grouse (*Bonasa umbellus*) | Q | 6% |
| | Ruffed grouse (*Bonasa umbellus*) | Q | 8% |
| | Ruffed grouse (*Bonasa umbellus*) | TA | 8% |
| | Northern bobwhite (*Colinuus virginianus*) | Q | 3-6% |
| | Grey partridges (*Perdix perdix*) and Capercaillies (*Tetrao urogallus*) | Q | |
| | Pecking duck | ST | |
| | Acorn woodpecker (*Melanerpes formicivorus*) | Q | |
| | Acorn woodpecker (*Melanerpes formicivorus*) | TA | |
| | Garden warbler (*Sylvia borin*) and Blackcap (*Sylvia atricapilla*) | TA | 5-10% |
| MARSUPIALS | Brushtail possum (*Trichosurus vulpecula*) | NP | |
| | Brushtail possum (*Trichosurus vulpecula*) | Q | 3-6% |
| | Ringtail possum (*Pseudocheirus peregrinus*) | Q | 2,9-4,6% |
| | Ringtail possum (*Pseudocheirus peregrinus*) | NP | |
| | Parma wallaby (*Macropus parma*) | Q | 6% |
| | Red-bellied pademelon (*Thylogale billardierii*) | Q | 6% |
| | Red-bellied pademelon (*Thylogale billardierii*) | Q | 3% |
| BEARS | Black bear (*Ursus americanus*) | Q | 3-6% |
| LAGOMORPHS | Rabbit (*Oryctolagus cuniculus*) | TA | |
| | Mountain hare (*Lepus timidus*) | NP | |
| | European hare (*Lepus europaeus*) | NP | |
| | Pika (*Ochotona princeps*) | NP | |
| RODENTS | Rats | Q | 4% |
| | Meadow vole (*Microtus pennsylvanicus*) and Prairie vole (*Microtus ochrogaster*) | NP | |
| | Prairie vole (*Microtus ochrogaster*) | TA | 3-6% |
| | Prairie vole (*Microtus ochrogaster*) | Q | 3-6% |
| | Meadow vole (*Microtus pennsylvanicus*) | Q | 3% |
| | Meadow vole (*Microtus pennsylvanicus*) | Q | 6% |
| | Mexican woodrat (*Neotoma mexicana*) | Q | 7% |
| | Degu (*Octodon degus*) | TA | 1-4% |
| | Grey squirrel (*Scirurus carolinensis*) | NP | |
| | Grey squirrel (*Scirurus carolinensis*) | Q | 3-6% |
| | Grey squirrel (*Scirurus carolinensis*) | TA | 4-8% |
| RUMINANTS | Black-tailed deer (*Odocoileus hemionus sitkensis*) | NP | |
| | Mule deer (*Odocoileus hemionus*) | Q | 3-6% |
| | Mule deer (*Odocoileus hemionus*) | TA | 3-6% |
| | Mule deer (*Odocoileus hemionus*) | NP | |
| | Red deer (*Cervus elaphus*) | NP | 5,1-8,4% |
| | Steenbok (*Raphicerus campestris*) | TA | 1% |
| | Sheep (*Ovis aries*) | Q | 4-16% |
| | Sheep (*Ovis aries*) | Q | 5% |
| | Sheep (*Ovis aries*) | Q | 5% |
| | Sheep (*Ovis aries*) | Q | 3-6% |
| | Sheep (*Ovis aries*) | Q | 3-6% |
| | Sheep (*Ovis aries*) | TA | 3-6% |

CP = crude protein; DM = dry matter; DMI = dry matter intake; BW = body weight; DE = digestible energy; ME = metabolisable energy; NDF = neutral detergent fibre.

| Effects | Source |
|---|---|
| **no effect** | Becker and Makkar 1999 |
| toxicity/ refusal to feed | Becker and Makkar 1999 |
| no effect, increase of caecal faeces volume | Hewitt et al. 1997 |
| loss of BM, reduced DMI | Hewitt et al. 1997 |
| extreme reduction in DMI and BW | Hewitt et al. 1997 |
| no effect but increase of caecal faeces volume | Hewitt et al. 1997 |
| lowered nitrogen concentration in caecal faeces | Luikkonen 2001 |
| reduction in energy and nitrogen absorption | King et al. 2000 |
| reduction of ME | Koenig 1991 |
| reduction of ME | Koenig 1991 |
| loss of BW, reduced DMI | Bairlein 1996 |
| depression of DMI, ME (urinary losses) and fibre aD | Foley and Hume 1987 |
| no reduction in DM aD, NDF aD, CP aD, nitrogen balance, no reduction of ME | McArthur and Sanson 1993b |
| no reduction in DM aD, NDF aD, CP aD, nitrogen balance, no reduction of ME | McArthur and Sanson 1993b |
| no reduction of weight gain, DMI, DM aD or CP aD | McArthur and Sanson 1991 |
| reduced DM aD and CP aD, all tannins recovered in faeces | McArthur and Sanson 1993a |
| no reduction in DM aD, increase of NDF aD, lower CP aD, tannin only partially recovered in faeces | McArthur and Sanson 1993a |
| no effect, tannin only partially recovered in faeces | McArthur and Sanson 1993a |
| reduction in DM aD, CP aD | Robbins et al. 1991 |
| Toxicity | Dollahite et al. 1962 |
| reduced DMI, CP aD, no reduction in DM aD, no increased renal sodium losses | Iason and Palo 1991 |
| reduced DMI, CP aD, no reduction in DM aD, increased renal sodium losses | Iason and Palo 1991 |
| reduction in DM aD, CP aD, fibre aD, increase of urinary losses | Dearing 1997 |
| reduced DMI, daily weight gain, CP aD, body fat deposition | Dawson et al. 1999 |
| reduced growth, CP aD, DM aD, increased DMI | Lindroth et al. 1986 |
| reduced growth | Lindroth and Batzli 1984 |
| drastic reduction of DMI | Lindroth and Batzli 1984 |
| no effects | Dietz et al. 1994 |
| reduced DMI (adaptation after several days), loss of BW (adaptation after several days), increase in mortality, lower CP aD | Dietz et al. 1994 |
| decrease in DMI, loss of BW, high mortality | Voltura and Wunder 1994 |
| no effect on BW, increase of DMI | Bozinovic et al. 1997 |
| reduction in DMI, CP aD, and increase of urinary losses | Chung-MacCoubrey et al. 1997 |
| reduced DE, CP aD | Chung-MacCoubrey et al. 1997 |
| reduced DE, CP aD, increase of urinary losses | Chung-MacCoubrey et al. 1997 |
| reduction in DM aD, DM aD, soluble cell contents aD | Hanley et al. 1992 |
| reduction in DM aD, CP aD, 100 % of ingested tannin excreted in faeces | Robbins et al. 1991 |
| no reduction in CP aD | Hagerman et al. 1992 |
| reduction in CP aD | Hagerman et al. 1992 |
| higher DMI, higher weight gains, greater carcass weights | Hoskin et al. 1999 |
| reduction DE, CP aD, fibre aD | Hay and Van Hoven 1988 |
| reduction of intestinal helminths; no impact on abomasal helminths | Athanasiadou et al. 2001 |
| reduced DM aD, CP aD, NDF aD, more nitorgen in faeces and less in urine, mucosal ulceration and histiocytes in jejunum and ileum | Dawson et al. 1999 |
| no depression of liveweight gain, reduction of faecal egg count | Butter et al. 2000 |
| reduction in faecal egg count | Athanasiadou et al. 2000 |
| reduction in DM aD, CP aD, NDF aD; only 60 % of ingested tannin excreted in faeces | Robbins et al. 1991 |
| no reduction in CP aD | Hagerman et al. 1992 |

livers than grazing ruminants of comparable body size (Hofmann 1989), and a similar observation has been made for the browser black rhino (*Diceros bicornis*) as compared to the grazer white rhino (*Ceratotherum simum*, Kock and Garnier 1993). It is likely that comparative data collections for other species, e.g. for primates, would reveal the same pattern.

Salivary proteins of many animals have been shown to bind tannins (table 3), and their occurence in browsing species and absence in grazing species has been interpreted as a physiological defense against potentially damaging effects of tannins. This dietary protection is an important contributing factor to the fact that some browsing animals do not show the same adverse or negative reactions to tannins as some other species (c.f. table 1 and 2). The exact mechanism by which tannin-binding salivary proteins function has not been elucidated yet, and experimental results are partially contradictory. The current state of knowledge is summarized by Foley et al. (1999). Browsing ruminants have larger salivary glands than grazing ruminants (Hofmann 1973, 1989, Kay 1987). The greater kudu (*Tragelaphus strepsiceros*) is a browser (Hofmann 1989) that has exceptionally small salivary glands (Robbins et al. 1995). Therefore, it should be exceptionally unprotected against secondary plant metabolites. Accordingly, the kudu is the only browsing ruminant for which mortalities due to secondary compounds of trees have been reported (Van Hoven 1991). Langurs have quite large salivary glands (Ayer 1948), and guerezas (*Colobus guereza*) as well (Kay et al. 1976). Large salivary glands are also reported in other colobine primates, tree kangaroos and sloths (Bauchop 1978).

Additionally, the gut microflora of browsing species can be adapted to the tannin content of the natural forage. Rumen fluid from goat, gazelle, Gunther's dik-dik (*Madoqua güntheri*) and impala (*Aepyceros melampus*) from African ranges effectively fermented tannin-rich fodders and therefore may harbour tannin-tolerant or -degrading microorganisms (Odenyo and Osuji 1998, Odenyo et al. 1999). In contrast, Jones et al. (2001) did not confirm these findings with rumen fluids from giraffe, greater kudu, eland (*Taurotragus oryx*), duiker, impala, nyala (*Tragelaphus angasi*), goat, wildebeest (*Connochaetus taurinus*) and sheep. Some rumen bacteria from goats (Brooker et al. 1994) and from bush duiker (*Cephalophus spp.*), giraffe, Grant's gazelle (*Gazella grantii*), sheep and goat from East Africa were shown to be tannin-tolerant (Odenyo et al. 2001), and the same has been shown for gut bacteria from free-ranging gorilla (*Gorilla gorilla*, Berry 1998). Gut bacteria capable of degrading tannin-protein complexes were isolated from koala (*Phascolarctos cinereus*, Osawa 1992) and from ringtail and brushtail possums (*Trichosurus vulpecula*, Osawa and Sly 1992).

All these morphophysiological adaptations to dietary tannins give rise to an "old question" in zoo animal management: should a certain (dietary, behavioural, climatic) stimulus that an animal is particularly adapted to be provided? This question could be answered more clearly if not only the morphophysiological adaptations to tannins were known, but also potentially positive effects that the animal might miss without them.

**Table 3.** Animals with demonstrated salivary tannin-binding proteins.

| Species | Source |
|---|---|
| Swamp wallabies (*W bicolor*) | McArthur et al. (1995) |
| Pademelon (*Thylogale thetis*) | McArthur et al. (1995) |
| Humans (*Homo sapiens*) | McArthur et al. (1995), Charlton et al. (1996), Bacon and Rhoades (1998) |
| Mouse (*Mus musculus*) | Mehansho et al. (1985), Asquith et al. (1985) |
| Rat (*Rattus norvegicus*) | Mehansho et al. (1983), Jansman et al. (1994) |
| Root vole (*Microtus oeconomus*) | Juntheikki et al. (1996) |
| Beaver (*Castor canadensis*) | Hagerman and Robbins (1993) |
| Pika (*Ochotona princeps*) | Dearing (1997) |
| Rabbit (*Oryctolagus cuniculus*) | Mole et al. (1990) |
| Mountain hare | McArthur et al. (1995) |
| Hare (*Lepus timidus*) | Mole et al. (1990) |
| Black bear (*Ursus americanus*) | Hagerman and Robbins (1993) |
| Black rhinoceros (*Diceros bicornis*) | Neiper (1998) |
| Camel (*Camelus dromedarius*) | Schmidt-Witty et al. (1994) |
| Roe deer (*Capreolus capreolus*) | Fickel et al. (1998) |
| White-tailed deer (*Odocoileus virginianus*) | Robbins et al. (1987b), Mole et al. (1990) |
| Mule deer (*Odocoileus hemionus*) | Austin et al. (1989), Robbins et al. (1987b), Hagerman and Robbins (1993) |
| Moose (*Alces alces*) | Hagerman and Robbins (1993), Juntheikki (1996) |

# 6 Potentially positive effects of tannins

## *6.1 Antioxidant capacities and vasculoprotective effects*

Recently the interest in food phenolics in humans has increased greatly because of a possible relation to civilisation diseases typically associated with "western" diets. The antioxidant and free radical-scavenging abilities associated with some phenolics have potential relevance for human health (Tebib et al. 1997, Bravo 1998). Epidemiologic studies have demonstrated a link between polyphenol intake and a reduced risk of cardiovascular disease (Green and Harari 1992, Stensvold et al. 1992, Hertog et al. 1993, 1995, Knekt et al. 1996). The so-called "paradoxic" low incidence of heart attacks in France has been correlated with the high intake of polyphenolic substances in red wine (Frankel et al. 1993). Tannins have been shown to lower the glycemic response and therefore the diabetogenic potential of carbohydrate foods in humans (Thompson et al. 1984). A semi-essential status for flavonoids and tannins has been postulated in human nutrition (Kühnau 1976, Hässig et al.

1999). Today, polyphenolic extracts from red grapes can be found on drug store shelves next to the vitamin pills.

### 6.2 Pathogen control: parasites

Tannins are effective against gastrointestinal stages of helminth parasites, both *in vitro* and *in vivo* (Niezen et al. 1995, Kabasa et al. 2000, Athanasiadou et al. 2000, 2001, Butter et al. 2000). Browsers are, on the one hand, in less contact with faeces of their own species anyhow, as they rarely or less frequently eat from ground level. On the other hand, they could have adapted to a certain degree on this external parasite control by tannins. Therefore, in theory browsers would not have needed to evolve as powerful endogenous parasite defenses as grazing animals. Interestingly, the mixed feeder impala has lower parasitic faecal egg counts in the dry season in which it depends to higher degrees on browse forage (Ocaido et al. 1999).

### 6.3 Pathogen control: bacteria

Tannins are effective against bacteria, fungi and viruses (reviewed by Chung et al. 1998). It has been suggested that the feeding of certain, tannin-containing plants can reduce the number of *Clostridium perfringens* (a pathogenic bacterium) in the faeces of sheep (Baumann et al. 1997). In theory, there should be notable differences in the quantitative bacterial composition of the faeces of free-ranging and captive browsers. As far as the author knows, such studies do not exist except for a comparison of the faecal microflora of free-ranging and captive capercaillies (*Tetrao urogallus*). Captive specimens had higher concentrations of pathogenic bacteria in their faeces than free-ranging animals (Schales 1992a). These bacteria were susceptible *in vitro* to extracts of the secondary plant compounds of the natural forage of the birds (Schales 1992b). In the wild, the gut flora of many animals might thus be kept in balance by secondary plant compounds.

### 6.4 Bloat prevention

Tannins are known to prevent bloat in domestic ruminants (Jones and Lyttleton 1971, Waghorn and Jones 1989, McMahon et al. 2000). Therefore, it has been attempted (in vain) to breed alfalfa species with a certain tannin content, in order to reduce the incidence of bloat in cattle ingesting fresh alfalfa (Goplen et al. 1980), but research in this respect in still ongoing (McMahon et al. 2000).

### 6.5 Protection of nutrients from forestomach fermentation

Generally, it is thought that tannins reduce protein availability in ruminants (Robbins et al. 1987a). Low levels of tannins, however, can reduce the protein degradation in the forestomach of ruminants and thereby increase the flow of more valuable amino acids to the small intestine (Driedger and Hatfield 1972, Barry and Manley 1984, Waghorn et al. 1987, Liu et al. 1998, Frutos et al. 2000) and enhance weight gains (Kaitho et al. 1998). It is also speculated that tannins in forages can protect soluble carbohydrates from rumen fermentation and therefore increase their nutritive value for ruminants (Barry and Manley 1984, Sreerangaraju et al. 2000).

### 6.6 Iron chelation

Tannins are known to chelate iron in the gastrointestinal tract and reduce its availability (Roy and Mukherjee 1979, Gillooly et al. 1983, Siegenberg et al. 1991, Jansman et al. 1993). The consumption of black tea, which contains polyphenolics, has been correlated with the occurrence of iron-deficiency anemia in children (Merhav et al. 1985). In the wild, many animals therefore would face very low dietary iron availabilities, whereas a captive diet without tannins would offer a relatively unrestrained iron provision.

## 7 Pathological conditions observed in captivity

### 7.1 Antioxidant deficiency and vascular disease

Wild animals in captivity are mostly fed a diet that is relatively low in polyphenolics. The usual hays, grasses, alfalfa and pelleted feeds do not contain significant amounts (Van Soest 1994). While this might suit the evolutionary adaptation of grazing species, especially the browsers could be hypothesized to face a situation where the antioxidant support from their natural forage that they have adapted to is missing in captive diets. A state of antioxidant deficiency has repeatedly been demonstrated in captive wildlife (e.g. Dierenfeld 1989). In this respect, the usual measurements of vitamin A, E and C might not be sufficient as comparative parameters for species that habitually depend on polyphenolic compounds in their blood. To test the hypothesis that the antioxidant status of folivorous animals is significantly lower in captivity than in the wild, tests would have to be available that not only measure the usual vitamins but other parameters like specific polyphenolic compounds or general antioxidant parameters, as reviewed – mostly for human medicine - by Pryor and Godber (1991), Hageman et al. (1992) and Papas (1996). To the knowledge of the author, such measurements have not been performed in wild animal species.

The natural diet of gorillas (Calvert 1985, Rogers et al. 1990, Barton et al. 1993), chimpanzees (Wrangham and Waterman 1983, Reynolds et al. 1998) and orangutans (*Pongo pygmaeus*, Hamilton and Galdikas 1994) contains significant amounts of tannins. (Potential) Atherosclerosis and/or high cholesterol levels have been reported in many primate species (Finlayson 1965, Luginbühl et al. 1977), and especially in chimpanzees (Brack et al. 1975), orangutans (Dierenfeld 1996) and gorillas (Morgan 1970, Gray and O'Neal 1981, Hruban et al. 1986, Allchurch 1993, Kenny et al. 1994, Scott et al. 1995). As the vasculoprotective effects of polyphenolics have repeatedly been demonstrated (e.g. Uchida et al. 1990, Kono et al. 1992, Tebib et al. 1994, Osman et al. 1998, Stein et al. 1999, Keevil et al. 2000), the long-term health of these animals might benefit from a certain polyphenol content in their diet. This hypothesis could be tested by evaluating necropsy and feeding history data. The general lack of correlated pathology and feeding history reports has prevented such studies so far.

### 7.2 Bloat and helminthic and bacterial gastrointestinal infection

Foregut fermenting browsers have been reported to be especially prone to bloat conditions in captivity, like langurs (Hill 1964, Hollihn 1971, Ruempler 1998), proboscis monkeys (*Nasalis larvatus*, Hollihn 1971) or colobines in general (Brack 1982, Davies et al. 1983), sloths (Stefani Diniz and Oliveira 1999), moose (Ritscher 1990) or giant eland (Edwards 1999). This occurs especially frequently during the transition from the wild into captivity and is often accompanied by parasitic and bacterial gastrointestinal infection. Gastrointestinal pathology due to parasitic and bacterial gastrointestinal infections is observed in recently imported, monogastric browsers as well, e.g. lemurs (Bernischke et al. 1985). It has been observed that browsers are, in zoo situations, more susceptible to parasite infections than grazers. The moose, a strict browser, has been reported to succumb extremely often to whipworm infection (Pfister et al. 1989) and diarrhea (Shochat et al. 1997) in captivity. Captive roe deer are prone to gastrointestinal *Clostridium* infections (Clauss, pers. obs.). Again, comparative studies or appropriate documentation – by which a hypothesis on the correlation of feeding type and gastrointestinal pathology could be tested - are lacking. An evaluation of the pathology data provided by Kiupel (1988) shows that captive browsing ruminants have a higher incidence of gastrointestinal disorders than grazing ruminants.

### 7.3 Iron storage disease

It is well-known that lemurs (Brygoo et al. 1964, Griener 1983, Bernischke et al. 1985, Gonzales et al. 1984, Spelman et al. 1989) and black rhinoceros (Kock et al. 1992, Smith et al. 1995, Paglia and Dennis 1999, Dierenfeld et al., subm.) develop iron storage disease in captivity. A relative "lack of tannins" in captive diets has been suspected to be the underlying cause (Spelman et al. 1989, Paglia and Dennis 1999). The line of thought is that these animals encounter tannins in their natural forages; these tannins reduce the iron availability, and the animals therefore did not have to evolve or could afford to loose absorption-limiting mechanisms. In captivity, in the absence of any absorption-reducing tannins, these uncontrolled absorption mechanisms lead to iron overload.

This hypothesis bears several consequences: (a) lemurs and black rhinos should be less able to limit iron uptake than comparable species, (b) other minerals than iron, whose absorption is also affected by tannins, should show a similar pattern and (c) other animals, not only lemurs and black rhinos, should be affected.

a. Gonzales et al. (1984) tested the comparative iron absorption in white ruffed lemurs (*Lemur variegatus*) and rhesus monkeys (*Macaca mulatta*) with a radioisotopic iron marker. The sample size was limited, and the application of the marker was problematic. The results obtained by this study did not indicate a difference in the efficiency of iron absorption between the species. However, it is not the efficiency of iron absorption that is of prime interest but the ability to limit iron absorption, which could not be tested by the trial design.

b. In experimental or domestic animals, tannins/polyphenolics have no effect on the absorption of calcium, magnesium (Jansman et al. 1993) or manganese (Fraile and Flynn 1992). The absorption of zinc was not affected in two studies (Flanagen et al. 1985, Jansman et al. 1993) and was decreased by polyphenolics in another (Greger and Lyle 1987). The evidence is equivocal for copper as well: copper availability was decreased in two studies (Kies and Umoren 1989, Jansman et al. 1993); however, another study (Vaquero et al. 1994) found an increase in copper absorption, and an increase in plasma and liver copper content with polyphenolics intake was demonstrated in two studies (Greger and Emery 1987, Greger and Lyle 1987). The type of polyphenolics used in the respective studies probably is the cause of partially equivocal results. It should be noted however, that all studies in which copper availability increased used black tea (Greger and Emery 1987, Greger and Lyle 1987, Vaquero et al. 1994), and that black tea is a potent inhibitor of iron absorption (Disler et al. 1975). Therefore, at least for a certain group of polyphenolics/tannins, the "lack" of this type of tannin might produce low copper and high iron levels. Copper levels in lemurs are not known. In a study on the mineral status of captive rhinoceros species, the browsing rhinos had a significantly lower copper status than the grazing rhinos (Dierenfeld et al., subm.). More data on copper status in wild and captive animals seems warranted. As it is, other minerals provide no clear evidence if the theory on a particularity of browsing animals with respect to mineral absorption could be true.

c. In a recent review, Clauss et al. (2002) showed that numerous other mammalian herbivores show excessive iron storage, and that only browsing hindgut fermenters but not foregut fermenters are affected – a difference these authors contributed to differences in digestive physiology. The comparative data on other mammalian species, therefore, supports the theory on a less effective absorption-limiting mechanism in animals that consume natural diets wit a low iron availability.

Mynahs, toucans, birds of paradise and other birds are very prone to excessive iron storage in captivity (Lowenstine and Munson 1999), although the clinical manifestation of the disease differs between species (Worell 1997). The theory that these birds lack tannins in their zoo diet has been promoted (c.f. Worell 1997). Most of these species are frugivores, and tropical fruits can contain significant amounts of tannins (e.g. Cipollini and Stiles 1993). The effect of secondary plant compounds on frugivorous birds was much discussed, but no clear statement can be derived from that discussion (Izhaki and Sfriel 1989, 1990, Mack 1990, Sedinger 1990). Mete et al. (2001) showed that mynahs have a particularly uncontrolled (or particularly effective) iron absorption mechanism. Excessive iron storage has also been reported in fruit-eating bats (Crawshaw et al. 1995).

## 8 Consequences for zoo diets

The question is whether these considerations bear any direct relevance for the deliberate inclusion of tannins in zoo diets. One has to keep in mind that the difference in tannin content is not the only difference between captive and natural diets. Most notably, most zoo animals receive pelleted concentrates with higher levels of soluble carbohydrates than is available to them in the wild, and with comparatively low fibre contents. These concentrates are often mineralized and supplemented with vitamins, and a consistent reliable mineral and vitamin supplementation is probably the most important argument for the use of this food type. However, some other considerations should be taken into account when deciding on the proportion pelleted feeds an animal is to receive.

### *8.1 Pelleted feeds: High levels of soluble carbohydrates*

High levels of concentrates can trigger gastrointestinal upset in many animals. For example, they have been associated with digestive upsets due to overgrowth of certain bacteria in the small and large intestine in domestic animals – e.g. *Clostridium spp*-induced enterotoxemia in sheep and goats and *E. coli*–induced enteritis in weaned piglets (Radostis et al. 1999). Concentrate feeds have been correlated to bloat conditions in foregut-fermenting primates (Hollihn 1971) and in ruminants (Fraser et al. 1991). Therefore, the nutritional contribution to the development of a pathogenic intestinal microflora and to bloat could possibly be reduced by simply reducing soluble carbohydrate levels in captive diets via increasing fibre content. In this respect, pelleted feeds with a high fibre content should be preferred in many situations.

### *8.2 Pelleted feeds: High levels of iron*

The usual concentrate feeds used in zoos not only have particularly high contents in soluble carbohydrates, but also in minerals, especially in iron. This is in contrast with generally low iron contents in leaves (e.g. Yeager et al. 1997). Results of an investigation of iron content of natural and desinged feedstuffs used in zoos are listed in table 4. The high iron levels in concentrate feeds seem rather unavoidable, and only especially manufactured diets can guarantee low iron levels. The author is not aware of publications addressing the problem in a scientific way. Potential sources of the high iron levels in usual commercial diets are iron contaminations in the mineral premixes used, and iron contaminations from the processing plants themselves. Thus, it could be hypothesized that the captive animal species mentioned before would not only benefit from a tannin-containing diet, but would already show a lesser degree of iron storage if their rations consisted to a lesser proportion of usual, pelleted feeds.

**Table 4.** Iron content of selected natural and artifically designed feedstuffs. Dicotyledonous browse from a temperate forest; pelleted feeds were commercially available and designed for domestic and captive wild animals (from Clauss 2000).

| Food/Forage | Iron content (mg/kg DM) |
|---|---|
| Temperate browse – leaves | 57–95 |
| Temperate browse – twigs | 32–44 |
| Temperate browse – bark | 35–36 |
| Oats | 73–268 |
| Grass hay | 167–996 |
| Grass pellets | 599–1025 |
| Lucerne hay | 115–136 |
| Lucerne pellets | 152–791 |
| Pelleted feeds (for domestic and wild animals) | 218–963 |

This concept is supported by anecdotal reports from the literature: The high incidence of iron storage disease in lemurs reported by Gonzales et al. (1984) was associated with the feeding of a pelleted diet for primates that had very high iron levels. Although other primate species on this diet did not develop iron storage disease, the pathology in lemurs might well have been prevented by feeding a diet with lower iron levels. Similarly, Miller et al. (1997) demonstrated that the iron content of a diet fed to common marmosets (*Callithrix jacchus*) was directly correlated to the extent of iron storage in the animals. Although iron levels of 350 mg/kg DM were reported to cause increasing liver iron storage, a commercial pelleted marmoset diet marketed for European zoos had a calculated iron content of 358 mg/kg (as fed basis, manufacturer information provided in 2000). Miller et al. (1997) quote two other commercial marmoset feeds with similar high iron contents. It has been suspected that a seemingly lower incidence of excessive iron storage in black rhino in Europe compared to North America is due to a higher proportion of natural feeds (hays) in their diet (Clauss, pers. obs.), and the same has been suspected for lemurs (C. Wood, pers. comm.). Evidence for a difference in feeding regimes and pathology between the continents has not been gathered yet, but is partly issue of ongoing research. The documentation of feeding regimes and recommendations, however, reveals a tendency to use high proportions of pelleted feeds in North America. In the "Fact Sheet" of the Nutrition Advisory Group of the American Association of Zoos and Aquaria, Lintzenich and Ward (1997) recommend that the diet of black rhinos and tapirs should contain 30 % (90 % dry matter basis) of a pelleted feed. In the "Fact Sheet" on the nutrition of leaf-eating primates, Edwards (1997) recommends that their diets should consist at least to 65 % of a pelleted ratio. In contrast, a diet for guerezas and a diet for langurs used at two European zoo contained no pelleted ingredient at all (Ludwig 1989, Ruempler 1998). The widespread use of concentrates in gorillas, and a similar difference in the feeding of this species between the continents, was documented by Müller and Schildger (1992). The habit of offering high-iron pelleted diets to callitrichids has already been mentioned and can probably be transferred to other primate species as well. Rock hyraxes (*Procavia capensis*) receive a high concentrate diet in captivity (Glick-Bauer and Dierenfeld 1999), and the pika (*Ochotona rufescens*) investigated by Madarame et al. (1990) had been fed a commercial laboratory animal pellet. Gorillas, callitrichids, hyraxes and pikas all belong to the animal group that develop excessive iron storage in captivity (Clauss et al. 2002).

A reduction in the use of pelleted feeds, or an increased use of low-iron pelleted feeds, might be particularly appropriate for browsing hindgut fermenters. The addition of tannins to a diet would probably reduce the iron availability for an animal. In human patients with iron storage disease with increased iron absorption, the use of black tea for a reduction of iron absorption has been proven useful (De Alarcon et al. 1979, Kaltwasser et al. 1998).

### 8.3 Antioxidant effects – longevity, and iron storage once more

The studies on the beneficial effects of chronic polyphenolics intake, especially in respect to vascular disease, would make a chronic supplementation of the diets of long-lived species, like gorillas, desireable. However, the effects of such a dietary regimen can only be assessed by retrospective long-term epidemiological studies, and other factors, like a poor supply of n-3 polyunsaturated fatty acids in captive diets (Clauss and Ghebremeskel 2001), will be of equal importance in this respect. Yet, there is reason to believe that captive animals could benefit from the antioxidative properties of tannins and other polyphenolics: For the black rhinoceros, several disease syndromes have been linked to the increased oxidative burden caused by the excessive iron stores (Paglia and Dennis 1999, Paglia et al. 2000a). Polyphenolic antioxidants like tannins have been recommended as the antioxidants of choice in iron storage disease (Hässig et al. 1993) as they prevent iron-associated oxidative damage very efficiently (Kühnau, 1976; Cook and Samman, 1996; Bravo, 1998).

## 9 Outlook

While a deliberate, controlled and moderate inclusion of tannin-containing ingredients into zoo diets would probably provide benefits for the animals, similar effects could also be achieved by other management strategies. Captive animals are generally treated regularly against parasites and might therefore not require the additional protection a tannin-containing diet might offer. Good food and enclosure hygiene, and a restriction in concentrate feeds, would probably reduce the incidence of gastrointestinal bacterial infection and of forestomach bloat. The potentially protective effect of tannins might, however, be especially appropriate when animals from the wild are introduced into captivity. A deliberate inclusion of tannins in their diet at least during the first months in captivity might render the transgression into captivity more gradual in terms of gastrointestinal environment, and therefore lessen the incidence of gastrointestinal diseases associated with this transgression. The high iron loads of several hindgut-fermenting browsing mammals could probably be reduced by a more restricted use of concentrate feeds and/or by using a concentrate feed with low iron content. But the additional offer of tannin-containing ingredients, or the inclusion of such ingredients into the concentrate diet, would probably contribute to the prevention of iron overload. Potential long-term health effects of a chronic ingestion of moderate tannin levels, though difficult to assess, might contribute to the antioxidant status, health and longevity of browsing species.

The deliberate addition of tannins into zoo diets will require other tannin sources than commercially available tannic acid or quebracho tannins. These are prohibitive due to their cost alone, and in the case of quebracho tannins, due to ecological considerations as well. Other sources of tannins need to be tested, amongst which the use of black tea instead of drinking water, the use of tannin-rich sorghum grains, peas and beans for the formulation of pelleted diets, and fruit pomaces, especially red grape pomace. Red grape pomace should be easily obtainable in vicinity of many western zoos. Red grapes have not only an antioxidant potential (Tebib et al. 1994) but should also reduce iron absorption (Bezwoda et al. 1985, Cook et al. 1995).

## 10 Conclusions

1. Although all animal species investigated tend to avoid or limit their intake of tannins in their natural diet, there is a large number of species that consistently consume (low) amounts of dietary tannins. Animals have evolved different morphophysiological adaptations to this nutritional challenge.

2. Apart from digestibility-reducing and toxic effects, tannins have a range of potentially beneficial effects. They can act as antioxidants, limit gastrointestinal helminths and pathogenic bacteria, prevent bloat, increase the escape of valuable protein from bacterial degradation in ruminants, and reduce the availability of iron.

3. Captive wild animals, particularly browsers, display disease symptoms that match these effects: bloat, parasitic infestation, bacterial enteritis, excessive iron storage, and atherosclerotic complications in long-lived species.

4. The addition of low amounts of tannins could prove beneficial for animals prone to displaying these symptoms. According research projects should be instigated.

5. However, other dietary measures, most notably a reduction in the use of conventional pelleted concentrates, or the use of high-fibre, low-iron pelleted feeds, could prevent many of the mentioned symptoms.

6. In view of a potential correlation of long-term tannin intake and antioxidant status and vascular health, it is recommended that feeding history records are saved by zoological institutions that will allow, in the future, to evaluate potential effects of feeding regimes on animal health in epidemiological studies.

## Acknowledgements

I thank M. Lechner-Doll, E. Dierenfeld, J. Gehrke, and J.-M. Hatt for discussions that stimulated the development of this review; E. Krebs for sharing her extensive literature and expertise on primates; and B. Peters and C. Witte for help with literature acquisition.

## References

Allchurch, A. F. (1993): Sudden death and cardiovascular disease in the lowland gorilla. *Dodo* 29: 172–178.

Asquith, T. N.; Mehansho, H.; Rogler, J.; Butler, L.; Carlson, D. M. (1985): Induction of proline-rich protein biosynthesis in salivary glands by tannins. *Fed. Proc.* 44: 1097.

Athanasiadou, S.; Kyriazakis, I.; Jackson, F.; Coop, R. L. (2000): Consequences of long-term feeding with condensed tannins on sheep parasitised with Trichostrongylus colubriformis. *Int. J. Parasitol.* 30: 1025–1033.

Athanasiadou, S.; Kyriazakis, I.; Jackson, F.; Coop, R. L. (2001): Direct anthelmintic effects of condensed tannins towards different gastrointestinal nematodes of sheep: In vitro and in vivo studies. *Vet. Parasitol.* 99: 205–219.

Atstatt, P. R.; Ingram, T. (1983): Adaptation to oak and other fibrous, phenolic-rich foliage by a small mammal, *Neotoma fusiceps*. *Oecologia* 60: 135–142.

Austin, P. J.; Suchar, L. A.; Robbins, C. T.; Hagerman, A. E. (1989): Tannin binding proteins in the saliva of deer and their absence in the saliva of sheep and cattle. *J. Chem. Ecol.* 15: 1335–1347.

Ayer, A. A. (1948): *The anatomy of Semnopithecus entellus*. Madras: The Indira Publishing House.

Bacon, J. R.; Rhoades, M. J. (1998): Development of a competition assay for the evaluation of the binding of human parotid salivary proteins to dietary complex phenolics and tannins using a peroxidase-labeled tannin. *J. Agric. Food Chem.* 46: 5083–5088.

Bairlein, F. (1996): Fruit-eating in birds and its nutritional consequences. *Comp. Biochem. Physiol.* 113A: 215–224.

Barry, T. N.; Manley, T. R. (1984): The role of condensed tannins in the nutritional value of *Lotus pedunculatus* for sheep. 2. Quantitative digestion of carbohydrates and proteins. *Br. J. Nutr.* 51: 493–504.

Barthelmess, E. L. (2001): The effects of tannin and protein on food preference in eastern grey squirrels. *Ethol. Ecol. Evol.* 13: 115–132.

Barton, R. A.; Whiten, A. (1994): Reducing complex diets to simple rules: food selection by olive baboons. *Behav. Ecol. Sociobiol.* 35: 283–293.

Barton, R. A.; Whiten, A.; Byrne, R. W.; English, M. (1993): Chemical composition of baboon plant foods: implications for the interpretation of intra- and interspecific differences in diet. *Folia Primatol.* 61: 1–20.

Bauchop, T. (1978): Digestion of leaves in vertebrate arboreal folivores. In: *The Ecology of Arboreal Folivores* (G. G. Montgomery, ed.). Washington DC: Smithsonian Institute Press, pp. 193–205.

Baumann, M.; Müller, W.; Greiling, J. (1997): Effect of fodder plants containing tannin on Clostridia flora in the intestine of sheep. *Anim. Res. Devel.* 45: 73–81.

Becker, K.; Makkar, H. P. S. (1999): Effects of dietary tannic acid and quebracho tannin on growth performance and metabolic rates of common carp. *Aquaculture* 175: 327–335.

Bergeron, J.M. ; Jodoin, L. (1987) : Defining "high quality" food resources of herbivores: the case for meadow voles. *Oecologia* 71: 510–517.

Bernischke, K.; Miller, C.; Ippen, R.; Heldstab, A. (1985): The pathology of prosimians, especially lemurs. *Adv. Vet. Sci. Comp. Med.* 30: 167–208.

Bernischke, K.; Adams, F. D. (1980): Gorilla diseases and causes of death. *J. Reprod. Fert.* (Suppl) 28: 139–148.

Berry, J. P. (1998): *The chemical ecology of mountain gorillas, with special reference to antimicrobial constituents in the diet.* [PhD Dissertation] Cornell University, Ithaca.

Bezwoda, W. R.; Torrance, J. D.; Bothwell, T. H.; Macphail, A. P.; Graham, B.; Mills, W. (1985): Iron absorption from red and white wines. *Scand. J. Haematol.* 34: 121–127.

Bozinovic, F.; Novoa, F. F.; Sabat, P. (1997): Feeding and digesting fiber and tannins by a herbivorous rodent, *Octodon degus*. *Comp. Biochem. Physiol.* 118A: 625–630.

Brack, M. (1982): Erkrankungen nichthumaner Primaten. Akute Magendilatation. *Kleintier-Praxis* 27: 313–317.

Brack, M.; Moore, G. T.; Kalter, S. S. (1975): Fatal atherosclerosis in two chimpanzees. *Verh. Ber. Erkr. Zootiere* 17: 231–236.

Bravo, L. (1998): Polyphenolics: chemistry, dietary sources, metabolism, and nutritional significance. *Nutr. Rev.* 56: 317–333.

Brooker, J. D.; O'Donovan, L. A.; Skene, I.; Clarke, K.; Blackall, L.; Mulera, P. (1994): *Streptococcus caprinus* sp. nov. A tannin-resistant ruminal bacterium from feral goats. *Lett. Appl. Microbiol.* 18: 313–318.

Bryant, J. P.; Provenza, F. D.; Pastor, J.; Reichardt, P. B.; Clausen, T. P.; du Toit, J. (1991): Interactions between woody plants and browsing mammals mediated by secondary metabolites. *Ann. Rev. Ecol. Syst.* 22: 431–446.

Brygoo, E.R.; Levaditi, J.; Destombes, P.; Guillon, J.C. (1964): Adéno-cancer avec « cirrhose bronzée » observé à Madagascar chez un lemur. *Bull. Soc. Pathol. Exot.* 57: 228–235.

Buchsbaum, R.; Valiela, I.; Swain, T. (1984): The role of phenolic compounds and other plant constituents in feeding by Canada geese in a coastal marsh. *Oecologia* 63: 343–349.

Butler, L. G.; Rogler, J. C. (1992): Biochemical mechanisms of the antinutritional effects of tannins. In: *Phenolic Compounds in Food and Their Effects on Health* (C. T. Ho, C. V. Lee, M. T. Huang, ed.). Vol. I, chapter 23. Washington DC: Am Chem Soc, ACS Symposium Series 506, pp. 298.

Butter, N. L.; Dawson, J. M.; Wakelin, D.; Buttery, P. J. (2000): Effect of dietary tannin and protein concentration on nematode infection in lambs. *J. Agric. Sci.* 134: 89–99.

Calvert, J. J. (1985): Food selection by western gorillas in relaion to food chemistry. *Oecologia* 65: 236–246.

Carrai, V.; Borgonini Tarli, S. M. (2001): Self-medication: a possible case in sifakas from the Kirindy Forest, Western Madagaskar. *Folia Primatol.* 72: 128–152.

Charlton, A. J.; Baxter, N. J.; Lilley, T. H.; Haslam, E.; McDonald, C. J.; Williamson, M. P. (1996): Tannin interactions with a full-length human salivary proline-rich protein display a stronger affinity than with single proline-rich repeats. *FEBS Letters* 382: 328–329.

Chung, K. T.; Wong, T. Y.; Wie, C. I.; Huang, Y. W.; Lin, Y. (1998): Tannins and human health: a review. *Crit. Rev. Food Sci. Nutr.* 38: 421–464.

Chung-MacCoubrey, A. L.; Hagerman, A. E.; Kirkpatrick, R. L. (1997): Effects of tannins on digestion and detoxification activity in gray squirrels. *Physiol. Zool.* 70: 270–277.

Cipollini, M. L.; Stiles, E. W. (1993): Fruit rot, antifungal defense, and palatability of fleshy fruits for frugivorous birds. *Ecology* 74: 751–762.

Clausen, T. P.; Provenza, F. D.; Burritt, E. A.; Reichardt, P. B.; Bryant, J. P. (1990): Ecological impliations of condensed tannin structure: a case study. *J. Chem. Ecol.* 16: 2381–2392.

Clauss, M. (2000): *Fütterungspraxis in der Haltung von Elchen.* [dissertation] University of Munich; Münster: Klaus Schüling Verlag.

Clauss, M.; Ghebremeskel, K. (2001): *n-6 and n-3 polyunsaturated fatty acids in the nutrition of wild animals.* 2nd European Zoo Nutrition Conference, April 6–9, Southhampton, UK. Abstract Book, p. 42.

Clauss, M.; Lechner-Doll, M.; Hänichen, T.; Hatt, J. M. (2002): Excessive iron storage in captive mammalian herbivores – a hypothesis for its evolutionary etiopathology. *Proc. EAZWV Conf.* 4: 123–131.

Cook, N. C.; Samman, S. (1996): Flavonoids – chemistry, metabolism, cardioprotective effects, and dietary sources. *J. Nutr. Biochem.* 7: 66–76.

Cook, J. D.; Reddy, M. B.; Hurrell, R. F. (1995): The effect of red and white wines on nonheme-iron absorption in humans. *Am. J. Clin. Nutr.* 61: 800–804.

Cooper, S. M.; Owen-Smith, N. (1985): Condensed tannins deter feeding by browsing ruminants in a South African savanna. *Oecologia* 67: 142–146.

Cooper, S. M.; Owen-Smith, N.; Bryant, J. P. (1988): Foliage acceptability to browsing ruminants in relation to seasonal changes in the leaf chemistry of woody plants in a South African savanna. *Oecologia* 75: 336–342.

Crawshaw, G.; Oyarzun, S.; Valdes, E.; Rose, K. (1995): Hemochromatosis (iron storage disease) in fruit bats. *Proc. NAG Conf.* 1: 136–147.

Davies, A. G.; Baillie, I. C. (1988): Soil-eating by red leaf monkeys in Sabah, Northern Borneo. *Biotropica* 20: 252–258.

Davies, A. G.; Caldecott, J. O.; Chivers, D. J. (1983): Natural foods as a guide to the nutrition of old world primates. In: *Standards in laboratory animal management* (J. Remfry, ed.). Potters Bar: UFAW.

Davies, A. G.; Bennet, E. L.; Waterman, P. G. (1988): Food selection by two South-east Asian colobine monkeys in relation to plant chemistry. *Biol. J. Linn. Soc.* 34: 33–56.

Dawson, J. M.; Buttery, P. J.; Jenkins, D.; Wood, C.; Gill, M. (1999): Effects of dietary quebracho tannin on nutrient utilisation and tissue metabolism in sheep and rats. *J. Sci. Food Agric.* 79: 1423–1430.

De Alarcon, P. A.; Donovan, M. E.; Forbes, G. B.; Landaw, S. A.; Stockman, J. A. (1979): Iron absorption in the thalassemia syndromes and its inhibition by tea. *N. Engl. J. Med.* 300: 5–8.

Dearing, M. D. (1996): Disparate determinants of summer and winter diet selection of a generalist herbivore, *Ochotona princeps*. *Oecologia* 108: 467–478.

Dearing, M. D. (1997): Effects of *Acomastylis rossil* tannins on a mammalian herbivore, the North American pika. *Oecologia* 109: 122–131.

Dierenfeld, E. S. (1996): Nutrition. In: *SSP Managemment Guidelines for Orangutans*, pp. 115–122.

Dierenfeld, E. S. (1989): Vitamin E deficiency in zoo reptiles, birds, and ungulates. *J. Zoo Wildl. Med.* 20: 3–11.

Dierenfeld, E. S.; Atkinson, S.; Craig, A. M.; Walker, K. C.; Clauss, M. (in prep.): Mineral concentrations in blood and liver tissue of captive and free-ranging rhinoceros species. Submitted to *J. Zoo Wildl. Med.*

Disler, P. B.; Lynch, S. R.; Charlton, R. W.; Torrance, J. D.; Bothwell, T. H.; Walker, R. B.; Mayet, F. (1975): The effect of tea on iron absorption. *Gut* 16: 193–200.

Dietz, B. A.; Hagerman, A. E.; Barrett, G. W. (1994): Role of condensed tannin on salivary tannin-binding proteins, bioenergetics, and nitrogen digestibility in the meadow vole. *J. Mammal.* 75: 880–889.

Dollahite, J. W.; Pigeon, R. F.; Camp, B. J. (1962): The toxicity of gallic acid, pyrogallol, tannic acid and quercus havardi in the rabbit. *Am. J. Vet. Res.* 23: 1264–1267.

Donnelly, E. D. (1954): Some factors that affect palatability in *Sericea lespedeza*. *Agron. J.* 46: 96–97.

Driedger, A.; Hatfield, E. E. (1972): Influence of tannins on the nutritive value of soybean meal for ruminants. *J. Anim. Sci.* 34: 465–468.

Edwards, M. E. (1997): *Leaf-eating primates: nutrition and dietary husbandry*. AZA Nutrition Advisory Group Handbook, Fact Sheet 007.

Edwards, M. E. (1999): Nutritional management of acute and chronic bloat in giant eland. *Proc. NAG Conf.* 3: 25–29.

Faurie, A. S.; Perrin, M. R. (1993): Diet selection and utilization in blue duikers and red duikers. *J. African. Zool.* 107: 287–299.

Fickel, J.; Göritz, F.; Joest, B. A.; Hildebrandt, T.; Hofmann, R. R.; Breves, G. (1998): Analysis of parotid and mixed saliva in roe deer. *J. Comp. Physiol.* B 168: 257–264.

Field, C. R. (1976): Palatability factors and nutritive values of the food of buffaloes in Uganda. *E. Afr. Wildl. J.* 14: 181–201.

Finlayson, R. (1965): Spontaneous arterial disease in exotic animals. *J. Zool. Lond.* 147: 239–343.

Flanagan, P. R.; Cluett, J.; Chamberlain, M. J.; Valberg, L. S. (1985): Dual-isotope method for determination of human zinc absorption: the use of a test meal of turkey meat. *J. Nutr.* 115: 111–122.

Foley, W. J. (1987): Digestion and energy metabolism in a small arboreal marsupial, the greater glider, fed high-terpene eucalyptus forage. *J. Comp. Physiol.* 157B: 355–362.

Foley, W. J.; Hume, I. D. (1987): Digestion and metabolism of high-tannin eucalyptus foliage by the brushtail possum. *J. Comp. Physiol.* 157B: 67–76.

Foley, W. J.; McLean, S.; Cork, S. J. (1995): Consequences of biotransformation of plant secondary metabolites on acid-base metabolism in mammals --a final common pathway? *J. Chem. Ecol.* 21: 721–743.

Foley, W. J.; Iason, G. R.; McArthur, C. (1999): Role of plant secondary metabolites in the nutritional ecology of mammalian herbivores: how far have we come in 25 years? In: *Nutritional ecology of herbivores*

(H. J. G. Jung, G. S. Fahey, eds.). Proc IVth Int Symp Nutr Herbivores. The American Society of Animal Science, pp. 130–209.

Fraile, A. L.; Flynn, A. (1992): The absorption of manganese from polyphenol-containing beverages in suckling rats. *Int. J. Food Sci. Nutr.* 43: 163–168.

Frankel, E. N.; Kanner, J.; German, J. B.; Parks, E.; Kinsella, J. E. (1993): Inhibition of oxidation of human low-density lipoprotein by phenolic substances in red wine. *Lancet* 341: 454–457.

Fraser, C. M.; Bergeron, J. A.; Mays, A.; Aiello, S. E. (eds.) (1991): The Merck Veterinary Manual. Rahway, NJ: Merck & Co Inc.

Freeland, W. J. (1991): Plant secondary metabolits: biochemical coevolution with herbivores. In: *Plant defenses against mammalian herbivory* (R.T. Palo, C. T. Robbins, eds.). Boca Raton: CRC Press Inc, pp. 61–81.

Frutos, P.; Hervas, G.; Giraldez, F. J.; Fernandez, M.; Mantecon, A. R. (2000): Digestive utilization of quebracho-treated soya bean meals in sheep. *J. Agric. Sci.* 134: 101–108.

Fürstenburg, D.; van Hoven, W. (1994): Condensed tannin as anti-defoliate agent against browsing by giraffe in the Krüger National Park. *Comp. Biochem. Physiol.* 107A: 425–431.

Ganzhorn, J. U. (1988): Food partitioning among Malagasy primates. *Oecologia* 75: 436–450.

Ganzhorn, J. U. (1989): Primate species separation in relation to secondary plant chemicals. *Human. Evol.* 4: 125–132.

Ganzhorn, J. U.; Abraham, J. P.; Razanahoera-Rakotomalala, M. (1985): Some aspects of the natural history and food selection of *Avahi laniger*. *Primates* 26: 452–463.

Gauthier, G.; Bedard, J. (1990): The role of phenolic compounds and nutrients in determining food preference in greater snow geese. *Oecologia* 84: 553–558.

Gauthier, G.; Bedard, J. (1991): Experimental tests of the palatability of forage plants in greater snow geese. *J. Appl. Ecol.* 28: 491–500.

Gillooly, M.; Bothwell, T. H.; Torrance, J. D.; MacPahil, A. P.; Derman, D. P.; Bezwoda, W. R.; Mills, W.; Charlton, R. W. (1983): The effect of organic acids, phytates and polyphenolics on the absorption of iron from vegetables. *Br. J. Nutr.* 49: 331–342.

Glander, K. E. (1981): Feeding patterns in mantled howling monkeys. In: *Foraing behavior. Ecological, Ethiological and Psychological Approaches* (A. C. Kamil, T. D. Sargent, eds.). Gartland: STPM Press, pp. 231–257.

Glick-Bauer, M.; Dierenfeld, E. S. (1999): Dietary intake and digestion in rock hyrax at the Prospect Park Wildlife Center. *Zool. Garten* NF 69: 293–300.

Gonzales, J.; Bernischke, K.; Saltman, P.; Roberts, J.; Robinson, P. T. (1984): Hemosiderosis in lemurs. *Zoo Biol.* 3: 255–265.

Goplen, B. P.; Howarth, R. E.; Sarkar, S. K.; Lesins, K. (1980): A search for condensed tannins in annual and perennial species of *Medicago, Trigonella,* and *Onobrychis*. *Crop Sci.* 20: 801–804.

Gray, R.; O'Neal, R. M. (1981): Sudden death associated with atherosclerosis in a gorilla. *J. Am. Vet. Med. Assoc.* 179: 1306–1307.

Green, M. S.; Harari, G. (1992): Association of serum lipoproteins and health-related habits with coffee and tea consumption in free-living subjects examined in the Israel CORDIS study. *Prev. Med.* 21: 532–545.

Greger, J. L.; Emery, S. M. (1987): Mineral metabolism and bone strength of rats fed coffee and decaffeinated coffee. *J. Agric. Food Chem.* 35: 551–556.

Greger, J. L.; Lyle, B. J. (1987): Iron, copper and zinc metabolism of rats fed various levels and types of tea. *J. Nutr.* 118: 52–60.

Griner, L. A. (1983): *Pathology of Zoo Animals*. San Diego: The Zoological Society of San Diego.

Hässig, A.; Liang, W. X.; Schwabl, H.; Stampfli, K. (1999): Flavonoids and tannins: plant-based antioxidants with vitamin character. *Med. Hypoth.* 52: 479–481.

Hageman, J. J.; Bast, A.; Vermeulen, N. P. E. (1992): Monitoring of oxidative radical damage in vivo: analytical aspects. *Chem. Biol. Interact.* 82: 243–293.

Hagerman, A. E.; Robbins, C. T. (1993): Specifity of tannin-binding salivary proteins relative to diet selection by mammals. *Can. J. Zool.* 71: 628–633.

Hagerman, A. E.; Butler, L. G. (1991): Tannins and lignins. In: *Herbivores: Their Interactions with Secondary Plant Metabolites* (G. A. Rosenthal, M. R. Berenbaum, eds.). Vol. I: The Chemical Participants. Academic Press Inc., pp. 355–388.

Hagerman, A. E.; Robbins, C. T.; Weerasuriya, Y.; Wilson, T. C.; McArthur, C. (1992): Tannin chemistry in relation to digestion. *J. Range Manage.* 45: 57–62.

Hamilton, R. A.; Galdikas, B. M. F. (1994): A preliminary study of food selection by the orangutan in relation to plant quality. *Primates* 35: 255–263.

Hanley, T. A.; Robbins, C. T.; Hagerman, A. E.; McArthur, C. (1992): Predicting digestible protein and digestible dry matter in tannin-containing forages consumed by ruminants. *Ecology* 73: 537–541.

Hay, L.; Van Hoven, W. (1988): Tannins and digestibility in the steenbok. *Comp. Biochem. Physiol.* 91A: 509–511.

Hertog, M. G. L.; Feskens, E. J. M.; Hollman, P. C. H.; Katan, M. B.; Kromhout, D. (1993): Dietary antioxidant flavonoids and risk of coronary heart disease: the Zutphen Elderly Study. *Lancet* 342: 1007–1011.

Hertog, M. G. L.; Kromhout, D.; Aravanis, C. (1995): Flavonoid intake and long-term risk of coronary heart disease and cancer in the Seven Countries Study. *Arch. Intern. Med.* 155: 381–386.

Hewitt, D. G.; Lafon, N. W.; Kirkpatrick, R. L. (1997): Effect of tannins on galliform cecal partitioning. *Physiol. Zool.* 70: 175–180.

Hill, W. C. O. (1964): The maintenance of langurs in captivity: experiences and some suggestions. *Folia primatol.* 2: 222–231.

Hjältén, J.; Palo, T. (1992): Selection of deciduous trees by free-ranging voles and hares in relation to plant chemistry. *Oikos* 63: 477–484.

Hladik, C. M.; Gueguen, L. (1974) : Géophagie et nutrition minérale chez les Primates sauvages. *C. R. Acad. Sci.* 279: 1393–1396.

Hofmann, R. R. (1973): The ruminant stomach. *E. Afr. Monogr. Biol.* 2: 1–354.

Hofmann, R. R. (1989): Evolutionary steps of ecophysiological adaptation and diversification of ruminants: a comparative view of their digestive system. *Oecologia* 78: 443–457.

Hollihn, K. U. (1971): Das Verhalten von Guerezas (*Colobus guereza und C. polycomos*), Nasenaffen (*Nasalis larvatus*) und Kleideraffen (*Pygathrix nemaeus*) bei der Nahrungsaufnahme und ihre Haltung. *Z. Saeugetierk.* 36: 65–95.

Hoskin, S. O.; Barry, T. N.; Wilson, P. R.; Charleston, W. A. G.; Kemp, P. D. (1999): Growth and carcass production of young farmed deer grazing sulla, chicory, or perennial ryegrass/white clover pasture in New Zealand. *N. Z. J. Agric. Res.* 42: 83–92.

Hruban, Z.; Meehan, T.; Wolff, P.; Wollman, R. L.; Glagov, S. (1986): Aortic dissection in a gorilla. *J. Med. Primatol.* 15: 287–293.

Huffman, M. A.; Seifu, M. (1989): Observations on the illness and consumption of a possibly medicinal plant by a wild chimpanzee in the Mahale Mountains, National Park, Tanzania. *Primates* 30: 51–63.

Iason, G. R.; Palo, R. T. (1991): Effects of birch phenolics on a grazing and a browsing mammal: a comparison of hares. *J. Chem. Ecol.* 17: 1733–1743.

Illius, A. W.; Jessop, N. S. (1995): Modeling metabolic costs of allelochemical ingestion by foraging herbivores. *J. Chem. Ecol.* 21: 693–719.

Izhaki, I.; Safriel, U. N. (1989): Why are there so few exclusively frugivorous birds? Experiments on fruit digestibility. *Oikos* 54: 23–32.

Izhaki, I.; Safriel, U. N. (1990): Weight losses due to exclusive fruit diet – interpretation and evolutionary implications: a reply to Mack and Sedinger. *Oikos* 57: 140–144.

Jachmann, H. (1989): Food slection by elephants in the Miombo biome, in relation to leaf chemistry. *Biochem. Syst. Ecol.* 17: 15–24.

Jansman, A. J. M.; Houdijk, J. G. M.; Verstegen, M. W. A. (1993): Effects of condensed tannins in faba beans on the availability of minerals in pigs.

In: *Bioavailability '93. Nutritional, Chemical, and Food Processing Implications of Nutrient Availability* (G. Schlemmer, ed.). Fed. Europ. Chem. Soc. 2: 48–52.

Jansman, A. J. M.; Fröhlich, A. A.; Marquardt, R. R. (1994): Production of proline-rich proteins by the parotid gland of rats is enhanced by feeding diets containing tannins from faba beans. *J. Nutr.* 124: 249–258.

Janzen, D. H. (1978): Complications in interpreting the chemical defenses of trees against tropical arboreal plant-eating vertebrates. In: *The Ecology of Arboreal Folivores* (G. G. Montgomery, ed.). Washington DC: Smithsonian Institute Press, pp. 73–84.

Johns, T.; Duquette, M. (1991): Detoxification and mineral supplementation as functions of geophagy. *Am. J. Clin. Nutr.* 53: 448–456.

Jones, W. T.; Lyttleton, J. W. (1971): Bloat in cattle. A survey of legume forages that do and do not produce bloat. *N. Z. J. Agr. Res.* 14: 101–107.

Jones, R. J.; Amado, M. A. G.; Dominguez, B. M. G. (2000): Comparison of the digestive ability of crop fluid from the folivorous hoatzin and cow rumen fluid with seven tropical forages. *Anim. Feed. Sci. Technol.* 87: 287–296.

Jones, R. J.; Meyer, J. H. F.; Bechaz, F. M.; Stoltz, M. A.; Palmer, B.; Van der Merwe, G. (2001): Comparison of rumen fluid from South African game species and from sheep to digest tanniniferous browse. *Aust. J. Agric. Res.* 52: 453–460.

Juntheikki, M. R. (1996): Comparison of tannin-binding proteins in saliva of Scandinavian and North American moose. *Biochem. Syst. Ecol.* 24: 595–601.

Juntheikki, M. R.; Julkunentiitto, R.; Hagerman, A. E. (1996): Salivary tannin-binding proteins in root vole. *Biochem. Syst. Ecol.* 24: 25–36.

Kabasa, J. D.; Opuda-Asibo, J.; ter Meulen, U. (2000): The effect of oral administration of polyethylene glycol on faecal helminth egg counts in pregnang goats grazed on browse containing condensed tannins. *Trop. Anim. Health Prod.* 32: 73–86.

Kaitho, R. J.; Umunna, N. N.; Nsahlai, I. V.; Tamminga, S.; Van Bruchem, J. (1998): Utilization of browse supplements with varying tannin levels by Ethiopian Menz sheep. 1. Intake, digestibility and live weight changes. *Agroforestry Syst.* 39: 145–159.

Kaltwasser, J. P.; Werner, E.; Schalk, K.; Hansen, C.; Gottschalk, R.; Seidl, C. (1998): Clinical trial on the effect of regular tea drinking on iron accumulation in genetic haemochromatosis. *Gut* 43: 699–704.

Kay, R. N. B. (1987): Weights of salivary glands in some ruminant animals. *J. Zool. Lond.* 211: 431–436.

Kay, R. N. B.; Hoppe, P. P.; Maloiy, G. M. O. (1976): Fermentative digestion of food in the colobus monkey. *Experientia* 32: 485–486.

Keevil, J. G.; Osman, H. E.; Reed, J. D.; Folts, J. D. (2000): Grape juice, but not orange juice or grapefruit juice, inhibits human platelet aggregation. *J. Nutr.* 130: 53–56.

Kenny, D. E.; Cambre, R. C.; Alvarado, T. P.; Prowten, A. W.; Allchurch, A. F.; Marks, S. K.; Zuba, J. R. (1994): Aortic dissection: an important cardiovascular disease in captive gorillas. *J. Zoo. Wildl. Med.* 25: 561–568.

Kies, C.; Umoren, J. (1989): Inhibition of copper bioutilization: fiber, lead, phytate, and tannis. *Adv. Exper. Med. Biol.* 258: 81–93.

King, D.; Fan, M. Z.; Ejeta, G.; Asem, E. K.; Adeola, O. (2000): The effects of tannins on nutrient utilisation in the White Pecking duck. *Br. Poultry Sci.* 41: 630–639.

Kiupel, H. (1988): Sektionsergebnisse bei Paarhufern (Artiodactyla). *Verh. Ber. Erkr. Zootiere* 30: 29–34.

Knekt, P.; Järvinen, R.; Reunanen, A.; Maatela, J. (1996): Flavonoid intake and coronary mortality in Finland: a cohort study. *Br. Med. J.* 312: 478–481.

Kock, R. A.; Garnier, J. (1993): Veterinary management of three species of rhinoceroses in zoological collections. In: *Rhinoceros Biology and Conservation* (O. A. Ryder, ed.). Zool. Soc. San Diego, pp. 325–345.

Kock, N.; Foggin, C.; Kock, M. D.; Kock, R. (1992): Hemosiderosis in the black rhinoceros: a comparison of free-ranging and recently captured with translocated and captive animals. *J. Zoo. Wildl. Med.* 23: 230–234.

König, W. D. (1991): The effects of tannins and lipids on digestion of acorns by acron woodpeckers. *Auk* 108: 79–88.

Kono, S.; Shinchi, K.; Ikeda, N.; Yanai, F.; Imanishi, K. (1992): Green tea consumption and serum lipid profiles: a cross-sectional study in northern Kyushu, Japan. *Prev. Med.* 21: 526–531.

Kool, K. M. (1992): Food selection by the silver leaf monkey in relation to plant chemistry. *Oecologia* 90: 527–533.

Kreulen, D. A. (1985): Lick use by large herbivores: a review of benefits and banes of soil consumption. *Mammal Rev.* 15: 107–123.

Kühnau, J. (1976): The flavonoids. A class of semi-essential food components: their role in human nutrition. *Wld. Rev. Nutr. Diet.* 24: 117–191.

Kumar, R.; Singh, M. (1984): Tannins, their adverse role in ruminant nutrition. *J. Agric. Food Chem.* 32: 447–453.

Leighton, M. (1993): Modeling dietary selectivity by Bornean orangutans: evidence for integration of multiple criteria in fruit selection. *Int. J. Primatol.* 14: 257–313.

Lindroth, R. L.; Batzli, G. O. (1984): Plant phenolics as chemical defenses: effects of natural phenolics on survival and growth of prairie voles. *J. Chem. Ecol.* 10: 229–244.

Lindroth, R. L.; Batzli, G. O.; Avildsen, S. I. (1986): Lespedeza phenolics and Penstemon alkaloids: effects on digestion efficiencies and growth of voles. *J. Chem. Ecol.* 12: 713–728.

Lintzenich, B. A.; Ward, A. M. (1997): *Hay and pellet ratios: consideration in feeding ungulates*. AZA Nutrition Advisory Group Handbook, Fact Sheet 006.

Liu, F. Y.; Hodgson, J.; Barry, T. N. (1998): Effects of grazing sequence and condensed tannins on ingestive behaviour, herbage intake, and performance of lambs grazing Yorkshire fog pasture. *N. Z. J. Agric. Res.* 41: 359–366.

Lowenstine, L. J.; Munson, L. (1999): Iron overload in the animal kingdom. In: *Zoo and Wild Animal Medicine* (M. E. Fowler, E. R. Miller, eds.). Current Therapy 4. Philadelphia: W.B. Saunders Co, pp. 260–268.

Ludwig, W. (1989): Zur Ernährung und künstlichen Aufzucht von Guerezas im Zoologischen Garten Dresden. *Zool. Garten* NF 59: 173–187.

Luginbühl, H.; Rossi, G. L.; Ratcliffe, H. L.; Müller, R. (1977): Comparative atherosclerosis. *Adv. Vet. Sci. Comp. Med.* 21: 421–448.

Luikkonen, A. T. (2001): Nutritional and genetic adaptation of galliform birds: Implicatons for hand-rearing and restocking. *Acta Univ. Oulu A: Sci. Rer. Nat.* 367: 1–73.

Mack, A. L. (1990): Is frugivory limited by secondary compounds in fruits? *Oikos* 57: 135–138.

Madarame, H.; Kumagai, M.; Suzuki, J. (1990): Pathology of excessive iron storage in the Afghan pika. *J. Comp. Pathol.* 103: 351–359.

Mahaney, W. C.; Aufreiter, S.; Hancock, R. G. V. (1995): Mountain gorilla geophagy: a possible seasonal behavior for dealing with the effects of dietary changes. *Int. J. Primatol.* 16: 475–488.

Makkar, H. P. S.; Blummel, M.; Becker, K. (1995): Formation of complexes between polyvinyl pyrrolidones or polyethylene glycols and tannins, and their implications in gas production and true digestibility in in vitro techniques. *Br. J. Nutr.* 73: 897–913.

Marks, D. L.; Swain, T.; Goldstein, S.; Richard, A.; Leigthon, M. (1987): Chemical correlates of rhesus monkey food choice: the influence of hydrolyzable tannins. *J. Chem. Ecol.* 14: 213–235.

McArthur, C.; Sanson, G. D. (1991): Effects of tannins on digestion in the common ringtail possum, a specialized marsupial folivore. *J. Zool. Lond.* 225: 233–251.

McArthur, C.; Sanson, G. D. (1993a): Nutritional effects and costs of a tannin in a grazing and a browsing macropodid marsupial herbivore. *Functional Ecol.* 7: 690–696.

McArthur, C.; Sanson, G. D. (1993b): Nutritional effects and costs of a tannin in two marsupial arboreal folivores. *Functional Ecol.* 7: 697–703.

McArthur, C.; Robbins, C. T.; Hagerman, A. E.; Hanley, T. A. (1993): Diet selection by a ruminant generalist browser in relation to plant chemistry. *Can. J. Zool.* 71: 2236–2243.

McArthur, C.; Sanson, G. D.; Beal, A. M. (1995): Salivary proline-rich proteins in mammals: roles in oral homeostasis and counteracting dietary tannin. *J. Chem. Ecol.* 21: 663–691.

McKey, D. B.; Gartlan, J. S.; Waterman, P. G.; Choo, G. M. (1981): Food selection by black colobus monkeys in relation to plant chemistry. *Biol. J. Linn. Soc.* 16: 116–146.

McMahon, L. R.; McAllister, T. A.; Berg, B. P.; Majak, W.; Acharya, S. N.; Popp, J. D.; Coulman, B. E.; Wang, Y.; Cheng, K. J. (2000): A review of the effects of forage condensed tannins on ruminal fermentation and bloat in grazing cattle. *Can. J. Plant. Sci.* 80: 469–485.

Mehansho, H.; Hagerman, A.; Clements, S.; Butler, L.; Rogler, J.; Carlson, D. M. (1983): Modulation of proline-rich protein biosynthesis in rat parotid glands by sorghums with high tannin levels. *Proc. Natl. Acad. Sci.* USA 80: 3948–3952.

Mehansho, H.; Clements, S.; Sheares, B. T.; Smith, S.; Carlson, D. M. (1985): Induction of proline-rich glycoprotein synthesis in mouse salivary glands by isoproterenol and by tannins. *J. Biol. Chem.* 260: 4418–4423.

Merhav, H.; Amitai, Y.; Palti, H.; Godfrey, S. (1985): Tea drinking and microcytic anemia in infants. *Am. J. Clin. Nutr.* 41: 1210–1213.

Mete, A.; Dorrestein, G. M.; Marx, J. J. M.; Lemmens, A. G.; Beynen, A. C. (2001): A comparative study of iron absorption in mynah birds, doves and rats. *Avian Pathology* 30: 479–486.

Miller, G. F.; Barnard, D. E.; Woodward, R. A.; Flynn, B. M.; Bulte, J. W. M. (1997): Hepatic hemosiderosis in common marmosets: effect of diet on incidence and severity. *Lab. Anim. Sci.* 47: 138–142.

Mole, S.; Waterman, P. G. (1987): Tannins as antifeedants to mammalian herbivores – still an open question? In: *Allelochemicals: Role in agriculture and forestry* (G. R. Waller, ed.). Washington DC: Am. Chem. Soc., pp. 572–587.

Mole, S.; Butler, L. G.; Iason, G. R. (1990): Defense against dietary tannin in herbivores: a survey for proline rich salivary proteins in mammals. *Biochem. Syst. Ecol.* 18: 287–293.

Moreno-Black, G. S.; Bent, E. F. (1982): Secondary compounds in the diet of *Colobus angolensis*. *Afr. J. Ecol.* 20: 29–36.

Morgan, D. G. (1970): Dissecting aneurysm of the aorta in a gorilla. *Vet. Rec.* 86: 502–505.

Mowry, C. B.; Decker, B. S.; Shure, D. J. (1996): The role of phytochemistry in dietary choices of Tana River red colobus monkeys. *Int. J. Primatol.* 17: 63–84.

Müller, K. H.; Schildger, B. J. (1992): Empfehlungen für eine artgerechte Ernährung von Flachlandgorillas in menschlicher Obhut auf der Grundlage einer quantitativen Nahrungsanalyse. *Zool. Garten* NF 62: 351–363.

Müller, P. J.; Hart, J. A.; Robertson, J. B. (1998): Food choice, digestion and body size among African rainforest duikers fed natural fruit diets. *Proc. Comp. Nutr. Soc.* 2: 145–149.

Munn, C. A. (1994): Winged rainbows – macaws. *National Geographic* 185: 118–140.

Neiper, F. M. (1998): *Aspects of nutrition concerning the black rhinoceros – regarding tannin-binding proteins and captive diet adequacy*. [honour's thesis], Agricultural Faculty, University of Sydney, Australia.

Niezen, J. H.; Waghorn, T. S.; Charleston, W. A. G.; Waghorn, G. C. (1995): Growth and gastrointestinal nematode parasitism in lambs grazing either lucerne or sulla which contain condensed tannins. *J. Agric. Sci.* 125: 281–289.

Oates, J. (1978): Water-plant and soil consumption by guereza monkeys: a relationship with minerals and toxins in the diet? *Biotropica* 10: 241–253.

Oates, J. F.; Swain, T.; Zantovska, J. (1977): Secondary compounds and food selection by colobus monkeys. *Biochem. Syst. Ecol.* 5: 317–321.

Oates, J. F.; Waterman, P. G.; Choo, G. M. (1980): Food selection by the South Indian leaf-monkey in relation to leaf chemistry. *Oecologia* 45: 45–56.

Ocaido, M.; Siefert, L.; Baranga, J. (1999): Seasonal changes of impala faecal helminth egg counts through a one-year period. *Afr. J. Ecol.* 37: 327–333.

Odenyo, A. A.; Osuji, P. O. (1998): Tannin-tolerant ruminal bacteria from East African ruminants. *Can. J. Microbiol.* 44: 905–909.

Odenyo, A. A.; McSweeney, C. S.; Palmer, B.; Negassa, D.; Osuji, P. O. (1999): In vitro screenig of rumen fluid samples from indigenous African ruminants provides evidence for rumen fluid with superior capacities to digest tannin-rich fodders. *Aust. J. Agric. Res.* 50: 1147–1157.

Odenyo, A. A.; Bishop, R.; Asefa, G.; Jamnadass, R.; Odongo, D.; Osuji, P. (2001): Characterization of tannin-tolerant bacterial isolates from East African ruminants. *Anaerobe* 7: 5–15.

Oh, H. I.; Hoff, J. E.; Haff, L. A. (1985): Immobilized condensed tannins and their interactions with proteins. *J. Food Sci.* 50: 1652–1654.

Osawa, R. (1992): Tannin-protein complex-degrading enterobacteria isolated from the alimentary tracts of koalas and a selective medium for their enumeration. *Appl. Environ. Microbiol.* 58: 1754–1759.

Osawa, R.; Sly, L. I. (1992): Occurence of tannin-protein complex degrading *Streptococcus sp.* in faeces of various animals. *Syst. Appl. Microbiol.* 15: 144–147.

Osman, H. E.; Maalej, N.; Shanmuganayagam, D.; Folts, J. D. (1998): Grape juice but not orange or grapefruit juice inhibits platelet activity in dogs and monkeys. *J. Nutr.* 128: 2307–2312.

Paglia, D. E.; Dennis, P. (1999): Role of chronic iron overload in multiple disorders of captive black rhinoceros. *Proc. AAZV*, pp. 163–171.

Paglia, D. E.; Kenny, D. E.; Dierenfeld, E. S.; Tsu, I. C. H. (2000): Potential role for iron overload in the pathogenesis of congenital leukoencephalomalacia in captive black rhinoceroses. *Am. J. Vet. Res.* 62: 343–349.

Papas, A. M. (1996): Determinants of antioxidant status in humans. *Lipids* 31: S77–S82.

Pfister, K.; Meister, V.; Robin, K.; Kipfer, H.; Lobsiger, L.; Henzi, M. (1989): Role and treatment of *Trichuris spp.* infections in moose and other non-domesticated ruminants. *Verh. Ber. Erkr. Zootiere* 31: 397–401.

Provenza, F. D.; Burritt, E. A.; Clausen, T. P.; Bryant, J. P.; Reichardt, P. B.; Distel, R. A. (1990): Conditioned flavor aversion: a mechanism for goats to avoid condensed tannins in blackbrush. *Am. Nat.* 136: 810–828.

Pryor, W. A.; Godber, S. S. (1991): Noninvasive measures of oxidative stress status in humans. *Free Radical Biol. Med.* 10: 177–184.

Radostis, O. M.; Gay, C. C.; Blood, D. C.; Hinchcliff, K. W. (1999): *Veterinary Medicine. A Textbook of the Diseases of Cattle, Sheep, Pigs, Goats and Horses.* 9th ed. London/New York: W.B. Saunders.

Reed, J. D. (1995): Nutritional toxicology of tannins and related polyphenolics in forage legumes. *J. Anim. Sci.* 73: 1516–1528.

Reynolds, V.; Plumptre, A. J.; Greenham, J.; Harborne, J. (1998): Condensed tannins and sugars in the diet of chimpanzees in the Budongo Forest, Uganda. *Oecologia* 115: 331–336.

Ritscher, D. (1990): Erkrankungen und Todesfälle bei Elchen im Zoologischen Garten Rostock. *Verh. Ber. Erkr. Zootiere* 32: 297–302.

Robbins, C. T. (1993): *Wildlife feeding and nutrition.* San Diego: Academic Press Inc.

Robbins, C. T.; Spalinger, D. E.; Van Hoven, W. (1995): Adaptation of ruminants to browse and grass diets: are anatomical-based browser-grazer interpretations valid? *Oecologia* 103: 208–213.

Robbins, C. T.; Hanley, T. A.; Hagerman, A. E.; Hjeljord, O.; Baker, D. L.; Schwartz, C. C.; Mautz, W. W. (1987a): Role of tannins in defending plants against ruminants: reduction in protein availability. *Ecology* 68: 98–107.

Robbins, C. T.; Mole, S.; Hagerman, T. A.; Hanley, T. A. (1987b): Role of tannins in defending plants against ruminants: reduction in dry matter digestion? *Ecology* 68: 1606–1615.

Robbins, C. T.; Hagerman, A. E.; Austin, P. J.; McArthur, C.; Hanley, T. A. (1991): Variation in mammalian physiological responses to a condensed tannin and its ecological implications. *J. Mammal.* 72: 480–486.

Rogers, M. E.; Maisels, F.; Williamson, E. A.; Fernandez, M.; Tutin, C. E. G. (1990): Gorilla diet in the Lopé Reserve, Gabon: a nutritional analysis. *Oecologia* 84: 326–339.

Roy, J.; Bergeron, J. M. (1990): Branch-cutting behavior by the vole. A mechanism to decrease toxicity of secondary metabolites in conifers. *J. Chem. Ecol.* 16: 735–741.

Roy, S. N.; Mukherjee, S. (1979): Influence of food tannins on certain aspects of iron metabolism: part I – absorption and excretion in normal and anemic rats. *Ind. J. Biochem. Biophys.* 16: 93–98.

Ruempler, U. (1998): Husbandry and breeding of Douc langurs at Cologne Zoo. *Int. Zoo Yb.* 36: 73–81.

Schales, K. (1992a): *Investigations on the aerobic flora and Clostridium perfringens in faecal specimens of free-ranging and captive capercaillies.* [dissertation] University of Munich, Germany.

Schales, C. (1992b): *In vitro-investigations on the antiibacterial effect of essential oils and hydrophilic contents from conifer needles on bacteria isolated from the faeces of captive capercaillies.* [dissertation] University of Munich, Germany.

Schmidt, K. A. (2000): Interactions between food chemistry and predation risk in fox squirrels. *Ecology* 81: 2077–2085.

Schmidt-Witty, U.; Kownatki, R.; Lechner-Doll, M.; Enss, M. L. (1994): Binding capacity of camel saliva mucins for tannic acid. *J. Camel Pract. Res.* 1: 121–122.

Schwartz, C. C.; Regelin, W. L.; Franzmann, A. W. (1987): Nutritional energetics of moose. *Swedish Wildl. Res.* (Suppl.) 1: 265–280.

Scott, N. A.; McManamon, R.; Strobert, E.; Cipolla, G. D.; Tarazona, N.; Swenson, R. B. (1995): In vivo diagnosis of coronary artery disease in a western lowland gorilla. *J. Zoo. Wildl. Med.* 26: 139–143.

Sedinger, J. S. (1990): Are plant secondary compounds responsible for negative apparent metabolizability of fruits by passerine birds? A comment on Izhaki and Safriel. *Oikos* 57: 138–140.

Setz, E. Z. F.; Enzweiler, J.; Solferini, V. N.; Amendola, M. P.; Berton, R. S. (1999): Geophagy in the golden-faced saki monkey in the Central Amazon. *J. Zool. Lond.* 247: 91–103.

Shahkhalili, Y.; Finot, P. A.; Hurrell, R.; Fern, E. (1990): Effects of foods rich in polyphenolics on nitrogen excretion in rats. *J. Nutr.* 120: 346–352.

Shochat, E.; Robbins, C. T.; Parish, S. M.; Young, P. B.; Stephenson, T. R.; Tamayo, A. (1997): Nutritional investigations and management of captive moose. *Zoo Biol.* 16: 479–494.

Siegenberg, D.; Baynes, R. D.; Bothwell, T. H.; Macfarlane, B. J.; Lamparelli, R. D.; Car, N. G.; MacPhail, P.; Schmidt, U.; Tal, A.; Mayet, F. (1991): Ascorbic acid prevents the dose-dependent inhibitory effects of polyphenolics and phytates on nonheme-iron absorption. *Am. J. Clin. Nutr.* 53: 537–541.

Simmen, B. (1994): Taste discrimination and diet differentiation among New World primates. In: *The Digestive System in Mammals: Food, Form and Function* (D. J. Chivers; P. Langer, eds.). Cambridge: Cambridge Univ Press, pp. 150–165.

Simmen, B.; Josseaume, B.; Atramentowicz, M. (1999): Frugivory and taste responses for fructose and tannic acid in a prosimian primate and didelphid marsupial. *J. Chem. Ecol.* 25: 331–346.

Smallwood, P. D.; Peters, W. D. (1986): Grey squirrel food preferences: the effects of tannin and fat concentration. *Ecology* 67: 168–174.

Smith, J. E.; Chavey, P. S.; Miller, R. E. (1995): Iron metabolism in captive black and white rhinoceroses. *J. Zoo. Wildl. Med.* 26: 525–531.

Spelman, L. H.; Osborn, K. G.; Anderson, M. P. (1989): Pathogenesis of hemosiderosis in lemurs: role of dietary iron, tannin, and ascorbic acid. *Zoo Biol.* 8: 239–251.

Sreerangaraju, G.; Krishnamoorthy, U.; Kailas, M. M. (2000): Evaluation of Bengal gram (*Cicer arietinum*) husk as a source of tannin and its interference in rumen and post-rumen nutrient digestion in sheep. *Anim. Feed. Sci. Technol.* 85: 131–138.

Stefani Munaó Diniz, L. de.; Oliveira, P. M. A. (1999): Clinical problems of sloths in captivity. *J. Zoo. Wildl. Med.* 30: 76–80.

Stein, J. H.; Keevil, J. G.; Wiebe, D. A.; Äschlimann, S.; Folts, J. D. (1999): Purple grape juice improves endothelial function and reduces the susceptibility of LDL cholesterol to oxidation in patients with coronary artery disease. *Circulation* 100: 1050–1055.

Stensvold, I.; Tverdal, A.; Solvoll, K.; Foss, O. P. (1992): Tea consumption. Relationship to cholesterol, blood pressure, and coronary and total mortality. *Prev. Med.* 21: 546–553.

Swain, T. (1976): Reptile-angiosperm co-evolution. In: *Secondary Metabolism and Coevolution* (M. Luckner, K. Mothes, L. Nover, eds.). Halle: Deutsche Akademie der Naturforscher Leopoldina, pp. 551–561.

Tahvanainen, J.; Helle, E.; Julkunen-Tiito, R.; Lavola, A. (1985): Phenolic compounds of willow bark as deterrents against feeding by mountain hare. *Oecologia* 65: 319–323.

Tebib, K.; Bitri, L.; Besancon, P.; Rouanet, J. M. (1994): Polymeric grape seed tannins prevent plasma cholesterol changes in high-cholesterol-fed rats. *Food Chem.* 49: 403–406.

Tebib, K.; Rouanet, J. M.; Besancon, P. (1997): Antioxidant effects of dietary polymeric grape seed tannins in tissues of rats fed a high cholesterol-vitamin E-deficient diet. *Food Chem.* 59: 135–141.

Thompson, L. U.; Yoon, J. H.; Jenkins, D. J. A.; Wolever, T. M. S.; Jenkins, A. L. (1984): Relationship between polyphenol intake and blood glucose response of normal and diabetic individuals. *Am. J. Clin. Nutr.* 39: 745–751.

Tixier, H.; Duncan, P.; Scehovic, J.; Yani, A.; Gleizes, M.; Lila, M. (1997): Food selection by European roe deer: effects of plant chemistry, and consequences for the nutritional value of their diets. *J. Zool. Lond.* 242: 229–245.

Uchida, S.; Ohta, H.; Niwa, M.; Mori, A.; Nonaka, G.; Nishioka, I.; Ozaki, M. (1990): Prolongation of life span of stroke-prone spontaneously hypertensive rats (SHRSP) ingesting perimmon tannin. *Chem. Pharm. Bull.* 38: 1049–1052.

Van Hoven, W. (1991): Mortalities in kudu populations related to chemical defence in trees. *J. Afr. Zool.* 105: 141–145.

Van Soest, P. J. (1994): *Nutritional ecology of the ruminant*. 2nd ed. Ithaca: Cornell University Press.

Vaquero, M. P.; Veldhuizen, M.; van Dokkum, W.; van den Hamer, C. J. A.; Schaafsma, G. (1994): Copper availability from breakfasts containing tea. Influence of the addition of milk. *J. Sci. Food. Agric.* 64: 475–481.

Verheyden-Tixier, H.; Duncan, P. (2000): Selection for small amounts of hydrolysable tannins by a concentrate-selecting mammalian herbivore. *J. Chem. Ecol.* 26: 351–358.

Voltura, M. B.; Wunder, B. A. (1994): Physiological responses of the Mexican woodrat to condensed tannins. *Am. Midl. Nat.* 132: 405–409.

Volz, T. J.; Clausen, T. P. (2001): Tannins in *Puccinellia arctica*: Possible deterrents to herbivory by Canada geese. *J. Chem. Ecol.* 27: 725–732.

Waghorn, G. C.; Jones, G. T. (1989): Bloat in cattle. Potential of dock as an antibloat agent for cattle. *N. Z. J. Agr. Res.* 32: 227–235.

Waghorn, G. C.; Ulyatt, M. J.; John, A.; Fisher, M. T. (1987): The effect of condensed tannins on the site of digestion of amino acids and other nutrients in sheep fed on *Lotus corniculatus*. *Br. J. Nutr.* 57: 115–126.

Westoby, M. (1974): An analysis of diet selection by large generalist herbivores. *Am. Nat.* 108: 290–304.

Wilkins, H. L.; Bates, R. P.; Hewson, R. P.; Lindahl, I.; Davis, R. E. (1953): Tannin and palatability in *Sericea lespedeza*. *Agron J.* 45: 335–336.

Wink, M.; Hofer, A.; Bilfinger, M.; Englert, E.; Martin, M.; Schneider, D. (1993): Geese and dietary allelochemicals – food palatability and geophagy. *Chemoecology* 4: 93–107.

Worell, A. B. (1997): Toucans and mynahs. In: *Avian Medicine and Surgery* (R. B. Altman, S. L. Clubb, G, M. Dorrestein, K. Queesenberry, eds.). Philadelphia: W.B. Saunders, pp. 910–917.

Wrangham, R. W.; Waterman, P. G. (1981): Feeding behaviour of vervet monkeys on *Acacia tortilis* and *Acacia xanthophloea* with special reference to reproductive strategies and tannin production. *J. Anim. Ecol.* 50: 715–731.

Wrangham, R. W.; Waterman, P. G. (1983): Condensed tannins in fruits eaten by chimpanzees. *Biotropica* 15: 217–222.

Yeager, C. P.; Silver, S. C.; Dierenfeld, E. S. (1997): Mineral and phytochemical influences on foliage selection by the Proboscis monkey. *Am. J. Primatol.* 41: 117–128.

*M. Clauss[1], E. Kienzle[1], H. Wiesner[2]*

# The botanical, structural and chemical composition of different pelleted feeds used in a captive browsing ruminant, the moose (*Alces alces*)

### *Abstract*

*The commercially available, pelleted moose food sold under the same brand name ("Mazuri Moose Maintenance") in North Amercia and Europe differs drastically in ingredient composition; the European formula does not contain the aspen sawdust that is regarded the crucial ingredient in the North American diet. Apart from these feeds, other pelleted foods designed for horses, domestic ruminants and cervids are used in feeding moose in European facilities. These pelleted feeds, and for comparison grass and browse samples, were submitted to a variety of analyses in order to isolate the potentially beneficial factors of the commercial moose feeds. All pelleted feeds had comparable particle size distributions, with the North American moose feed as the notable exception, as the sawdust particles were not as finely ground as the other ingredients. All pelleted feeds were similar in nutrient composition; however, the commercial moose feeds had higher percentages of fibre, due to a higher cellulose (and in the European pellets also hemicellulose) content. The commercial moose pellets did not display significantly higher amounts of lignin than the other pelleted feeds, in spite of the sawdust ingredient. Due to their high cellulose content, they even had lower lignin:cellulose-ratios than the other feeds and therefore rather resembled grass than browse in their fibre composition. Thus, the reported success of the commercial moose diets is most likely explained by their comparatively low energy density and high fibre content, and not by the sawdust ingredient itself. Additionally, the fact that they do not contain corn starch is considered beneficial. The nutritional contribution to husbandry problems in captive moose is considered to be generally due to the widespread use of pelleted feeds high in energy density and poor in structural fibre components.*

### *Keywords*

*nutrition, browse, grass, fibre, starch, lignin*

1 Institute of Animal Physiology, Physiological Chemistry and Animal Nutrition, Ludwig-Maximilians-University, Munich, Germany. Corresponding author: Marcus Clauss, Institute of Animal Physiology, Physiological Chemistry and Animal Nutrition, Veterinaerstr. 13, 80539 Muenchen, Germany, FAX: ++49-89-21803208, clauss@tiph.vetmed.uni-muenchen.de.

2 Zoological Garden "Hellabrunn", Munich, Germany.

## 1 Introduction

While there is common agreement on the fact that moose are notoriously difficult to keep in captivity in the literature from both North America and Europe, three major differences exist in the conceptual approach to moose husbandry between the continents. (1) Intraspecific aggression is reported to be a major limiting factor in Europe only (Clauss et al. 2002). (2) Parasitic infections with whipworms (*Trichuris spp.*) are regarded as the one most dangerous disease of captive moose in Europe, while this parasite is hardly mentioned in North American literature (Clauss et al. 2002). (3) Most notably, the commercially available moose feed, sold under the same brand name (Mazuri Moose Maintenance) by different companies in North America (Purina Mills, Missouri) and Europe (Special Diets Services, Essex, UK), differs drastically in ingredient composition. This difference reflects the North American history of developing a pelleted diet for moose based on aspen sawdust (Schwartz 1980), a development that seemingly went unnoticed in Europe. The use of the aspen-containing pelleted food has been regarded as the most important contribution to moose husbandry, and has led to a recognized improvement of the health of captive moose (see Shochat et al. 1997 for a review). In order to identify the ingredient or the property of the aspen-containing moose foods that could be the cause of its beneficial effect, we submitted a variety of feedstuffs fed to captive moose to botanical, physical and chemical analyses.

Moose are classified as browsers/concentrate selectors (Hofmann 1989). The morphophysiological adaptations of browsers, their consequences for captive feeding regimes, and the proneness of this feeding type for digestive problems in captivity, are discussed in another contribution to this volume (Clauss et al. 2003).

## 2 Methods

Feed samples were obtained in 25 moose facilities, including pelleted feeds, hays, and freshly cut grass. Browse samples (*Salix alba, Salix caprea, Fagus sylvatica, Fraxinus excelsior, Betular pubescens, Acer pseudoplatanus, Corylus cornuta, Quercus rubra, Quercus robur*) were obtained directly from the forests around Munich, Bavaria. Two samples of the North American commercial moose feed (Mazuri Moose Maintenance, Mazuri Moose Breeder, Purina Mills) were obtained from a North American facility.

Two sub-samples of the Mazuri Moose Maintenance, one from Purina Mills, one from SDS, were submitted to the Institute of Applied Botany of the University of Hamburg, Germany (sample ID 3371/97 and 3372/97) for botanical analysis.

Several pelleted feeds were analyzed by wet sieving for particle composition. Sieve sizes were 3.55, 1.40, 1.00, 0.80, 0.56, 0.40 and 0.20 mm, respectively (linear dimension of holes). After soaking in 2 liters of water for 12 hours, app. 50 g of the original substance (OS) was given onto the sieve column, and flushed with an additional 4 l of water. Weight of each particle size class was determined after drying. Results were expressed as the percentage of dry matter (DM).

Feed samples were analyzed for DM, crude ash (CA), crude protein (CP), crude fat (CF), crude fibre (FIB), neutral detergent fibre (NDF), acid detergent fibre (ADF), acid detergent lignin (ADL) by standard procedures. Pelleted feeds were incubated with alpha-amylase prior to NDF analysis (McQueen and Nicholson 1979). In determining NDF content of browse, sodium sulfite was omitted from the standard procedure (Mould and Robbins 1981).

**Table 1.** Botanical analysis of the North American and the European "Mazuri Moose Maintenance" pelleted feed.

| Ingredient | Estimated proportion (app.) |
|---|---|
| SDS (Europe) | |
| Soy product | 20–25 % |
| Sunflower | 15 % |
| Oats | 20–25 % |
| Wheat | 8 % |
| Barley | 2–3 % |
| Grass product | 20–25 % |
| Mineral mix | 1–2 % |
| | |
| Purina Mills (North America) | |
| Soy product | 15–20 % |
| Beet pulp | 25–30 % |
| Wood product (Aspen*) | 40–45 % |
| Alfalfa product (plus some grass) | 20–25 % |
| Mineral mix | 1 % |

Additions of fat, oil, molasses and other additives cannot be determined and estimated in their quantity by microscope. Thus, significant variations in the estimated proportions of ingredients are possible.

* Wood species determined by Dr. Grosser, Institute for Wood Research, Munich, Germany.

Nitrogen-free extracts (NfE) content was calculated (DM-CP-CF-CA-FIB), as was cellulose (C) (ADF-ADL) and hemicellulose (HC) (NDF-ADF) content. In order to better differentiate between foodstuffs, we additionally calculated the lignin:cellulose-ratio of the feeds and expressed fibre fractions as a percentage of NDF. For a comparison with the NfE values, the "residual carbohydrates" (RCH) were calculated by substituting NDF for FIB in the NfE equation.

## 3 Results

The results of the botanical analyses are presented in table 1. They are in accord with the information provided by the manufacturers. While there is a high proportion of aspen sawdust in the North American product, there are

**Table 2.** Particle size distribution of selected pelleted feeds, expressed as size classes in % DM.

| Sieve size (mm) | Mazuri Moose Maintenance USA | Mazuri Moose Maintenance Europa | Horse pellets | Cattle pellets | Cervid pellets |
|---|---|---|---|---|---|
| 3.55 | 1.9 | — | 0.2 | — | — |
| 1.40 | 33.0 | 0.1 | 10.3 | 5.5 | 4.6 |
| 1.00 | 8.7 | 2.0 | 9.5 | 7.8 | 9.3 |
| 0.80 | 4.7 | 4.1 | 5.9 | 6.9 | 5.9 |
| 0.56 | 6.8 | 11.9 | 11.6 | 11.5 | 11.7 |
| 0.40 | 6.1 | 14.7 | 7.9 | 9.1 | 10.1 |
| 0.20 | 6.8 | 17.1 | 11.7 | 11.3 | 21.7 |
| < 0.20 | 32.0 | 50.0 | 42.9 | 47.9 | 36.6 |
| < 1.40 mm | 65.1 | 99.9 | 89.4 | 94.5 | 95.4 |

**Table 3.** Proximate analysis of different feeds fed to moose (average, S.D., range). See text for explanations.

| Feed | n | DM % OS | CA % DM | CF % DM | FIB % DM | CP % DM | NfE % DM | RCH % DM |
|---|---|---|---|---|---|---|---|---|
| Horse pellets | 7 | 88.5 ± 1.8 (86.0–90.6) | 9.7 ± 1.6 (7.7–12.6) | 3.4 ± 1.0 (2.1–4.9) | 14.4 ± 2.8 (11.6–20.2) | 13.7 ± 1.5 (11.7–15.9) | 58.7 ± 2.8 (53.8–61.5) | 47.7 ± 9.5 (40.2–68.2) |
| Cattle pellets | 3 | 85.8 ± 0.6 (85.2–86.3) | 8.1 ± 0.5 (7.6–8.6) | 3.6 ± 0.6 (3.1–4.3) | 10.9 ± 3.1 (8.1–14.3) | 18.8 ± 3.2 (15.1–20.9) | 58.6 ± 5.2 (53.4–63.8) | 43.5 ± 12.1 (30.4–54.1) |
| Cervid pellets | 9 | 88.0 ± 1.9 (85.9–90.4) | 10.1 ± 1.5 (7.4–12.4) | 3.4 ± 0.9 (1.9–5.1) | 16.9 ± 4.0 (7.8–21.5) | 14.4 ± 2.5 (11.2–17.7) | 55.2 ± 3.5 (50.0–60.9) | 37.9 ± 5.5 (30.2–49.6) |
| Mazuri Moose Maintenance (USA) | 1 | 90.1 | 7.8 | 5.9 | 27.7 | 13.4 | 45.1 | 31.9 |
| Mazuri Moose Breeder (USA) | 1 | 90.3 | 9.6 | 5.2 | 22 | 19.2 | 44.1 | 29.6 |
| Mazuri Moose Maintenance (Europa) | 3 | 88.6 ± 0.6 (87.9–89.1) | 7.7 ± 0.8 (7.0–8.6) | 5.1 ± 0.7 (4.5–5.9) | 21.4 ± 1.2 (20.2–22.5) | 15.7 ± 0.4 (15.3–16.0) | 50.2 ± 0.7 (49.7–51.0) | 28.8 ± 1.6 (27.5–30.6) |
| Lucerne hay | 2 | 90.1 (89.9–90.3) | 7.85 (7.5–8.2) | 0.95 (0.9–1.0) | 40.4 (40.2–40.6) | 12.6 (12.3–12.8) | 38.3 (37.8–38.7) | 16.9 (14.7–19.0) |
| Grass hay | 8 | 89.8 ± 1.9 (85.0–90.8) | 8.0 ± 2.5 (4.3–11.1) | 1.6 ± 0.4 (1.0–2.5) | 31.2 ± 4.1 (27.4–40.0) | 11.5 ± 2.5 (7.4–14.8) | 47.8 ± 4.4 (38.6–51.6) | 13.9 ± 5.4 (5.8–22.2) |
| Grass (fresh) | 9 | 15.3 ± 2.7 (12.6–20.8) | 15.3 ± 4.0 (10.9–23.3) | 2.3 ± 0.7 (1.4–3.2) | 24.9 ± 4.8 (18.8–35.8) | 16.8 ± 1.5 (14.3–18.9) | 40.7 ± 3.9 (36.1–47.7) | 15.1 ± 4.5 (10.0–25.3) |
| Tree leaves (fresh) | 9 | 37.5 ± 3.9 (31.7–42.3) | 8.2 ± 2.9 (2.9–11.7) | 4.2 ± 1.7 (1.9–6.6) | 19.9 ± 4.1 (13.1–25.9) | 15.1 ± 1.7 (13.4–17.9) | 52.5 ± 5.5 (45.6–62.9) | 22.9 ± 4.8 (16.9–29.8) |
| Twigs (fresh) | 5 | 46.7 ± 3.0 (42.4–50.4) | 5.6 ± 0.8 (4.4–6.6) | 2.3 ± 1.2 (1.1–4.2) | 34.7 ± 9.1 (20.1–42.3) | 5.2 ± 1.6 (3.0–7.2) | 52.1 ± 10.3 (43.6–69.4) | 14.7 ± 4.6 (6.9–18.2) |

**Table 4.** Fibre fractions of different feeds fed to moose (average, S.D., range).

| Feed | n | NDF % DM | ADF % DM | ADL % DM | C % DM | HC % DM | HC % NDF | C % NDF | ADL % NDF | ADL:C |
|---|---|---|---|---|---|---|---|---|---|---|
| Horse pellets | 7 | 29.7<br>± 3.3<br>(25.8–35.7) | 16.4<br>± 3.3<br>(12.9–23.5) | 3.6<br>± 0.3<br>(3.3–4.0) | 12.8<br>± 3.2<br>(9.5–19.6) | 13.3<br>± 2.0<br>(9.6–16.0) | 45.0<br>± 6.9<br>(34.1–53.1) | 42.8<br>± 7.1<br>(34.6–54.8) | 12.2<br>± 1.4<br>(10.3–13.9) | 0.29<br>± 0.06<br>(0.20–0.37) |
| Cattle pellets | 3 | 26.0<br>± 9.8<br>(20.1–37.3) | 14.4<br>± 5.9<br>(9.5–20.9) | 3.2<br>± 2.8<br>(0.9–6.3) | 11.2<br>± 3.8<br>(7.1–14.6) | 11.6<br>± 4.5<br>(7.4–16.4) | 50.6<br>± 10.1<br>(39.3–58.7) | 44.2<br>± 12.8<br>(34.6–58.7) | 10.9<br>± 6.2<br>(4.4–16.8) | 0.28<br>± 0.18<br>(0.08–0.43) |
| Cervid pellets | 9 | 34.2<br>± 6.7<br>(17.7–40.5) | 20.8<br>± 4.5<br>(10.5–26.2) | 4.8<br>± 1.1<br>(3.6–6.5) | 16.0<br>± 4.0<br>(6.9–21.8) | 13.4<br>± 3.5<br>(7.3–18.4) | 39.2<br>± 6.1<br>(30.6–47.5) | 46.4<br>± 6.3<br>(38.9–56.5) | 14.5<br>± 3.5<br>(11.0–20.2) | 0.32<br>± 0.10<br>(0.20–0.52) |
| Mazuri Moose Maintenance (USA) | 1 | 41.0 | 29.8 | 4.8 | 25.0 | 11.2 | 27.3 | 61.0 | 11.7 | 0.19 |
| Mazuri Moose Breeder (USA) | 1 | 36.4 | 24.7 | 4.2 | 20.5 | 11.8 | 32.3 | 56.1 | 11.6 | 0.20 |
| Mazuri Moose Maintenance (Europa) | 3 | 42.6<br>± 2.1<br>(40.5–44.6) | 23.6<br>± 1.2<br>(22.5–24.8) | 3.4<br>± 0.5<br>(2.9–3.8) | 20.2<br>± 0.7<br>(19.6–21.0) | 19.0<br>± 0.9<br>(18.1–19.8) | 44.6<br>± 0.3<br>(44.3–44.9) | 47.4<br>± 0.9<br>(46.6–48.4) | 8.0<br>± 0.8<br>(7.1–8.6) | 0.17<br>± 0.02<br>(0.15–0.18) |
| Lucerne hay | 2 | 61.8<br>(59.0–64.6) | 42.8<br>(42.4–43.2) | 9.0<br>(8.2–9.8) | 33.9<br>(33.5–34.2) | 19.0<br>(15.7–22.2) | 30.6<br>(26.7–34.4) | 54.9<br>(52.9–56.8) | 14.6<br>(12.7–16.5) | 0.27<br>(0.24–0.29) |
| Grass hay | 8 | 65.0<br>± 4.0<br>(59.7–70.6) | 35.1<br>± 3.0<br>(31.3–41.8) | 5.3<br>± 1.1<br>(3.6–7.3) | 29.8<br>± 2.6<br>(25.0–34.5) | 30.0<br>± 4.0<br>(25.2–36.1) | 46.0<br>± 4.4<br>(38.5–51.1) | 45.8<br>± 3.5<br>(41.9–50.8) | 8.2<br>± 1.9<br>(5.3–10.8) | 0.18<br>± 0.04<br>(0.12–0.25) |
| Grass (fresh) | 9 | 50.5<br>± 5.9<br>(41.3–61.9) | 35.0<br>± 3.1<br>(32.1–41.0) | 8.2<br>± 1.7<br>(6.0–10.8) | 26.8<br>± 3.1<br>(22.5–32.1) | 15.5<br>± 4.0<br>(8.3–20.9) | 30.3<br>± 5.3<br>(20.2–36.6) | 53.2<br>± 2.4<br>(50.2–57.9) | 16.5<br>± 4.5<br>(11.0–25.4) | 0.31<br>± 0.09<br>(0.21–0.47) |
| Tree leaves (fresh) | 9 | 49.6<br>± 3.8<br>(43.3–53.6) | 30.6<br>± 6.4<br>(19.5–39.7) | 15.5<br>± 4.9<br>(8.1–24.1) | 15.1<br>± 3.0<br>(8.4–20.0) | 18.9<br>± 5.6<br>(12.4–26.7) | 38.3<br>± 11.6<br>(25.4–57.8) | 30.6<br>± 6.7<br>(18.1–42.0) | 31.1<br>± 8.5<br>(18.8–45.3) | 1.05<br>± 0.32<br>(0.54–1.54) |
| Twigs (fresh) | 5 | 72.1<br>± 6.1<br>(66.9–81.4) | 49.9<br>± 6.3<br>(40.5–56.4) | 20.6<br>± 4.5<br>(14.0–24.7) | 29.3<br>± 3.4<br>(24.9–32.5) | 22.3<br>± 8.2<br>(13.5–33.2) | 30.5<br>± 9.8<br>(19.8–41.2) | 40.7<br>± 4.6<br>(37.1–47.7) | 28.8<br>± 7.2<br>(20.3–36.9) | 0.71<br>± 0.18<br>(0.53–0.99) |

no wooden ingredients in the European one. There is a notable absence of corn products, of which only fragments were found in the European moose feed.

The results of the sieve analyses are shown in table 2. The particle distribution in the different pellet types is quite uniform, and generally more than 90 % of the DM is of a particle size of less than 1.4 mm. The only notable exception is the North American moose pellet, which contains a high proportion of relatively large particles.

The results of the nutrient analyses are presented in tables 3 and 4. All pelleted feeds were similar in nutrient composition; however, the commercial moose feeds had higher percentages of fibre, due to a higher cellulose (and in the European pellets also hemicellulose) content, and accordingly lower NfE and RCH-values. The commercial moose pellets did not display significantly higher concentrations of lignin than the other pelleted feeds, in spite of the sawdust ingredient. Due to their high cellulose content, they even had lower lignin:cellulose-ratios than the other feeds and therefore rather resembled grass than browse in their fibre composition.

## 4 Discussion

The results demonstrate that RCH values provides a more detailed information for these kinds of feeds than NfE. Note, e. g., that the NfE content of twigs and the European moose pellets are quite similar, but their RCH content differs significantly. The same applies, e. g., to grass hay and the North

American moose pellets. Using NDF instead of FIB in the calculation of the fraction of soluble, nitrogen-free nutrient allows a more precise estimate of the proportion of sugars and starches within a feed.

The results obtained in this study for the nutrient composition of browse are in good accord with literature data on the nutrient composition of moose brose (Regelin et al. 1987, Schwartz et al. 1988, Risenhoover 1989) or the actual diet of free-ranging moose (Regelin et al. 1987)

The pelleted feeds investigated in this study are quite similar in their nutrient composition. The only significant difference is the higher fibre content of the three moose pellets, which is mainly due to an increase in cellulose, and in the case of the European product, in hemicellulose as well.

The work of Shochat and others (1997) and the historical development of moose feeds that they summarize strongly implies a nutritional contribution to, if not cause of the "wasting syndrome complex" (WSC), the most important disease of captive moose. The development of a pelleted diet on the basis of aspen sawdust by Schwartz (1980) at the Moose Research Center, Alaska (MRC) is still regarded as the initial breakthrough in moose nutrition. The refinement of this diet by the replacement of sucrose, molasses and beet pulp for the corn of the original MRC diet led to further improvements, although WSC still occurs frequently in moose (Shochat and others 1997). Four possible explanations come to mind for the success of the original MRC formulation.

1. The first follows the initial thoughts of Schwartz (1980) that moose are adapted to the physical properties of browse and can not handle those of grass, with grass or hay ingestion leading to a filled forestomach with a slow particle clearance and a subsequent suppression of further, supposedly necessary food intake. This explanation is supported by several findings. Grass and browse have been shown to differ in their physical properties (Spalinger et al. 1986). The content of moose rumens, like those of other browsing ruminants, is naturally not stratified (Renecker and Hudson 1990), in contrast to the contents of grazing ruminants; this stratification is due to the physical structure of grass fibre (Lechner-Doll et al. 1991). Browsing ruminants have been reported to suffer from forestomach blockage due to hay ingestion (Spalinger et al. 1993). Interestingly, while moose consume grass hay in only limited amounts, they increase their intake if the physical structure of the hay is altered by cutting it into smaller pieces (Bo and Hjeljord 1991). However, while these reflections hold true for natural forage, they are unlikely to play a role in pelleted feeds that consist of material that is already ground to small pieces; therefore the notion of Schwartz (1980) that *pellets* based on grass material could induce rumen blockage is contradictory in itself. The results of the sieve analysis (Table 2) show that both pellets based on sawdust and on grass fibre consist almost exclusively of particles that pass a 3.55 mm aperture. As moose faeces contain particles up to a size of 4 mm and more (Nygren and Hofmann 1990, Nygren et al. 2001), neither pellet type can be expected to cause forestomach blockage or be advantageous due to its physical structure.

2. Due to the wood ingredient, the fibre fractions of the MRC formula could resemble natural moose forage more closely than grass-based pellets. The digestive system of moose could be especially adapted to a high proportion of lignin in the fibre fraction. If moose consume grass-based feeds, a higher percentage of fermentable cellulose is likely to reach the hindgut, whereas when consuming browse, the ingesta should contain higher percentages of indigestible lignin. A low lignin:cellulose-ratio therefore might induce increased hindgut fermentation in captive as compared to free-ranging animals.

   Right as this theory may be, it can not apply to the observed success of the MRC formula. The inclusion of aspen sawdust in the formula does not increase its lignin content significantly (Table 4). The fibre fraction of all pelleted feeds is low in lignin, compared to browse. The higher fibre content of the commercial moose pellets is mainly due to a higher cellulose content. Whereas in browse, the three fibre fractions HC, C and lignin occur in nearly equal proportions, their distribution in the pelleted feeds tends to consist first of C, then HC, and only of a little lignin – like in grass or hays. Therefore, the lignin:cellulose ratio of all pelleted feeds is between 0.2 and 0.3, with the moose pellets at the lower end of the range, due to their higher C content. These values correspond to the range of grass and hays. Browse, on the other hand, has a higher lignin:cellulose-ratio of 0.7 to 1.0.

   These results are in accord with the ADL content of 5.2 % DM Schwartz and others (1985) give for the MRC diet, and lead to the conclusion that sawdust is not a very efficient source of lignin. However, it is a high-fibre, low-energy ingredient that dilutes other nutrients. The deliberate inclusion of a lignin component into pelleted feeds has, to our knowledge, not been assessed in zoo animal nutrition to date.

3. In theory, the sawdust-based pellets could contain secondary plant compounds of beneficial effect. However, aspen was chosen by Schwartz (1980) for its lack of secondary compounds. These compounds have not been analyzed for, so no data-based statement can be made.

4. This leaves us with the last possible explanation, namely that it is simply the high fibre content of the MRC diet in general and the according lower NfE and RCH values that make this feed so beneficial for moose. Used as a sole feed and fed *ad libitum*, this food is less likely to cause rumen acidosis, or excessive or malfermentation in the hindgut. Hofmann and Nygren (1992) diagnosed subclinical acidosis in all 7 cases of captive moose they investigated, which suggests that captive moose are generally fed too energy-dense a diet. The use of one of the commercial moose pellets as the sole, *ad libitum* trough food for moose, combined with an appropriate source of structured fibre (see below) should prevent rumen acidosis from occurring, although RCH values are still higher than in natural forage.

The fact that the exclusion of corn starch from North American moose diets resulted in an additional improvent (Shochat et al. 1997) supports the notion that in moose, high-energy and hard-to-digest materials can lead to hindgut problems. While it has been demonstrated that moose produce the starch-digesting enzyme amylase (Schwartz et al. 1996) and can handle high loads of proprionate (the ruminal metabolite of starch, Shochat et al. 1997), there is no reason to believe that they are not susceptible to differences in starch digestibility like domestic animals. Starches from different sources vary enormously in their digestibility (Dreher et al. 1984), and corn starch has been shown to be especially hard to digest in both domestic ruminants (Orskov and Kay 1987) and horses (Kienzle 1994). It has repeatedly been observed that significant amounts of corn starch pass the rumen and the small intestine of grazing domestic ruminants undigested and reach the hindgut (Tucker et al. 1968, Orskov et al. 1969), where it is fermented and can lead to changes in cecal microflora and feces consistency (Orskov et al. 1970). Drochner and Meyer (1991) correlated the feeding of corn starch to a higher incidence of hindgut tympanies and torsions in domestic ruminants. This effect of hard-to-digest starch is very likely to be even accentuated in moose due to their digestive physiology: moose have faster passage rates compared to domestic ruminants (Hubbert 1987, Renecker and Hudson 1990). Therefore, because the ingesta leaves the rumen relatively fast, some substances are probably less subjected to ruminal degradation or fermentation, like soluble carbohydrates (necessitating glucose transporters in the mucosa of the small intestine of moose that are absent in cattle, Rowell et al. 1996) or polyunsaturated fatty acids (leading to higher proportions of polyunsaturated fatty acids in moose depot fat compared to domestic ruminants, Meyer et al. 1998). Starch should be no exception. The exclusion of corn starch from moose diets therefore is reasonable, and an increased use of other carbohydrate sources that do not induce malfermentation or acidosis, like the pectins of beet pulp, is a promising new way of designing formulated rations (Van Soest 1996). Corn was, according to the available batch labels, an ingredient in all of the pelleted diets for horses, cattle and cervids investigated in this study. The higher fibre and lower RCH content, and the absence of corn, therefore are the most significant differences between the moose pellets and the other pelleted feeds.

Whereas the use of pelleted feeds makes forestomach blockage unlikely, it reduces rumination activity (Kick et al. 1937), and it increases the likelihood of ruminal acidosis by reducing the pH of rumen contents (Hinders et al. 1961). This is probably due to the reduction of rumination and the consequent lack of stimulation for the production of buffering saliva (Cullison 1961). The feeding of small amounts of structure material like hay or straw increases rumen pH back to physiological levels (Cullison 1961). We are not aware of a study that demonstrates the behavioral regulation of rumen pH through selective foraging by ruminants; yet common experience shows that ruminants will ingest any larger, fibrous material in order to achieve rumination stimulation. If no browse is available, captive moose will therefore graze in their enclosure if possible, and grazing is regarded as the triggering factor for the wasting syndrome complex (Shochat et al. 1997, Clauss et al. 2002). While the development of more suitable, refined and palatable pelleted feeds is a constant, important challenge to zoo nutritionists, pelleted formulas are unlikely to fulfil the need for coarse, structured material. As grass and grass hays seem unsuitable for moose (see above), other feeds of a coarser structure should be tested if browse is not available. Chopped hay, chopped grass, apple pomace mixed with chopped hay or – for better storage – according silages might offer alternatives.

## 5 Conclusions

1. The main difference between the commercially available, pelleted moose feeds and other pelleted feeds used in European moose husbandry is the higher fibre content and the absence of corn starch in the former.
2. This higher fibre content is due to an increase mainly in cellulose. The fibre composition of the commercially available moose feeds therefore resembles grass rather than browse, in spite of the sawdust ingredient of the North American product.
3. It is suggested that the main effect of the sawdust ingredient in the North American product is a dilution of digestible nutrients, an effect that is achieved by grass meal in the European product.
4. According to literature reports on the effects of corn starch and the digestive physiology of moose, the absence of corn starch in pelleted feeds should be beneficial for these animals.
5. While the refinement of pelleted diets is a continuous challenge for zoo nutritionists, the development of a coarse feed other than grass hay that is suitable for browsing ruminants is warranted.

## References

Bo, S.; Hjeljord, O. (1991): Do continental moose ranges improve during cloudy summers? *Can. J. Zool.* 69: 1875–1879.

Clauss, M.; Kienzle, E.; Wiesner, H. (2002): The importance of the wasting syndrome complex in captive moose. *Zoo Biology* 21(5): 499–506.

Clauss, M.; Kienzle, E.; Hatt, J.M. (2003): Feeding practice in captive wild ruminants: peculiarities in the nutrition of browsers/concentrate selectors and intermediate feeders. A review. (this volume).

Cullison, A. E. (1961): Effect of physical form of the ration on steer performance and certain rumen phenomena. *J. Anim. Sci.* 20: 478–483.

Dreher, M. L.; Dreher, C. J.; Berry, J. W. (1984): Starch digestibility of foods: a nutritional perspective. *CRC Crit. Rev. Food Sci. Nutr.* 20: 47–71.

Hinders, R. C.; Vidacs, G. Y.; Ward, G. M. (1961): Effects of feeding dehydrated alfalfa pellets as the only roughage to dairy cows. *J. Dairy Sci.* 44: 1178.

Hofmann, R. R.; Nygren, K. (1992): Ruminal mucosa as indicator of nutritional status in wild and captive moose. *Alces Suppl.* 1: 77–83.

Hubbert, M. E. (1987): *The effect of diet on energy partitioning in moose.* [PhD dissertation]. Fairbanks: University of Alaska.

Kick, C. H.; Gerlaugh, P.; Schalk, A. F. (1937): The effect of mechanical processing of feeds on the mastication and rumination of steers. *J. Agric. Res.* 55: 587–592.

Kienzle, E. (1994): Small intestinal digestion of starch in the horse. *Revue Méd. Vét.* 145: 199–204.

Lechner-Doll, M.; Kaske, M.; von Engelhardt, W. (1991): Factors affecting the mean retention time of particles in the forestomach of ruminants and camelids. *Proc. Int. Symp. Ruminant Physiol.* 7: 455–482.

Meyer, H. H. D.; Rowell, A.; Streich, W. J.; Stoffel, B.; Hofmann, R. R. (1998): Accumulation of polyunsaturated fatty acids by concentrate selecting ruminants. *Comp. Biochem. Physiol.* 120A: 263–268.

Nygren, K.; Hofmann, R. R. (1990): Seasonal veriations of food particle size in moose. *Alces* 26: 44–50.

Nygren, K. F. A.; Lechner-Doll, M.; Hofmann, R. R. (2001): Influence of papillae on post-ruminal regulation of ingesta passage in moose. *J. Zool. Lond.* 254: 375–380.

Orskov, E. R.; Kay, R. N. B. (1987): Non-microbial digestion of forages by herbivores. In: *The nutrition of herbivores* (J. B. Hacker, J. H. Ternouth, eds.). Sydney: Academic Press, pp. 267–280.

Orskov, E. R.; Fraser, C.; Kay, R. N. B. (1969): Dietary factors influencing the digestion of starch in the rumen and small and large intestine of early weaned lambs. *Br. J. Nutr.* 23: 217–226.

Orskov, E. R.; Fraser, C.; Mason, V. C.; Mann, S. O. (1970): Influence of starch digestion in the large intestine of sheep on caecal fermentation, caecal microflora and faecal nitrogen excretion. *Br. J. Nutr.* 24: 671–682.

Regelin, W. L.; Schwarz, C. C.; Franzmann, A. W. (1987): Effects of forest succession on nutritional dynamics of moose forage. *Swedish Wildl. Res. Suppl.* 1: 247–263.

Renecker, L. A.; Hudson, R. J. (1990): Digestive kinetics of moose, wapiti, and cattle. *Anim. Prod.* 50: 51–61.

Risenhoover, K. L. (1989): Composition and quality of moose winter diets in interior Alaska. *J. Wildl. Manage.* 53: 568–577.

Rowell, A.; Dyer, J.; Hofmann, R. R.; Lechner-Doll, M.; Meyer, H. H. D.; Shirazi-Beechey, S. P.; Wood, I. S. (1996): The expression of intestinal sodium-glucose cotransporters in cervids. *Proc. Int. Symp. Physiol. Ethol. Wild Zoo Anim.* 1: 204–208.

Schwartz, C. C. (1980): A formulated ration for captive moose. *Alces* 16: 82–105.

Schwartz, C. C.; Regelin, W. L.; Franzmann, A. W. (1988): Estimates of digestibility of birch, willow, and aspen mixtures in moose. *J. Wildl. Manage.* 52: 33–37.

Schwartz, C. C.; Harmon, D. L.; Hundertmark, K. J.; Robbins, C. T.; Lintzenich, B. A. (1996): Carbohydrase activity in the pancreas and small intestine of moose and cattle. *Alces* 32: 25–29.

Schwartz, C. C.; Regelin, W. L.; Franzmann, A. W. (1985): Suitability of a formulated ration for moose. J. Wildl. Manage. 49: 137–141.

Shochat, E.; Robbins, C. T.; Parish, S. M.; Young, P. B.; Stephenson, T. R.; Tamayo, A. (1997): Nutritional investigations and management of captive moose. *Zoo Biol.* 16: 479–494.

Spalinger, D. E.; Robbins, C. T.; Hanley, T. A. (1986): The assessment of handling time in ruminants: the effect of plant chemical and physical structure on the rate of breakdown of plant particles in the rumen of mule deer and elk. *Can. J. Zool.* 64: 312–321.

Spalinger, D. E.; Robbins, C. T.; Hanley, T. A. (1993): Adaptive rumen function in elk and mule deer. *Can. J. Zool.* 71: 601–610.

Tucker, R. E.; Mitchell, G. E.; Little, C. O. (1968): Ruminal and postruminal starch digestion in sheep. *J. Anim. Sci.* 27: 824–826.

Van Soest, P. J. (1996): Allometry and ecology of feeding behavior and digestive capacity in herbivores: a review. *Zoo Biol.* 15: 455–479.

*E. J. Flach*[1], *M. Clauss*[2], *A. Hunt*[3]

# Copper deficiency in yak (*Bos grunniens*) at Whipsnade Wild Animal Park


### *Abstract*

*Copper deficiency was suspected in the herd of yak (Bos grunniens) at Whipsnade Wild Animal Park. Animals were suffering from a range of conditions, including chronic diarrhoea, poor body condition and dull coats, despite daily supplementation with 36 mg of copper per animal. The copper concentration in yak blood samples collected in 1994 ranged from 0.8 to 3.3 µmol/L (mean 1.8, n = 10), well below the normal cattle range of 12 to 19 µmol/L. The copper supplement was therefore increased to 720 mg copper per adult per day (1.8 g copper sulphate) and blood copper concentrations rose each year, apart from low concentrations in juveniles in 1998, to plateau between 8.1 and 20.1 µmol/L (mean 13.3, n = 21). Over the same period general body and coat condition improved, again with the exception of 1998, and herd size grew. Other factors which may have been involved in the improvement in the health of the herd were the importation of a new herd male in 1992, and an intensification of anthelminthic treatment over the same period.*



### *Keywords*

*yak, Bos grunniens, copper, molybdenum, parasitism, fertility, depigmentation*


## 1 Introduction

Copper is an essential mineral for tissue oxidation, and a deficiency can cause disorders of keratinization, formation of melanin, elastin and haemoglobin, and reduced osteoblastic activity (Radostits et al. 1994). Typical clinical signs include retarded growth, poor quality and/or depigmented fur or wool, diarrhoea, anaemia, and ataxia. Reduced fertility and immunity have also been ascribed to copper deficiency in some species.

The supplementation of zoo diets with copper has been found to improve fertility, reduce the number of stillbirths and immature offspring, and inten-


[1] Veterinary Science Unit, Institute of Zoology, Whipsnade Wild Animal Park, Dunstable, Beds. LU6 2LF, United Kingdom, Tel.: ++44 1582 872171, Fax: 0044 1582 873989.

[2] Institute of Animal Physiology, Physiological Chemistry and Animal Nutrition, Ludwig-Maximilians University, Veterinärstr. 13, D-80539, Munich, Germany.

[3] Clinical Chemistry Unit, Veterinary Laboratories Agency, Kendal Road, Harlescott, Shrewsbury SY1 4HD, United Kingdom.

sify rutting behaviour in several ungulate groups (Senf & Zscheile 1978). For one species, the blesbok (*Damaliscus dorcas phillipsi*) a deficiency state has been demonstrated both in captivity (Jones 1980) and in the wild (Turkstra et al. 1978), and this may reflect an unusually high requirement for the element (Dierenfeld et al. 1988). A condition resembling enzootic ataxia has been described in yak (*Bos grunniens*) (Whitehead 1950), but no diagnostic investigations were reported. However, Liu, Zhang and Huang (1995) found very low liver copper concentrations in apparently healthy yak, and Clauss and Dierenfeld (1999) reported on clinical deficiency in yak, and presented evidence for a particular susceptibility to deficiency of the element.

Copper deficiency has been diagnosed, or suspected, in a number of ruminants at Whipsnade Wild Animal Park including bontebok (*Damaliscus dorcas*) (Jones 1980), llama (*Llama glama*) (Palmer et al, 1980), European bison (*Bison bonasus*), wapiti (*Cervus elaphus*) and yak (Ashton et al. 1979). Clinical signs recorded in yak included debility, weight loss, anaemia, diarrhoea, hindleg ataxia, exercise intolerance, alopecia, depigmentation around the eyes, stillbirths and poor neonatal survival. Between 1972 and 1979, 43 yak serum samples were analysed and found to contain between 10 and 100 µg/dl copper, with a mean of 40 (1.6 to 15.7 µmol/l; mean 6.2, Ashton et al. 1979). During the same period the liver copper concentration of four yak ranged from 8.5 to 26 µg/g dry matter (DM), with a mean of 13.4 (133 to 408 µmol/kg DM; mean of 210). Both means were below the normal copper ranges for cattle established by the Veterinary Laboratories Agency, UK: 9–19 µmol/l serum and 300–8000 µmol/kg DM liver. A grass sample from the yaks' paddock contained 10.6 mg copper/kg DM (166.4 µmol/kg DM), thought to be a mildly inadequate concentration, while repeated, seasonal testing of six paddocks between 1983 and 1984 for molybdenum, known to interfere with copper absorption, only revealed one sample out of 48 with a concentration of molybdenum above 2.0 mg/kg DM (2.3 mg/kg DM, all others were below 1.5 mg/kg DM). Between 1979 and 1992 the yak diet was supplemented with copper sulphate, but the inclusion rate was variable and never greater than 180 mg copper per adult per day.

Between 1992 and 1994 it was evident that yak were still suffering from a range of conditions which could be due to copper deficiency. We present here the results of opportunistic investigations of the copper status of the herd before and after increases in dietary supplementation.

## 2 Materials and Methods

Yak were introduced to Whipsnade in 1944 and have been kept as a closed herd with occasional new animals. The only arrival in the last 20 years was a new breeding male imported from Sweden in 1992. Details of individuals and the herd population were taken from animal management records which since 1989 have been stored on the ARKS database (International Species Information System, Apple Valley, MN, USA).

From 1990 to the present day the yak were kept in a large grassed drive-through exhibit on a dense loam (limestone and clay) soil, which they shared with Bactrian camels (*Camelus bactrianus*) and Père David's deer (*Elaphurus davidianus*). They had permanent access to shelters and, during the winter, were housed at night. Supplementary hay was offered during the winter, but in the winter of 1998/1999 silage was fed, and in 1999–2000 haylage. Approximately 1.25 kg of grazer concentrate pellets (14 % protein) were offered per adult per day. Up to 1994 these contained 21 mg/kg (Zoo Grazer G. P. Diet) and since 1994 25 mg/kg (Whipsnade Grazer). Copper sulphate was supplemented daily, applied to the concentrate pellets as an aqueous solution, and allowed to soak in before feeding exclusively to the yak. Between 1991 and 1994 40 ml of a 2.5 % solution was given to 11 animals, or approximately 36 mg of copper per animal. In June 1994 the supplement was increased to 144 mg per animal per day, the same rate as used in 1979, and then after analysis of blood results (see below) increased further to 720 mg per animal per day from September 1994. The allowance for calves was half of the adult dose until they were over one year of age. Anthelminthic drugs were administered in the feed three times yearly (April, July and September). Prior to 1995 fenbendazole (Panacur 1.5 % pellets) was offered as an addition to normal food on one day, but from 1995 onwards fenbendazole (Panacur 4 % powder) and ivermectin (Ivomec Premix for Pigs) were used on alternate years, incorporated into the concentrate feed and fed for three consecutive days.

Jugular venous blood samples were collected from yak immobilized for any management or veterinary procedure and stored with lithium heparin. This routine testing started in 1994, therefore the small numbers of samples tested between 1989 and 1993 were not analysed. Liver samples were collected during routine *post mortem* examinations of animals which died or were euthanased. Both were submitted to laboratories of the Veterinary Investigation Service, formerly of the Ministry of Agriculture, Fisheries and Food, and latterly the Veterinary Laboratories Agency. The copper content of the whole, heparinised, blood was determined by graphite furnace atomic absorption spectrophotometry using a GBC 906 AAS at 324.7 nm following a sample dilution of 50 µl with 1.00 ml of 0.05 % Triton-X-100 diluent. The copper content of liver samples was measured by flame atomic absorption spectrophotometry using a GBC 908 AAS, after sample dissolution in nitric acid. Blood values were compared with the normal range for cattle (whole, heparinised blood) established by the VLA: 12–19 µmol/l. Grass was collected from the enclosure in 1994, and submitted for analysis at the Royal Veterinary College, North Mymms, and again in 1998 when it was analysed at the VLA, Sutton Bonington by flame atomic absorption spectrophotometry using a GBC 932 AAS after digestion with nitric, perchloric and sulphuric acids. Unfortunately, conserved forages were not tested.

# 3 Results

## 3.1 Clinical cases

In 1992 several cases of diarrhoea were recorded in the yak herd, and two individuals, a 17-year-old female and a sub-adult male, were euthanased because of the chronic nature of the diarrhoea and loss of body condition. The copper concentration of the female's liver was 132 µmol/kg DM, less than half of the low end of the normal cattle range. In 1994 a sub-adult female, approximately 18 months old, was euthanased due to chronic hindlimb ataxia and poor body condition. The copper concentration of her liver was similarly low; 162 µmol/kg DM.

Since 1994 the general body condition of the herd has improved, and it has been noticeable that coat colour is now black, with some grey in older animals, whereas there used to be a brownish tinge. Recurrent diarrhoea, as noted in 1992 and previous years, has not been seen since. There are still cases of diarrhoea, but they are isolated cases for which a cause can normally be established, for example gastro-intestinal parasitism.

In the autumn of 1998 the calves born during the summer had depigmentation of the hair around the eyes, but were otherwise in good health. Their blood copper concentrations ranged from 0.8 to 5.0 µmol/L (mean 2.8), and the four male calves, which were culled, also had extremely low liver copper concentrations (17 to 135 µmol/kg DM, mean 73), plus moderate gastro-intestinal nematode burdens (50–3550 abomasal worms, mean 2350, and 700 to 4350 small intestinal worms, mean 2950). The female calves were injected intra-muscularly with 62.5 mg copper heptonate (Cuvine) and sub-cutaneously with 0.2 mg/kg body-weight ivermectin (Ivomec), and no further clinical signs were seen. A calf born in 2000 was euthanased at three months of age because of poor growth. Its liver copper concentration (366 µmol/kg DM) was within the normal cattle range, but at the low end of the range.

## 3.2 Blood copper results

The copper concentration in blood samples taken from animals immobilised for clinical or management purposes in 1994 ranged from 0.8 to 3.3 µmol/L (mean 1.8, $n = 10$), well below the normal cattle range of 12 to 19 µmol/L (figure 1). The copper supplement was increased in September 1994, and over the period 1995–2000 blood copper concentrations rose steadily, apart from 1998, to plateau in 1999–2000 between 8.1 and 20.1 µmol/L (mean 13.3, $n = 21$).

The low concentrations in 1998 were primarily those of the ten calves born during the summer and tested in the autumn. Two yearlings which were examined at the same time also had low concentrations (0.5 and 1.3 µmol/L), but three adult females sampled during the year had much higher concentrations (8.4, 17.0 and 18.1 µmol/L).

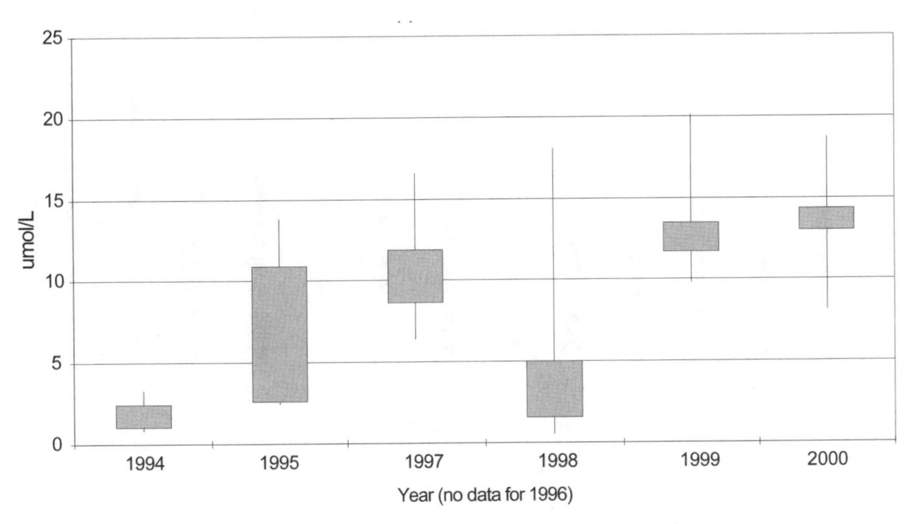


**Fig. 1.** Yak blood copper concentrations (1994–2000).

### 3.3 Liver copper concentrations

The liver concentrations of adult yak which died between 1995 and 2000 ranged from 557 to 4808 μmol/kg DM (mean 3125, $n = 5$), all within the normal cattle range. Ten neonates which were culled in 1999 had liver copper concentrations between 1699 and 6343 μmol/kg DM (mean 3948), also well within this range. However, the four male calves culled in 1998 had low values (see above) and a yearling female culled earlier in 1998 was also deficient (168 μmol/kg DM).

### 3.4 Pasture analysis

In 1994 the grass in the yak paddock was found to contain 8.3 mg copper/kg DM (130 μmol/kg DM). A further check in 1999 revealed a concentration of 19.7 mg/kg DM (309 μmol/kg DM).

### 3.5 Breeding

Breeding in the yak herd from 1988 remained fairly static at between two and four calves per year until after the introduction of the new male in 1992. The following year there were five calves born (figure 2), but in 1994 only two. However, from 1995 onwards the number of births increased each year until population control measures had to be taken in 1999 and 2000. The number of deaths peaked in 1988 and 1992, but in all other years were less than three, consequently the population grew from 1995 and animals were exported or culled each year except 1996.

Fertility was assessed as the number of live calves produced by female yak older than 1.5 years-old on the 1st January of that year, and still present during the calving period (March to August). This percentage was 60 % or greater in every year from 1990 to 2000 except one, 1994 (figure 3).

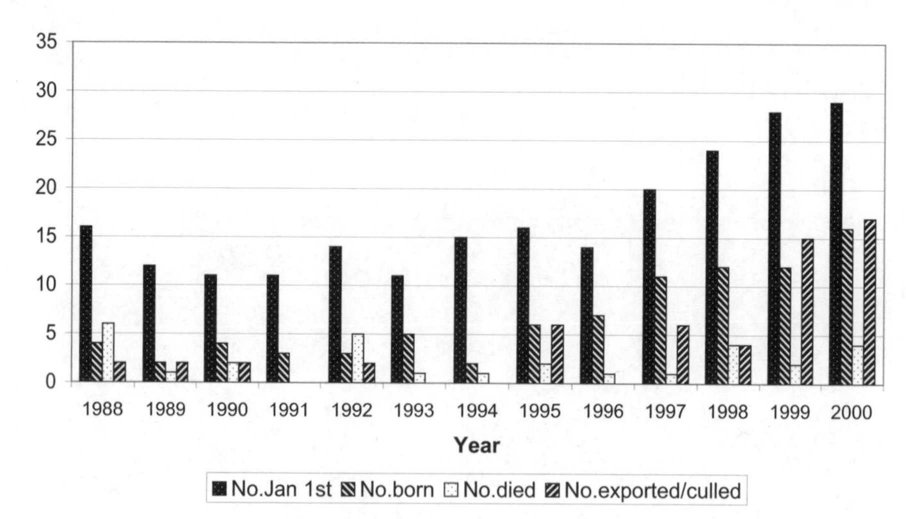


**Fig. 2.** Population growth 1988–2000.

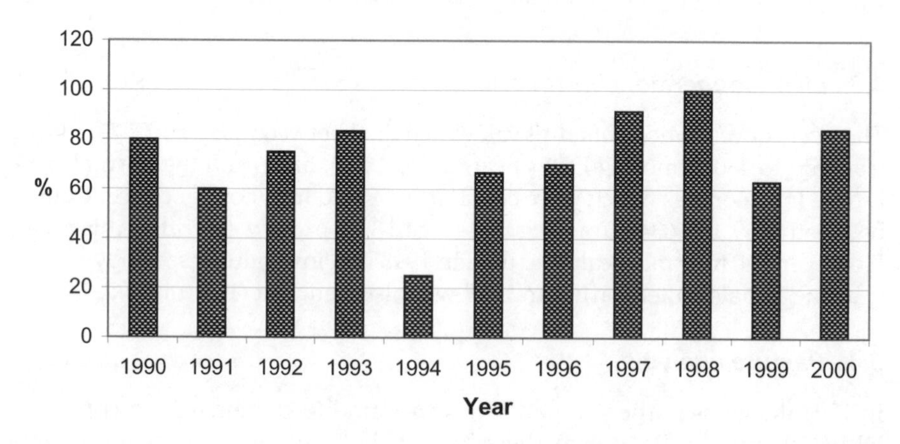


**Fig. 3.** Percentage of mature yak cows (> 1.5 yr) producing live calves.

## 4 Discussion

Increased supplementation with copper sulphate, either alone or in combination with other changes in husbandry, such as the importation of the new male and intensification of anthelminthic treatment, led to a marked improvement in the health and reproduction of the yak herd at Whipsnade. Opportunistic blood sampling provided the evidence that blood copper values in the yak rose simultaneously with these improvements, but because of the limitations of a clinical study it was not possible to obtain enough samples to prove cause and effect. Also, it was not possible to perform enough haematological examinations to study the association between red blood cell parameters and copper concentration, and to compare with yak results from the 1970s and early 1980s (Hawkey et al. 1983).

The diet offered to the yak between 1992 and 1994 was thought to contain sufficient copper. The minimum requirements for cattle are 10 mg copper per kg dry matter (Radostits et al. 1994) and, although the grass concentration in 1994 was slightly below this figure, the concentrate pellets (21–25 mg/kg) and existing supplement should have compensated. Moreover, at this stage all ages of animals, and dominant as well as lower-ranking individuals, had low blood copper concentrations, suggesting that lack of access to concentrates was not an important factor. Instead, there was probably a combination of secondary deficiency, due to one or more factors reducing the absorption of copper, and a uniquely high requirement by yak for the element (Clauss & Dierenfeld 1999). Neither the bactrian camels nor the Père David's deer sharing the pasture, but not receiving any supplement, were affected in the same way, underlining the particular sensitivity of yak. The final dose of copper supplement which was necessary for effective prophylaxis, 720 mg per animal per day, was consistent, on a comparative weight basis, with the daily figure of 1200 mg required for cows suffering from molybdenum-induced secondary deficiency (Radostits et al. 1994).

The conditioning factor for secondary copper deficiency is often not known, but the most commonly identified factor is an excessive dietary intake of molybdenum. This appears unlikely in this situation because extensive testing in the 1980s failed to show any elevation of the element. Other elements, such as sulphur and iron, have not been tested, but the paddock used by the yak is grazed very heavily, and so it is likely that animals do ingest soil as they graze.

Two other factors which could potentially have acted over the same time period were the importation of a new herd male in 1992, and an intensification of anthelminthic treatment over the same period. The new male was responsible for introducing new genes into the in-bred herd and undoubtably this helped improve reproductive success, but this improvement was mainly apparent from 1995 after the copper supplement was increased, and not from 1993 when the new male's first offspring were born. The parasite control protocol for all ungulates was reviewed in 1994, at the same time as the review of copper supplementation, and the treatment of the yak was incorporated into the concentrates, and given over three days to ensure that all individuals received a therapeutic dose. However, the impact of gastro-intestinal parasitism is difficult to assess. Both parasitism and copper deficiency affect the same individuals, primarily the young, and both were treated in the food, and so young and sub-dominant animals would have had reduced access to anthelminthic drug and copper sulphate. There is evidence that the two interact: intestinal nematodes may reduce the absorption of copper, but copper supplementation has an anthelminthic effect (Sykes 1987, Poppi et al. 1990). Copper deficiency is also thought to reduce an individual's immune response. It was notable, therefore, that the calves which showed signs of copper deficiency in 1998 also had moderate nematode infections.

There was not a clear-cut association between low blood copper concentrations and fertility, although the very low figure in 1994 reflected the poor health and low copper status at the time, and there was an increase in parallel with copper supplementation between 1995 and 1998, with a dip in 1999 possibly caused by the copper deficiency seen in juveniles the previous year. Fertility was 60 % or greater during the period 1990–1993, but unfortunately comparable herd blood copper concentrations were unavailable. The herd did increase slightly in size over this period, but the main increase occurred from 1995 onwards when there were more births each year, but no comparable increase in mortality.

## 5 Conclusions

1. Successful treatment of copper deficiency in yak required large doses of copper sulphate. Supplementation has been continued for several years.
2. The copper concentration of whole blood samples, collected whenever animals were immobilised, reflected the copper status of the herd, and indicated a deficiency in juveniles despite supplementation.
3. Improvements in herd reproductive success may require correction of several factors, including genetic inbreeding and diseases such as copper deficiency and gastrointestinal parasitism.

## Acknowledgements

We should like to thank all past and present veterinary colleagues at Whipsnade who have helped with sampling and analyses over the years. Shaun Ferneley carried out a review of copper sample results in 1994 which formed the basis of the increase in supplementation which has proved so successful. Vivian Heys, Royal Veterinary College, kindly undertook pasture copper analyses in 1994. Amelie Malgras performed the worm counts on stored samples of abomasal and small intestinal contents.

## Products mentioned in the text

**Cuvine**: copper heptonate, 12.5 mg/ml, injectable copper supplement, manufactured by Vericore, Litlington, Herts., UK.

**Ivomec Injection for Cattle**: ivermectin 10 mg/ml, injectable anthelminthic, manufactured by Merial Animal Health Ltd., Harlow, Essex, UK.

**Ivomec Premix for Pigs:** ivermectin 0.6 %, manufactured by Merial Animal Health Ltd.

**Panacur 1.5 % pellets:** fenbendazole 1.5 % oral pellets, manufactured by Intervet UK Ltd., Milton Keynes, Bucks., UK.

**Panacur 4 % powder**: fenbendazole 4 %, manufactured by Intervet UK Ltd.

**Whipsnade Grazer**: manufactured by Clarke & Butcher, Soham, Cambs., UK

**Zoo Grazer G.P. Diet**: manufactured by SDS/Mazuri, Witham, Essex, UK

## References

Ashton, D. G.; Jones, D. M.; Lewis, G.; Cinderey, R. N. (1979): Some preliminary studies on the blood and liver copper levels in ungulates at Whipsnade. *Verhandlungsbericht Erkrankungen der Zootiere* 21: 135–144.

Clauss, M.; Dierenfeld, E. (1999): Susceptibility of yak (*Bos grunniens*) to copper deficiency. *Veterinary Record* 145: 436–437.

Dierenfeld, E. S.; Dolensek, E. P.; McNamara, T. S.; Doherty, J. G. (1988): Copper deficiency in captive blesbok antelope. *Journal of Zoo Animal Medicine* 19: 126–131.

Hawkey, C. M.; Ashton, D. G.; Hart, M. G.; Cinderey, R. N.; Jones, D. M. (1983): Normal and clinical haematology in the yak (*Bos grunniens*). *Research in Veterinary Science* 34: 31–36.

Jones, D. (1980): A complex, debilitating syndrome in blesbok as an example of a problem of maintaining antelopes from arid lands on temperate grassland. In: *The comparative pathology of zoo animals* (R. J. Montali, G. Migaki, eds.). Washington DC: Smithsonian Institute Press, pp. 73–76.

Liu, Z. P.; Zhang, Q. B.; Huang, L. (1995): Serum biochemical values and mineral element contents of tissues in yaks. *Veterinary Research Communications* 19: 473–478.

Palmer, A. C.; Blakemore, W. F.; O'Sullivan, B.; Ashton, D. G.; Scott, W. A. (1980): Ataxia and spinal cord degeneration in llama, wildebeeste and camel. *Veterinary Record* 107: 10–11.

Poppi, D. P.; Sykes, A. R.; Dynes, R. A. (1990): The effect of endoparasitism on host nutrition – the implications for nutrient manipulation. *Proc. New Zeal. Soc. Anim. Prod.* 50: 237–243.

Radostits, O. M.; Blood, D. C.; Gay, C. C. (1994): *Veterinary Medicine. A Textbook of the Diseases of Cattle, Sheep, Pigs, Goats and Horses.* 8th edition. London: Baillière Tindall. P. 1379–1394.

Senf, W.; Zscheile, D. (1978): Beitrag zur erfolgreichen Bekämpfung von Kup fermangelerscheinungen bei Zootieren. *Verhandlungsbericht Erkrankungen der Zootiere* 20: 123–130.

Sykes, A. R. (1987): Endoparasites and herbivore nutrition. In: *Nutrition of herbivores* (Hacker, Teynouth, eds.). Marrickwale, New South Wales: Academic Press, pp. 211–232.

Turkstra, J.; de Vos, V.; Biddlekombe, F.; Dow, R. J. (1978): The characterisation of the concentration of various trace elements in liver tissue of blesbok and bontebok. *Z. Tierphysiol., Tierernährg. U. Futtermittelkde* 40: 149–154.

Whitehead, G. K. (1950): *Deer and their management in the deer parks of Great Britain and Ireland*. London: Country Life Ltd.

K. Foster[1]

# Assessing diets for Congo peafowl, *Afropavo congensis*, at Jersey Zoo

### Abstract

*Congo peafowl, Afropavo congensis, are considered vulnerable in the wild although little is known about their ecology and population density. They have been kept in captivity since the 1940s; however, the captive birds suffer from health and breeding problems. Chick mortality is high, resulting in low population growth. Causes of adult death (n = 15) and disorders identified at post-mortem in Congo peafowl at Jersey Zoo (1998–2000) were reviewed, and included several which may be diet-related: obstruction of the oviduct caused by egg retention, egg peritonitis, kidney failure, heart failure, fat accumulation around the heart, hyperlipaemia, hepatic lipidosis, gout and myocardial degeneration. This study was undertaken in order to evaluate the nutrient quality of the Congo peafowl diet.*

*The diet provided to and consumed by the Congo peafowl was quantified, analysed and compared to the nutrient requirement levels of domestic pheasants. Although the precise nutrients required by Congo peafowl are unknown, this analysis is still a valuable tool in assessing nutrient status, until more work has been done in the wild to understand their specific needs. This study highlighted some imbalances in the Congo peafowl diet, such as insufficient levels of calcium and protein, and an elevated fat content, which correlate with the findings at post-mortem. The diet was modified, to try to rectify some of the nutrient imbalances, to help provide well balanced diets to maintain healthy birds in captivity.*

### Keywords

*Calcium, fat, health, nutrients, protein, reproduction*

## 1 Introduction

### 1.1 Background

Congo peafowl, *Afropavo congensis,* are vulnerable in the wild through hunting and the loss of habitat, despite being protected in the Democratic Republic of Congo since 1938 (McGowan 1994; Hart and Ukopi 1997; Birdlife

[1] Research Department, Durrell Wildlife Conservation Trust, Les Augrès Manor, Trinity, Jersey, JE3 5BP, Channel Islands. Tel. 01534 860078; Fax. 01534 860001; Email: austinkatebrown@hotmail.com.

International 2000; Hilton-Taylor 2000). They were discovered in 1936, and have been in captivity since the 1940s. There is a managed captive breeding programme (EEP) for this species. However, there have been problems maintaining and breeding Congo peafowl in captivity (Van Bocxstaele 2000). Chick mortality is high, resulting in low population growth. Causes of adult death at Jersey Zoo (1998–2000) were reviewed and disorders identified at post-mortem in 15 adult Congo peafowl (9 males, 6 females) are illustrated in figure 1. Some of these problems (such as obstruction of the oviduct caused by egg retention, egg peritonitis, kidney failure, heart failure, fat accumulation around the heart, hyperlipaemia, hepatic lipidosis, gout and myocardial degeneration; MedARKS 2000; Van Bocxstaele 2000), may highlight possible dietary imbalances, so a nutritional study was initiated in order to establish whether the diet provided to these birds was adequate in terms of essential nutrients.

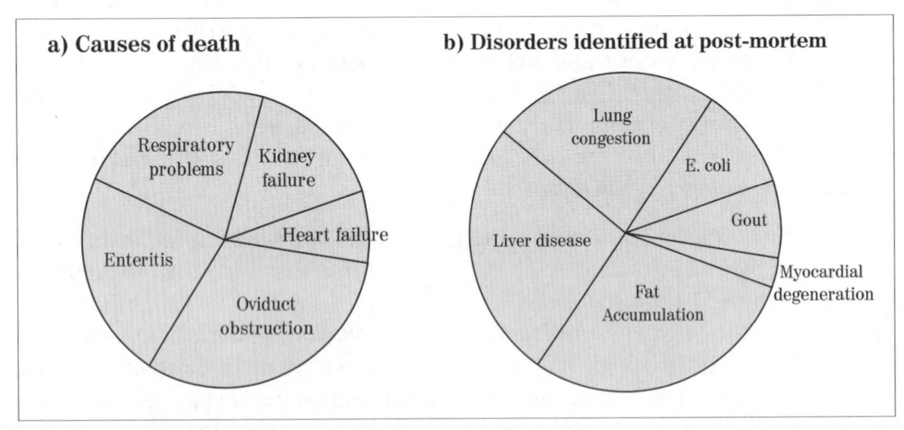


**Figure 1.** Causes of death and disorders identified at post-mortem in adult Congo peafowl ($n$ = 15) at Jersey Zoo (1998–2000). Oviduct obstruction is percentage of female birds, other causes are percentage of all birds.

### *1.2 Nutrition of Phasianidae*

Congo peafowl are from the order Galliformes, family Phasianidae, and they are the only species of pheasant to occur in Africa. They are endemic to the equatorial forests of the Democratic Republic of Congo in West Africa, in areas with prolific undergrowth and well-drained soil. In the wild, Congo peafowl are thought to be omnivorous, feeding on seeds and fruits of trees and plants in the understorey, and also on invertebrates and aquatic insects (McGowan 1994).

Limited data are available about the precise nutritional requirements of Congo peafowl, and much of the information on the nutritional requirements of this family of birds has been collated from other well-studied related genera, such as domestic pheasants and poultry (ARC 1975; King 1977; NRC 1994). However, a study reviewing ecological data for pheasants (Sheppard et al. 1998), classified Congo peafowl as belonging to a largely insectivorous group, likely to feed in the wild on a high protein diet containing over 35 % protein, which is substantially higher than the domestic pheasant protein requirement of approximately 17 % (NRC 1994). This highlights the difficulties in classifying species according to diet when limited data are available, and emphasises the need to study species in the wild in order to make robust comparisons to the species in captivity.

The breeding and maintenance requirements for some nutrients are listed in table 1, based on information compiled from a number of sources (Scott et al. 1959 a,b,c; ARC 1975; King 1977; NRC 1994, Sheppard et al. 1998). Growing pheasants have a higher protein requirement than adults, with newly hatched chicks requiring 31 % protein, decreasing to 20 % by around 3–4 months (NRC 1994). Calcium levels are given as 2.8 % of the diet of a domestic pheasant, although this level is likely to be only applicable to commercial birds laying multiple clutches. A calcium level of 0.5–1.5 % is likely to be more appropriate for wild birds (Chambers et al. 1966), and so this value was used for comparison.

## 2 Animals and methods

### 2.1 *Study animals*

At the time of the study (August 2000) there were 11 Congo peafowl at Jersey Zoo. The birds were all captive born, either at Jersey Zoo or Bronx Zoo, and were between one and 15 years old. The average body weight was 1296.4 g ± 306.7 g. The birds were housed in five aviaries, all of which were mixed-species exhibits, with either pink pigeons (*Columba mayeri*) or red-crested turacos (*Tauraco erythrolophus*). The enclosures were made up of an outside aviary with sand and vegetation (trees and ground cover), and an indoor area.

### 2.2 *2000 Diet*

The Congo peafowl were provided with a diet that consisted of a variety of fruits, a dry mixture and mealworms. A mean of seven (range 5–8) different chopped fruits and vegetables were provided each day (apple, banana, celery, cucumber, grape, kiwi, mango, melon, nectarine, papaya, pear, plum, tomato). Fruit items were sprinkled with the supplement Nutrobal, to provide additional vitamins and minerals. The dry mixture consisted of Pheasant Breeder Pellets, Universal Insectivorous Mix, bread crumbs, grated carrot, cracked corn, and hard-boiled egg. The fruit and dry food mixtures were provided at 1100 daily, and the mealworm feeds, consisting of 12–15 mealworms per bird per day, were provided at approximately 08:00 and 17:00 hrs.

### 2.3 *Feeding Trials*

The feeding trials were carried out during the breeding season in August 2000, and consisted of a total of 10 days of data collection for each group. Each fruit item was chopped and weighed before being mixed together and presented to the birds. Each item in the dry mixture was also weighed prior to being

**Table 1.** Nutrients required and levels in the Congo peafowl diet (dry matter)

| CATEGORY | NUTRIENT | | REQUIREMENT | *DIET* | |
|---|---|---|---|---|---|
| | | | | Provided | Consumed |
| Protein | Crude protein | % | 17.0–20.0<br>35.0 * | 8.4 | 13.3 |
| | Cystine | % | 0.3 | 0.1 | 0.1 |
| | Lysine | % | 0.8 | 0.3 | 0.4 |
| | Methionine | % | 0.3 | 0.1 | 0.2 |
| Fats | Crude fat | % | 5.0 | 4.6 | 6.6 |
| | Linoleic acid | % | 1.1 | 0.7 | 0.7 |
| Energy | ME Poultry | kcal/g | 3.1 | 0.8 | 1.6 |
| | Energy | kcal/day | 150.0 | 265.4 | 108.4 |
| Ash/ Minerals | Ash | % | | 3.4 | 4.0 |
| | Calcium | % | 2.8<br>0.5–1.5 ** | 0.4 | 0.6 |
| | Ca:P | | > 2:1 | 1.6:1 | 1.5:1 |
| | Chlorine | % | 0.1 | 0.04 | 0.08 |
| | Iron | mg/kg | | 44.4 | 50.8 |
| | Magnesium | % | | 0.1 | 0.1 |
| | Manganese | mg/kg | 66.7–95.0 | 26.0 | 34.9 |
| | Phosphorus | % | 0.4–0.8 | 0.2 | 0.4 |
| | Potassium | % | | 1.0 | 0.8 |
| | Selenium | mg/kg | | 1.7 | 3.4 |
| | Sodium | % | 0.2 | 0.1 | 0.2 |
| | Zinc | mg/kg | 66.7 | 39.3 | 50.0 |
| Vitamins | Choline | mg/kg | 1111.1 | 256.0 | 461.8 |
| | Folacin | mg/kg | | 1.7 | 1.7 |
| | Niacin | mg/kg | 33.3 | 39.4 | 41.4 |
| | Pantothenic acid | mg/kg | 17.8 | 13.6 | 16.5 |
| | Riboflavin | mg/kg | 4.4 | 2.5 | 2.5 |
| | Thiamin | mg/kg | | 2.7 | 2.9 |
| | Vitamin A | IU/g | 8.0 | 97.1 | 175.1 |
| | Vitamin $B_6$ | mg/kg | | 6.81 | 4.7 |
| | Vitamin C | mg/kg | | 694.5 | 403.9 |
| | Vitamin $D_3$ | IU/g | 2.0 | 1.0 | 0.9 |
| | Vitamin E | mg/kg | | 30.9 | 30.8 |

Data from Scott et al., 1959a,b,c; ARC, 1975; King, 1977; NRC, 1994

* Estimated protein intake by wild Congo peafowl (Sheppard et al., 1998)

** Estimated calcium requirement of wild birds (Chambers et al., 1966) mixed, and the amount of each mixture provided per aviary was recorded. All food remains were collected the following day at approximately 11:00 hrs and reweighed. The total amounts of food provided and remaining were recorded per aviary, and the amount of food consumed per individual was calculated on the assumption that each bird in one aviary consumed the same amount of food, as it was not possible to analyse individual consumption. Control feeds were used to calculate the amount of water that was lost or gained by the feeds during the time that they were in the aviary (approximately 24 hours), and subsequently used to apply a correction factor to the feed remains.

Some assumptions had to be made regarding the food remains. As it was not possible to separate the Nutrobal from the fruit remains, it was assumed that the Nutrobal was consumed in the same proportions as the fruit. It was also assumed that 75 % of the mealworms provided were consumed, as any uneaten were not possible to collect.

The Congo peafowl diets were analysed using the dietary management software Zootrition (WCS 1999). The Zootrition database of food composition was used to analyse the diets, as no analyse of actual food items were undertaken. Zootrition was also used to calculate nutritional breakdowns of the diets provided and consumed during the study. The composition of the diets was subsequently compared to the nutritional requirements of pheasants during breeding and maintenance seasons (table 1). A Kruskal Wallis test (Siegel and Castellan 1998) was used to compare the amount of nutrients consumed by the birds in each aviary during the study.

## 3 Results

### *3.1 Diet composition*

The average amount of food provided per bird per day was 409.8 g, of which 25.6 % (105.1 g) was consumed (wet weights). The average amount of fruit consumed per bird per day was 65.2 g (±18.5) and the average amount of the dry food consumed was 39.9 g (± 9.1) (wet weights). The diet provided consisted of 85.4 % fruit and 14.6 % of the dry mixture, and the diet consumed consisted of 61.3 % fruit and 38.7 % dry mixture (by wet weight).

### *3.2 Nutrient analyses*

The mean amounts of nutrients provided and consumed per bird during the study are given in table 1. There was no difference between the nutrients consumed by birds in each aviary during the study ($H = 1.24$, d.f. $= 4$, $p = 0.871$). The average composition of the diet provided was different to that of the diet consumed. The amount of protein consumed was proportionally 1.6 times greater than the amount of protein provided. The calcium content of the diet consumed was also greater than that provided, at 0.6 % and 0.4 % respectively. The diet contained almost twice as much vitamin A as the diet provided, but just over half of the amount of vitamin C provided.

The nutrient composition of the diets provided and consumed were then compared to the domestic pheasant requirements (NRC 1994) or to wild data estimates (Shepard et al. 1998). Figure 2 shows the average percentage of each breeding requirement that was consumed per bird during the study. Fat and niacin were consumed in amounts over the recommended levels whereas all other nutrients were consumed below the recommended levels. Crude protein was consumed at just under 80 % of the breeding requirement, although this was less than 40 % of the estimated protein intake by wild Congo peafowl (Shepard et al. 1998). Calcium levels were 20 % of that listed for breeding poultry (NRC 1994).

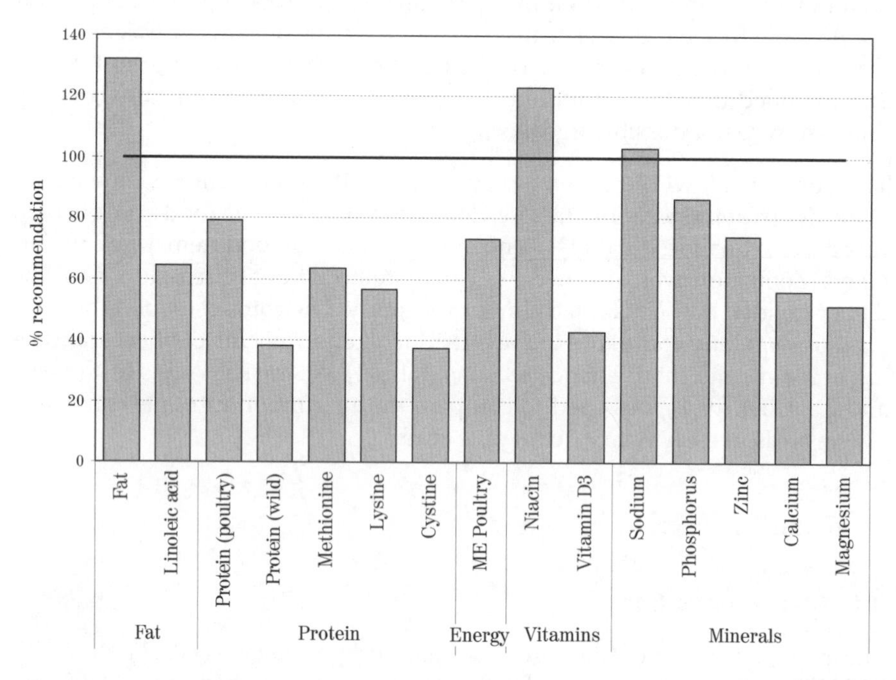


**Figure 2.** The percentage of each requirement that was consumed (dry matter) based on NRC, (1994) requirements. Protein (poultry) based on NRC (1994) requirement; Protein (wild) based on Sheppard et al. (1998)

## 4 Discussion

There are some dietary deficiencies in the diets consumed by Congo peafowl at Jersey Zoo when compared to the requirements of breeding pheasants. However, some of the apparent lack of nutrients is caused not by dietary deficiencies but by the absence of some data. Only 4.5 % of the food items provided (1 out of 22) contained an analysis of ME Poultry in their breakdown. Some amino acids were also deficient in composition data; 59 % of food items contained an analysis of cystine, 73 % contained an analysis of lysine, and 73 % contained an analysis of methionine. Data for choline was also only available for 14 % of the food items provided (3 out of the 22 items in the diet). Therefore the analysis will represent the minimum amount of these nutrients present in the diet. There are also difficulties when comparing diets to related species when wild data are limited. Using food composition data from a database, rather than conducting analysis on the actually food items provided will also have been a source of error, as the composition of food is very dependant upon the conditions in which they have been produced, e. g. soil in which plants are grown, substrate on which mealworms and crickets have been raised. However, this is still a useful tool in assessing the nutrient intake of captive species, until more work is done in the wild to fully understand their needs.

### 4.1 Diet content

The Congo peafowl were provided with an average of seven fruit items per day. The feeding of a large variety of items per day can be an important factor in influencing the nutritional intake of captive wild animals, and a heterogeneous diet can result in dietary deficiencies in individual animals, arising out of food preferences (Robbins 1993). Reducing the number of items that are provided per day would help prevent the skewing of nutrients consumed due to selective consumption.

The difference in the relative proportions of fruit and dry mixture in the diets provided and consumed showed that the Congo peafowl were selecting the dry food in preference to the fruit. The selective consumption of foods has affected the nutritional composition of the diets, as demonstrated by the differences in the proportions of nutrients present in the diets provided and consumed. Protein, calcium and vitamin A form greater proportions of the diet provided than consumed, which was primarily due to the consumption of the pellets and dry mixture in preference to the fruit. Vitamin C was consumed at 60% of that provided, again because of the fruit forming a smaller component of the diet consumed than the diet provided.

### 4.2 Protein

The Congo peafowl consumed a diet containing an average of 13.3 % protein, which was 79 % of the protein required by breeding pheasants (NRC 1994). However, this was only 38 % of the estimated protein content of the wild diet (Shepard et al. 1998). Levels of the amino acids cystine, lysine and methionine were all below the recommended levels of domestic pheasants. Deficiencies of methionine and cystine have also been suggested to cause hepatic lipidosis, which has been identified in Congo peafowl. Protein and amino acids are important for growth and egg production (Robbins 1993). Newly hatched chicks have a protein requirement of 31 % (NRC 1994), and amino acids may be one of the most important factors affecting chick survival (Lloyd et al. 2000). Congo peafowl have shown egg problems and low chick survival, so an increase in protein and essential amino acids content of the diets would be beneficial, particularly during the breeding season for reproductive adults and chicks, as in the wild breeding coincides with periods of increased availability of insect life and new plant growth, both of which are good sources of high quality protein (King 1977).

However, an increase in dietary protein should be monitored, as there have been cases of kidney failure and gout at Jersey Zoo in the past (MedARKS 2000), although this may also be associated with protein quality rather than quantity, particularly the lysine and methionine content (Slifka 1991; Fidgett and Robert 1993), though both of these amino acids were low in the 2000 diet.

### 4.3 Fats

Congo peafowl consumed a diet that contained 132 % of the fat required for breeding pheasants. Elevated fat levels have caused problems in the past, with 61 % of 15 adult birds showing fat accumulation around the heart and excessive amounts of lipase in the blood at post-mortem (Jersey Zoo, 1998 to 2000). There have also been cases of hepatic lipidosis, where fat accumulates in the liver beyond normal levels. This is particularly common in young animals with a low nutritional status (C. Dutton, in MedARKS 1998), and as already mentioned may be linked with deficiencies of methionine and cystine. The accumulation of fat around the kidneys and over the lower abdominal wall can interfere with ovulation and egg laying (King 1977), which may help to explain the high incidence of death caused by egg retention in Congo peafowl at Jersey Zoo, although egg retention is also related to dietary calcium levels (discussed below). The Congo peafowl could benefit from a reduction of the fat content in the diet to help reduce these problems.

### 4.4 Minerals

The calcium consumed per bird was below the recommended level, forming 0.56 % of the diet; only 50 % of the average wild bird requirement (Chambers et al. 1966). The average Ca : P ratio was between 1.4 : 1 and 1.5 : 1, although it should ideally be closer to 2 : 1. The dietary phosphorus consumed was 86 % of the amount of phosphorus required by breeding domestic pheasants. Historically, at Jersey Zoo there have been calcium deficiency-related problems, such as eggs being thin-shelled, and obstruction of the oviduct caused by egg retention, and egg peritonitis (which was the cause of death in 4 of 6 female Congo peafowl between 1998 and 2000). An increase in calcium levels would be beneficial, particularly during breeding. However, it is important to ensure that calcium concentration in the diet varies according to season, as continuously high levels of calcium can adversely affect the hatchability of poultry, reduce male fertility and reduce the uptake of trace minerals such as zinc and manganese (ARC 1975), both of which are low in the diet, at 75 % and 52 % of the recommended domestic pheasant level.

### 4.5 Vitamins

Niacin was consumed in quantities above the required level (123 %), although it is a water-soluble vitamin, which means that it is not stored in the body and thus will not be harmful when present in excess in the diet.

Low dietary concentrations of vitamin $D_3$ in the diet consumed by the Congo peafowl are not a cause for concern, as all the Congo peafowl have unlimited access to natural sunlight in outside aviaries, enabling them to synthesise it in the body (Albers et al. 1984). Natural vitamin $D_3$ is found in very few feed materials, such as whole milk and fish oils, and birds cannot utilize vitamin $D_2$ efficiently (the form found in sun-dried green forage), making solar irradiation the most important source of this vitamin.

Dietary concentrations of vitamin A appear to be extremely high, although 90 % of the vitamin A in the diet consumed was represented by vitamin A precursors (carotenoids), primarily from the carrot. Carotenoids occur in plant material, and are converted as required (McDonald et al. 1988), and the active form of vitamin A (retinol), is only present in animal products and commercially produced foods. Unlike retinol, which is stored in fat and tissues (particularly the liver), carotenoids are only stored in the body to a very small extent (Albers et al. 1984), and so are not harmful when present in excess. Carotenoids are also readily destroyed by oxidation, losing their vitamin A potency (McDonald et al. 1988), which would lower the dietary levels further. If only the preformed retinol was analysed, it would result in a dietary level of 17.5 IU/g consumed as opposed to 175.1 IU/g when the carotenoids are included. Although this is twice the pheasant requirement of 8 IU/g, the maximum tolerable level of vitamin A is presumed to be between 4 and 8 times the requirement (NRC 1987).

Choline was provided and consumed at levels of 23 % and 42 % of the pheasant requirement. However, as already mentioned, only 14 % of the food items provided contained a value for this vitamin in their nutrient breakdown, so part of this deficiency is likely to be due to a lack of nutrient composition data.

## 5 Recommendations

The following recommendations are suggestions as to how the diet could be modified in order to correct some of the nutrient imbalances apparent following the analysis of the Congo peafowl diet.

- Calcium: Increase content by increasing the relative proportions of calcium rich foods such as pheasant pellets and leafy green vegetables (including pak choi, watercress, clover and dandelion greens but excluding high oxalate containing foods such as spinach).
- Fat: Reduce content in diet to 5 % during breeding (possibly lowered during maintenance) to prevent fat accumulation around the heart, by restricting high fat foods such as egg and insectivorous mix. Providing crickets, locusts and earthworms in place of mealworms would also help to lower fat levels, due to the high fat content of mealworms.
- Protein: Increase content, particularly during breeding, by increasing the relative proportion of pheasant pellets. The inclusion of legumes and leafy green vegetables would help to raise dietary protein and levels of essential amino acids. Increasing the proportion of insects in the diet

would also increase protein levels. Insects are also important as enrichment, as Congo peafowl are likely to be largely insectivorous in the wild, and foraging for insects increases activity and stimulates more natural behaviour.

- Minerals: Elevate the manganese and zinc levels in the diet by increasing the relative proportions of pheasant pellets and other foods that are high in these minerals.
- Varying the nutrient content of the diet (e. g. protein, calcium) according to season, may help to stimulate breeding responses and reduce the harmful effects of continuously high levels of some nutrients, although identifying seasonal breeding patterns can be difficult as captive birds can sometimes breed throughout the year.
- Reduce the number of different items provided per day, as a heterogeneous diet can result in dietary deficiencies in individuals due to specific feeding preferences. Maintaining a variety over a week would help to prevent boredom arising from a restricted diet.

## 6 Diet modification

The Congo peafowl diet was modified to try to rectify some of the imbalances of the 2000 diet. A diet consisting of 60 g pellet mixture (60 % pheasant pellets, 15 % bread, 20 % carrot and 5 % hard-boiled egg, by wet weights), 40 g fruit and vegetables (2–3 different items per day), and invertebrates (crickets, locusts, earthworms, mealworms), would provided a diet that contained 23 % protein (also with an increased level of essential amino acids), 5 % fat, and a Ca : P of 2 : 1. Mealworms should only form a small proportion of the invertebrate content of the diet, due to their high fat content. The increase in the relative proportion of pheasant pellets has also increased levels of trace minerals (such as zinc an manganese). Until more work has been done to understand their requirements, and these changes have been monitored further, the protein content has not initially been increased up to the estimated wild levels, due to concerns over gout. However, as already mentioned, this may be at least partially due to protein quality rather than quantity.

During maintenance, the calcium and fat content of the diet could be reduced by changing the relative proportions of food items in the diet, e. g. reducing the amount of mealworms relative to crickets to lower the fat content, reducing the amount of pellet mixture relative to fruit and vegetables to lower calcium levels. However, implementing a diet that varies seasonally may be problematic, as a maintenance season can be difficult to identify when the Congo peafowl appear to be able to breed year-round in captivity (D. Jeggo, pers. comm.). This needs to be further investigated.

The change in the nutrient content of the diet should be monitored both in terms of adverse effects and benefits on health and reproduction. The increase in the relative proportion of pheasant pellets in the diet is currently being assessed at Jersey Zoo. It is hoped that it will improve the health of the population of Congo peafowl, resulting in a reduction in the cases of egg peritonitis and fat accumulation, and an increase in chick survival, as the nutritional status of the adults is critical in determining the nutritional status of the chicks, and hence their survival.

## 7 Conclusions

There were some imbalances in the diets that were consumed by Congo peafowl when compared to the requirements of breeding pheasants and estimated wild diets, which could help to explain why health and breeding problems have been apparent in the captive population.

1. Calcium levels were low; calcium deficiency is likely to be a major contributory factor in the death of female Congo peafowl by causing egg retention, the most common cause of death in female Congo peafowl at Jersey Zoo.
2. Fat levels were high; 61 % of the adult birds that underwent post-mortem at Jersey Zoo between 1998 and 2000 showed signs of fat accumulation and hyperlipaemia.
3. Protein levels were low; protein deficiency can impair egg production, growth and chick survival, all problems which have been identified in Congo peafowl, at Jersey Zoo and in the rest of the EEP population.

Although the precise nutrients required by Congo peafowl are unknown, this analysis is still a valuable tool in assessing nutrient status, until more work has been done to understand their specific needs. The effect of changing the diet is being monitored, and it is hoped that the improvement in nutrient status should help to improve the health and reproduction of these birds in captivity.

## Acknowledgements

Many thanks go to all the staff and students working on the Bird Department for their assistance and advice throughout the study and during the subsequent write-up; in particular, Austin Brown, John Condron, Simon James, David Jeggo and Andrew Plant. Thanks also go to Ellen Dierenfeld (Department of Nutrition, Wildlife Conservation Society) for advice on aspects of animal nutrition, and to Anna Feistner and Eluned Price for help and comments during data collection and the write-up of the report.

## Products mentioned in text

**Nutrobal:** vitamin and mineral supplement, manufactured by Vetark Animal Health, P.O. Box 60, Winchester, Hampshire, SO23 9XN, England.

**Pheasant Breeder Pellets:** pelleted food, manufactured by Special Diet Services, P.O. Box 705, Witham, Essex, CM8 3AD, England.

**Universal Insectivorous Mix:** seed and invertebrate mix, manufactured by Bogena BV, Waalwijk, Holland.

## References

[ARC] Agricultural Research Council (1975): *The nutritional requirements of farm livestock*. N°. 1 Poultry. London: ARC.

Albers, N.; Behm, G.; Dressler, D.; Klaus, W.; Küther, K.; Lindner, H. (1984): *Vitamins in animal nutrition*. Arbeitsgemeinschaft für Wirkstoffe in der Tierernährung e. V. (AWT).

BirdLife International. (2000): *Threatened Birds of the World*. Barcelona, Spain and Cambridge, UK: Lynx Edicions and BirdLife International.

Chambers, G. D.; Sadler, K. C.; Breitenback, R. P. (1966): Effects of dietary calcium levels on egg production and bone structure of pheasants. *Journal of Wildlife Management* 30: 65–73.

Foster, K. J. (2000): *Nutritional analysis of the diet of captive Congo peafowl, Afropavo congensis, at Jersey Zoo*. Jersey (UK): Durrell Wildlife Conservation Trust.

Fidgett, A. L.; Robert, J. N. (1993): An investigation into nutrition and mortality in captive St. Lucia parrots *Amazona versicolor*. *Dodo, Journal of the Wildlife Preservation Trusts* 29: 103–125.

Hart, J. A.; Upoki, A. (1997): Distribution and conservation status of Congo peafowl *Afropavo congensis* in eastern Zaire. *Bird Conservation International* 7: 295–316.

Hilton-Taylor, C. (compiler) (2000): *2000 IUCN Red List of Threatened Species*. IUCN, Gland, Switzerland and Cambridge, UK.

King, G. J. (1977): Pheasant breeding and diets at the Jersey Zoological Park. *Dodo, Journal of the Wildlife Preservation Trusts* 14: 86–91.

Lloyd, P.; Durrans, L.; Gous, R.; Little, R. M.; Crowe, T. M. (2000): The diet and nutrition of the Namaqua sandgrouse, an arid-zone granivore. *Journal of Arid Environments* 44(1): 105–122.

McDonald, P.; Edwards, R. A.; Greenhalgh, J. F. D. (1988): *Animal Nutrition*. Harlow, UK: Longman Scientific & Technical.

McGowan, P. J. K. (1994): Family Phasianidae (pheasants and partridges). In: *Handbook of the birds of the world* (J. del Hoyo, A. Elliot, J. Sargatal). Vol. 2, *New World vultures to guineafowl*. Barcelona: Lynx Edicions, pp. 434–553.

MedARKS (2000): *Medical Animal Record Keeping System*. Jersey, UK: Durrell Wildlife Conservation Trust.

[NRC] National Research Council (1994): *Nutrient requirements of poultry*. Washington, DC: National Academy Press.

Robbins, C. T. (1993): *Wildlife Feeding and Nutrition*. Second Edition. London: Academic Press.

Scott, M. L.; Holm, E. R.; Reynolds, R. E. (1959a): Studies in pheasant nutrition 2: Protein and fibre levels in diets for young pheasants. *Poultry Science* 32: 1237–1244.

Scott, M. L.; Holm, E. R.; Reynolds, R. E. (1959b): The calcium, phosphorus and vitamin D requirements of young pheasants. *Poultry Science* 37: 1419–1425.

Scott, M. L.; Holm, E. R.; Reynolds, R. E. (1959c): Studies on the niacin, riboflavin, choline, manganese and zinc requirements of young ring-necked pheasants for growth, feathering and prevention of leg disorders. *Poultry Science* 38: 1344–1350.

Siegel, S.; Castellan, N. J. Jr. (1988): *Non-parametric Statistics for the Behavioural Sciences*. New York: McGraw-Hill Inc.

Sheppard, C.; Dierenfeld, E.; Burnett, M. (1998): Recommendations for diets of captive pheasants, based on information from diets of wild birds. *World Pheasant Association News* 56: 27–33.

Slifka, K. A. (1991): Visceral gout in birds and reptiles. In: *Proceedings of the 9th Dr Scholl Conference on Nutrition of Captive Wild Animals*. Chicago: Lincoln Park Zoological Society.

Van Bocxstaele, R. (2000): Congo peafowl (*Afropavo congensis*) EEP Annual Report 1998. In: *EEP Yearbook 1998/99* including Proceedings of the 16th EAZA Conference, Basel, 7–12 September 1999 (F. Rietkerk, B. Hiddinga, K. Brouwer, S. Smits, eds.). EAZA Executive Office, Amsterdam, pp. 45–46.

Watkins, B. E. (1985): Protein and amino acid requirements of animals. In: *Proceedings of the 4th and 5th Annual Dr Scholl Conferences on the Nutrition of Captive Wild Animals*. Chicago: Lincoln Park Zoological Society.

[WCS] Wildlife Conservation Society (1999): *Zootrition: Dietary Management Software*. New York: Wildlife Conservation Society.

*K. Foster[1], A. Feistner[1], D. Wormell[2]*

# Assessing dietary modifications for pied tamarins, *Saguinus bicolor*, at Jersey Zoo

***Abstract***

*Pied tamarins, Saguinus bicolor, have suffered from a number of health and breeding problems in captivity, at Jersey Zoo and elsewhere, such as wasting marmoset syndrome, chronic diarrhoea, metabolic bone disorders and breeding problems. A nutritional study at Jersey Zoo was initiated in order to investigate whether some of these problems may in part be linked to diet. When compared to the requirements of Callitrichids and New World monkeys, the pied tamarin diets contained an imbalance of some nutrients, such as low levels of protein and vitamin E. The diet was modified to try to correct some of these imbalances, and the modified diet provided and consumed was analysed to establish whether the diet modifications had been successful in altering nutrient composition, and whether new food items were palatable. The modified diet increased the total amount of food consumed per tamarin per day, as well as increasing intake of pellets, high-protein items and gum. The modifications to the diet had succeeded in increasing the levels of some key nutrients, such as protein, vitamin E and vitamin $D_3$, which is hoped will improve the health of the captive population. Further recommendations, primarily in terms of food palatability, have been made to continue to modify the diet.*

***Keywords***

*Diet modification, health, nutrition, protein, vitamins*

## 1 Introduction

### *1.1 Background*

Pied tamarins, *Saguinus bicolor*, are an endangered primate (Hilton-Taylor 2000). They are from the family Callitrichidae and are found in a restricted area of forest around the Brazilian city of Manaus in central Amazonia (Egler 1993; Mittermeier et al. 1993). Their habitat is under severe threat from

[1] Research Department, Durrell Wildlife Conservation Trust, Les Augrès Manor, Trinity, Jersey, JE3 5BP, Channel Islands. Corresponding author: Katherine Foster, Durrell Wildlife Conservation Trust, Tel. 01534 860078, Fax. 01534 860001, Email: austinkatebrown@hotmail.com

[2] Mammal Department, Durrell Wildlife Conservation Trust.

deforestation, making them an important conservation priority, as the population is still decreasing (Hilton-Taylor 2000).

In the wild, pied tamarins spend 24 % of their total activity time foraging. Of this time, they spend 59.1 % of their time feeding on insects and other animal prey, 39.6 % feeding on fruit and plant material, and 1.3 % feeding on exudates, although they do feed on exudates more during the dry season when there are fewer fruits and insects available (Egler 1992).

### 1.2 Pied tamarins in captivity

Pied tamarins have proved difficult to breed and maintain successfully in captivity (de Boer 2000). They have suffered from a number of health problems at Jersey Zoo and elsewhere, such as wasting marmoset syndrome, chronic diarrhoea, metabolic bone disorders, low infant survival, premature and stillbirths, and appear to be more susceptible to stress and environmental disturbances than other callitrichid species (Wormell et al. 1996; de Boer 2000; Wormell 2000; Lopez et al. 2001). Although they have been maintained well and bred regularly at Jersey Zoo, the health problems of the population have been re-occurring, and so an assessment of their nutritional status was initiated at Jersey Zoo in January 2001 (Foster et al. 2001) to investigate whether some of these problems may in part be linked to diet. The results of that investigation indicated that the diets being provided to and consumed by the pied tamarins contained an imbalance of some nutrients, specifically there were deficiencies of protein and vitamin E. Recommendations were put forward as to how the diet could be modified to improve the nutrient content, which in turn would hopefully improve the condition and health of the tamarins. A new diet was formulated by altering the proportions of food items in the diet, introducing novel food items and investigating the use of different flavours to make the primate pellets more palatable. This follow-up study was carried out in June 2001, in order to establish whether the pied tamarins accepted the modified diet, and thus whether the nutritional composition of the diet consumed had been improved.

## 2 Animals and Methods

### 2.1 Study animals

The modified diet was provided to four groups of pied tamarins, a total of 10 individuals. They were all between two and six years old, were captive born, and the average body weight was 456.1 g ± 39.8. Only 4 groups were studied, as any groups with sick individuals, or pregnant or lactating females were excluded from the trials to ensure that there would be no adverse effects on sensitive individuals if the tamarins found the modified diet unpalatable. The enclosures were made up of indoor cages furnished with branches and ropes, with wood shavings on the floor, and outside access with trees, shrubs, branches and ropes (Wormell and Brayshaw 2000).

### 2.2 Modified diet

The content of the modified diet is listed in table 1, along with the number of times each food was provided (out of a total of seven days). The pied tamarins were feed three times a day. All food was provided indoors, in several dishes to prevent dominant animals restricting the feeding of subordinates.

**Table 1.** Amount of each food provided and consumed per tamarin per occasion fed (fresh weights).

| FOOD ITEMS | | PROVIDED (g) | | CONSUMED (g) | | | |
|---|---|---|---|---|---|---|---|
| | | No. days | Mean | Mean | Maximum | Minimum | Mean % |
| Fruit | Banana | 4 | 28.7 | 20.5 | 36.4 | 8.4 | 71.4 |
| | Grapes | 4 | 28.4 | 25.8 | 40.8 | 12.7 | 90.8 |
| | Kiwi | 4 | 24.2 | 14.0 | 24.7 | 4.1 | 57.9 |
| | Pear | 2 | 18.1 | 15.3 | 20.6 | 3.7 | 76.9 |
| | Pomegranate | 1 | 18.0 | 8.8 | 16.9 | 1.2 | 39.1 |
| Protein items | Chicken | 2 | 13.3 | 5.9 | 10.4 | 3.4 | 44.4 |
| | Egg | 3 | 16.8 | 5.9 | 7.8 | 3.2 | 35.1 |
| | Kidney beans | 2 | 25.0 | 3.5 | 5.2 | 2.3 | 14.0 |
| | Mushrooms | 3 | 13.6 | 0.9 | 3.1 | 0 | 6.6 |
| | Ox heart | 2 | 13.8 | 3.8 | 6.5 | 1.3 | 27.3 |
| | Peanuts | 2 | 6.6 | 2.0 | 3.0 | 1.6 | 27.0 |
| | Peas | 2 | 12.3 | 1.2 | 2.6 | 0.6 | 9.8 |
| Pellet mixture | Yakult flavour | 3 | 70.4 | 30.9 | 74.7 | 7.9 | 43.9 |
| | Peanut flavour | 4 | 53.1 | 17.6 | 43.4 | 0 | 33.1 |
| Insects | Locusts | 7 | 1.5 | 1.5 | 1.5 | 1.5 | 100.0 |
| | Waxworms | 7 | 2.3 | 2.3 | 2.3 | 2.3 | 100.0 |
| Other items | Acacia gum | 7 | 19.2 | 19.2 | 29.7 | 10.3 | 100.0 |
| | Bread | 7 | 5.0 | 5.0 | 5.0 | 5.0 | 100.0 |

The morning feed was provided at approximately 08:00 hrs, and consisted of high-protein primate pellets, which had been soaked in water overnight to soften them, before being mixed with the flavour items. Two different foods were introduced to flavour the pellets to make them more palatable, and were used on alternate days. The two flavours used were Yakult (a skimmed milk drink containing live *Lactobacillus casei shirota* to aid digestion) and peanut butter (a mixture which also included baby cereal, All Bran cereal and egg to help increase vitamins and protein levels). In the original diet, the pellets were flavoured with mango juice, cranberry juice, Ribena or honey; these flavours were not used in the modified diet in order to establish what effect the introduction of novel flavours would have on pellet consumption.

The midday feed consisted of a mixture of two chopped fruits (e. g. banana, grapes, kiwifruit, pear, pomegranate) and two high-protein items (roasted chicken breast, hard-boiled egg, kidney beans, mushrooms, boiled ox heart, peanuts, peas). Egg and ox heart were provided in the original diet; the other foods had not been provided before, or not formed part of the diet during the previous year.

The afternoon feed was provided at approximately 16 : 30 hrs, and consisted of a locust, a few waxmoth larvae and a piece of egg-soaked bread per tamarin. Acacia gum was provided at the same time as the insect feed and left in the enclosure until morning, so any gum eaten would be retained in their gastrointestinal tract overnight, allowing more effective digestion and absorption of the nutrients (Heymann and Smith 1999).

### 2.3 Feeding trials

The assessment of the consumption of the modified diet was carried out in June 2001 (seven days of data collection) two weeks following the implementation of the modified diet. All food items were weighed to the nearest 0.1 g. The relative proportion of each ingredient in the pellet mixture was calculated by weighing the amount of each item as the mixture was being made up. The amount of each food that was provided per enclosure was weighed prior to being mixed and offered to the tamarins. All food remains were collected and weighed at approximately 16 : 00, with the exception of the gum, insects and bread, which were provided at this time. It was assumed (following pilot observations) that all the insects and egg-soaked bread provided were consumed. Any gum remains were collected the following morning.

Control feeds consisted of portions of each of the food items that were provided to the tamarins each day, and were put in place daily to take into account variations in environmental temperature and humidity. This allowed the calculation of the amount of water that was lost or gained by the food during the period that it was in the enclosure. It was assumed that any changes in weight that were recorded in the control feeds would also have applied to the actual feeds. This weight change was subsequently used to apply a correction factor to the food remains. The amount of food that was consumed per group was calculated, allowing an estimation of the amount consumed per tamarin. It was assumed that each tamarin in one enclosure consumed the same amount of food, as it was not possible to separate individual consumption. The mean consumption per enclosure was averaged to obtain an estimate of the mean consumption per tamarin.

The food composition database in the dietary management software, Zootrition™ (WCS 1999) was used to provide data on the nutritional content of the food items provided. No compositional analyses were carried out on the actual food items provided. This is a source of error, as food composition will vary according to production methods and conditions, e. g. the content of soil nutrients in which plants were grown will affect the composition of the food items. The composition of insects will also vary according to production conditions, particularly the diet on which they were reared. However, it still provides a useful estimate of food composition. Zootrition was also used to establish nutritional breakdowns of the diets that were provided and consumed by the pied tamarins. The composition of the diets was subsequently compared to the nutritional requirements of Callitrichids and New World monkeys. (TAG Husbandry Guidelines, Zootrition database; NRC 1978).

## 3 Results

### 3.1 Diet content

The amount of each food that was provided and consumed per tamarin per day is shown in table 1, along with average maximum and minimum consumptions. 100 % of the acacia gum, insects and bread provided to the tamarins was consumed. The amount of chicken consumed per tamarin per day increased from an average of 3.4 g at the beginning of the study, to an average of 10.4 g. There was variation in the amount of each food that was consumed, both between different groups and within the same groups on different days. The tamarins in one group consumed over eight times the amount of egg as those in another group. Mushrooms and peas had the lowest average consumption of the protein items, egg and chicken were consumed on average in the greatest amounts.

The average amount of pellets consumed per tamarin per day when they were flavoured with Yakult was 30.9 g, and an average of 17.6 g of pellets were consumed when they were flavoured with the peanut butter mixture, indicating a preference for the Yakult flavour pellets.

The amount of food that was provided and consumed per tamarin per day in the original and the modified diets is compared in table 2. The amount of

**Table 2.** Amount of food provided and consumed in original and modified diets per tamarin per day (fresh weights).

| | PROVIDED (g) | | CONSUMED (g) | | % CONSUMED | |
|---|---|---|---|---|---|---|
| | ORIGINAL | MODIFIED | ORIGINAL | MODIFIED | ORIGINAL | MODIFIED |
| Fruit and vegetables | 81.0 | 52.2 | 37.1 | 38.6 | 45.8 | 73.9 |
| Pellet mixture | 31.7 | 58.8 | 14.0 | 24.3 | 44.2 | 46.5 |
| Rice mixture | 22.5 | * | 9.4 | * | 41.8 | * |
| Acacia gum | 16.8 | 19.2 | 4.8 | 19.2 | 28.6 | 100.0 |
| Yakult | 10.0 | * | 10.0 | * | 100.0 | * |
| Protein items | 7.4 | 32.2 | 1.5 | 7.6 | 20.3 | 63.0 |
| Bread | 4.4 | 5.0 | 4.4 | 5.0 | 100.0 | 100.0 |
| Insects | 2.9 | 3.8 | 2.9 | 3.8 | 100.0 | 100.0 |
| TOTAL | 176.7 | 171.2 | 84.1 | 96.3 | – | – |

* Food not provided in this form in modified diet.

fruit provided was reduced, and the amount of primate pellets, protein items and insects was increased compared to the original diet. The modified diet resulted in an overall increase in the total amount of food that was consumed. Five times as much of the protein items, and 1.6 times as much pellet mixture were consumed in the modified diet than in the original diet. Providing the gum in the late afternoon as opposed to with the lunchtime feed (as in Foster et al. 2001) resulted in a four-fold increase in the amount of gum consumed per tamarin per day.

### 3.2 Nutrient composition

The nutrient composition of the diets that were provided and consumed is shown in Table 3 (dry matter). The composition of the original diets provided and consumed is shown along with the modified diets for comparison. The diet modifications have increased the levels of many nutrients provided, particularly crude protein, fat, vitamin E and vitamin $D_3$. The amount of protein provided has doubled, and the amount of protein consumed has increased from 13.0 % to 20.8 %. The amount of vitamin E provided in the modified diet is seven times that in the original diet. The diets consumed contained nutrients in different proportions to those provided, indicating that the tamarins were feeding selectively.

The nutrient content of the diet was compared to the requirements of callitrichids (TAG Husbandry Guidelines) and New World monkeys (NRC 1978). The percentage of each requirement that was consumed in the original and modified diets for some key nutrients is shown in figure 1. The amount of protein provided and consumed in the modified diet was 91 % and 75 % of the

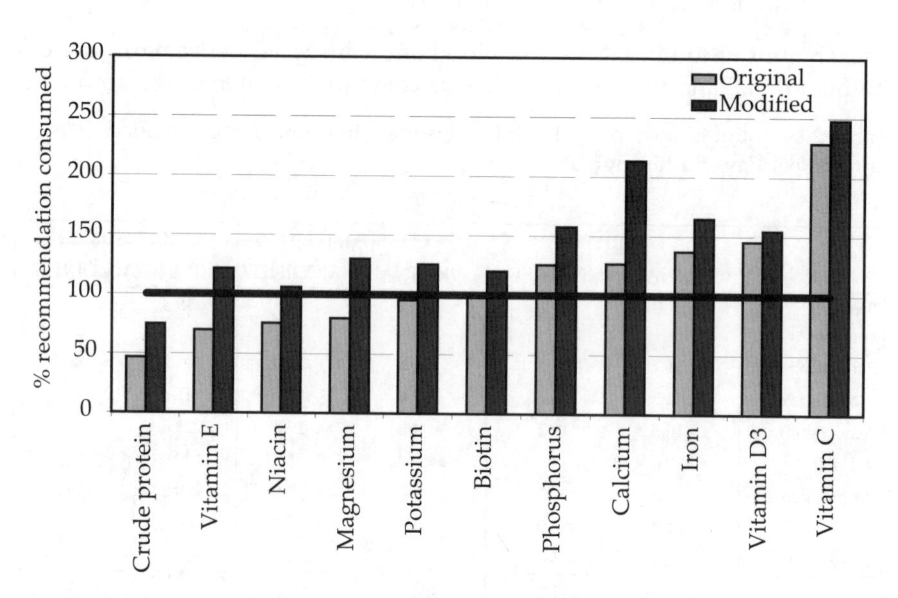


**Figure 1.** Percentage of recommended levels of nutrients consumed (original and modified diets)

**Table 3.** Nutrient composition of the diets (dry matter).

| NUTRIENT | RECOMMENDED LEVEL ** | MEAN PROVIDED | | MEAN CONSUMED | |
|---|---|---|---|---|---|
| | | ORIGINAL | MODIFIED | ORIGINAL | MODIFIED |
| ME Primate (kcal/g) | * | 2.60 | 3.67 | 2.93 | 3.35 |
| Crude fat (%) | * | 5.70 | 12.9 | 5.77 | 11.0 |
| Linoleic acid (%) | 1.00 | 1.03 | 2.91 | 0.98 | 2.15 |
| Crude protein (%) | 27.8 | 12.8 | 26.0 | 13.0 | 20.8 |
| Biotin (mg/kg) | 0.10 | 0.11 | 0.17 | 0.10 | 0.12 |
| Folacin (mg/kg) | 0.20 | 3.28 | 5.19 | 3.10 | 3.71 |
| Niacin (mg/kg) | 55.6 | 43.0 | 79.5 | 42.1 | 58.9 |
| Pantothenic acid (mg/kg) | 16.7 | 16.6 | 26.2 | 15.6 | 18.4 |
| Riboflavin (mg/kg) | 5.60 | 2.11 | 4.19 | 2.34 | 3.25 |
| Thiamin (mg/kg) | 5.60 | 1.83 | 2.20 | 1.93 | 2.19 |
| Vitamin A (IU/g) | 14.0 | 22.7 | 15.5 | 17.6 | 11.4 |
| Vitamin $B_6$ (mg/kg) | 2.80 | 8.47 | 10.6 | 9.66 | 9.47 |
| Vitamin $B_{12}$ (mcg/g) | 0.60 | 11.2 | 16.5 | 10.4 | 11.6 |
| Vitamin C (mg/kg) | 500 | 1232.0 | 1570.0 | 1143.0 | 1240.0 |
| Vitamin $D_3$ (IU/g) | 2.2 | 3.48 | 4.86 | 3.18 | 3.40 |
| Vitamin E (mg/kg) | 56.0 | 10.7 | 72.9 | 39.1 | 68.0 |
| Calcium (%) | 0.60 | 0.88 | 1.30 | 0.76 | 1.28 |
| Calcium : Phosphorus | 1.5:1 | 1.7:1 | 1.7:1 | 1.5:1 | 2:1 |
| Copper (mg/kg) | 1.50 | 7.26 | 11.2 | 7.23 | 8.54 |
| Iodine (mg/kg) | 0.10 | 0.98 | 1.43 | 0.90 | 1.00 |
| Iron (mg/kg) | 80.0 | 113.1 | 178.8 | 109.7 | 132.1 |
| Magnesium (%) | 0.20 | 0.17 | 0.24 | 0.16 | 0.26 |
| Manganese (mg/kg) | 44.4 | 30.1 | 42.4 | 29.4 | 32.4 |
| Phosphorus (%) | 0.40 | 0.51 | 0.78 | 0.50 | 0.63 |
| Potassium (%) | 0.90 | 0.85 | 1.02 | 0.86 | 1.13 |
| Selenium (mg/kg) | 0.10 | 0.15 | 0.22 | 0.17 | 0.20 |
| Sodium (%) | 0.30 | 0.20 | 0.28 | 0.21 | 0.26 |
| Zinc (mg/kg) | 11.1 | 29.3 | 46.0 | 29.0 | 35.7 |

* Denotes no information on the requirement level for that nutrient.

** Amount of nutrient required by Callitrichids, as given by the TAG Husbandry Manual in the Zootrition (WCS, 1999) database. The protein recommendation is that for New World monkeys (NRC, 1978) as no data were available in the Callitrichid recommendations.

recommended level respectively, as compared to 46 % and 47 % in the original diet. The amount of vitamin E provided and consumed is now above the requirement, as are the levels of niacin, magnesium and potassium.

# 4 Discussion

## 4.1 Diet content

The pied tamarins consumed more food on average per day when fed on the modified diet than on the original diet, including the amounts of pellets, high-protein items and gum, consumption of which has historically been low. Providing the gum in the afternoons as opposed to at midday resulted in a four-fold increase in gum intake per tamarin per day, which has increased the dietary calcium levels and should be providing a good source of carbohydrates and energy. Providing the gum in the afternoons also prolongs the amount of time that the gum is in their gastro-intestinal tract, which increases assimilation of nutrients, as some carbohydrates can only be fermented microbially if they are retained in the intestine for extended periods (Heymann and Smith 1999).

Using Yakult and the peanut butter mixture to flavour the pellets increased the amount of pellets consumed per tamarin per day, from an average of 14.0 g in the original diet, to an average of 24.3 g, with a particular preference being shown for the Yakult flavour pellets. There have been difficulties in making the pellets palatable to the tamarins, and historically pellet consumption has remained low (Price et al. 1999). An increase in pellet consumption should prove to be beneficial to the health of the tamarins, by increasing the intake of protein, vitamins and minerals. The increase in pellet consumption could have been due to the increased palatability of the Yakult and the peanut butter mixture, the novelty of these flavours, or due to a reduction in the amount of fruit provided, an effect that was also recorded in Price et al. (1999). It could be beneficial to use the Yakult and peanut butter flavours as well as some of the fruit juices used in the original diet, in order to give more variation and help to prevent boredom arising out of the consumption of the same food items daily, as the consumption of even preferred food items can decrease if fed daily.

It appeared that consumption of protein items changed over time, as the tamarins became more used to the food items. The amount of chicken consumed per tamarin per day increased during the study period, indicating that it takes time for the tamarins to become accustomed to novel food items, causing food intake to vary over time. This has implications when analysing diets, particularly immediately following the implementation of a new diet, as intake may differ according to the provision of novel food items. The amount of mushroom that was consumed per tamarin per occasion provided remained very low throughout the study. If mushroom consumption does not increase, they could be removed from the diet and chicken or egg provided instead, as these high-protein items were consumed in the greatest amounts.

## 4.2 Nutritional analysis

The diets provided and consumed were compared to the recommended levels of callitrichids and New World monkeys, as although some data were available on the food items consumed by wild pied tamarins, no data concerning the nutritional composition of those food items were available. However, comparisons to other taxa should be interpreted with caution, as requirements are likely to vary from one species to another, e.g. pied tamarins are thought to have higher protein and vitamin $D_3$ requirements than other callitrichids (Wormell et al. 1996). Pied tamarins have suffered from more metabolic bone problems (associated with a deficiency of vitamin $D_3$) than other callitrichid species housed in the same environment, indicating a difference in requirements of this vitamin, although how much it differs is unknown. This highlights the need for further study on the feeding ecology and nutrient requirements of these primates in the wild and in captivity.

There were some nutrient data missing in the breakdown of some of the food items in the Zootrition database. This means that the diet analysis represents the minimum amount of these nutrients present in the diet, and an apparent nutrient deficiency could be partly due to a lack of data rather than a dietary deficiency. For example, of the 17 different food items provided, only the pellet mixture contained an estimation of the iodine composition.

The diet modifications have altered the nutrient composition of the diets provided and consumed. Vitamin E levels have increased from 10.7 mg/kg in the original diet provided, to 72.9 mg/kg in the modified diet provided, which exceeds the requirement of 56.0 mg/kg. The composition of the diet consumed also contained vitamin E at above the requirement level. This should benefit the health of the tamarins, as vitamin E deficiency has been linked to muscular wasting (Ialeggio and Baker 1995; Meydani 1995). Increasing dietary levels of this vitamin beyond the requirement will not be harmful, because even though vitamin E is a fat soluble vitamin, it is not stored well, which means that excess levels are unlikely to cause toxicity problems (Albers et al. 1984; Allen and Oftedal 1996).

Although dietary protein levels are still below the recommendation of forming 27.8 % of the diet, the diet modifications have doubled the amount of protein provided, and the protein consumed now falls within the 20–25 % range (Portman 1970; Martin 1986). This is important, as protein deficiencies have been linked to a number of health problems that have often been apparent in captive callitrichids, such as wasting, reduced growth, loss of muscle and an increased susceptibility to disease and infection (Coates 1972; Flurer and Zucker 1985; Flurer 1988; Wormell et al. 1996). However, the diet consumed contained a mean of 20.8 % protein, which indicates that the tamarins are still selecting lower protein items in preference to the high protein items. This makes it important to further investigate palatability. The increase in dietary protein levels may become apparent in the health of the tamarins, as increased protein and carbohydrate levels have been shown to reverse symptoms of weight loss and diarrhoea (Barnard et al. 1988). Although the modified diet had the desired effect of increasing the intake of pellets, the effect of a gluten-free diet is being monitored in a group of pied tamarins at Jersey Zoo, as gluten intolerance can result in diarrhoea and wasting (Gore et al. 1998), and wasting symptoms have been reversed by the feeding of a gluten-free biscuit

(Crook 1998). An immune reaction to gliadin, a wheat protein, has also been observed in callitrichids (Gore et al. 2001), so the effect of wheat-based diets should be investigated further.

Although vitamin $D_3$ was not found to be deficient in the original diet analysis, it was decided to increase levels in the modified diet, as metabolic bone disorders had been identified in the population, despite the levels of vitamin $D_3$ exceeding the callitrichid requirement. This reinforces the theory that pied tamarins have higher vitamin $D_3$ requirements than other callitrichids. It is likely to be more effective to provide an environmental source of UV light to allow the synthesis of vitamin D, as absorption of dietary vitamin D can be prevented if the animal is suffering from gastrointestinal disease and diarrhoea (Lopez et al. 2001). The diet modifications have increased dietary levels of this vitamin in the diet, and with access to ultra-violet light, this should help to alleviate some of these bone disorders.

The increase in fat levels in the modified diet when compared to the original diet is likely to be beneficial, as pied tamarins have shown symptoms of lipid and fatty acid deficiency, such as alopecia, reproductive problems and immune disorders (Robbins 1993; de Boer 2000; Wormell 2000). The fatty acid linoleic acid meets the essential fatty acid requirements of most animals that have been studied (Allen and Oftedal 1996), and it now exceeds the recommended level in the modified diets, both provided and consumed.

Proportionally more magnesium and potassium were consumed than provided in the modified diet, indicating that the tamarins were selecting for these nutrients. The pellet mixture contributed 68 % and 40 % of magnesium and potassium respectively in the diet consumed. Banana (a high preference food) contributed 25 % of the dietary potassium consumed, and 10 % of the magnesium consumed.

### *4.3 Diet modifications*

Suggestion have been made to modify the diet again, to try to take into account some of the preferences that were highlighted, although individual differences make it difficult to formulate a diet that all the tamarins will find palatable. Food preferences also change over time, making a variable diet important. Food items should be offered on a rota basis to try to prevent boredom associated with the provision of the same items daily. Supplements of vitamins, minerals or probiotics should be provided with the preferred food items to ensure consumption (e. g. insects, bread and gum were 100 % consumed). This diet would hopefully be more palatable, as well as providing an appropriate balance of nutrients. The amount of food to be provided per tamarin per day is listed below (average body weight of 450 g).

- Morning: 40 g soaked pellet (flavoured with Yakult, peanut butter, Ribena, mango juice, or honey on alternate days)

- Midday: 30 g high-protein items (one or two per day, e. g. egg, chicken, nuts, pulses, tofu, cheese); 30 g fruit (two per day, e. g. banana, grape, kiwifruit, mango, papaya, pear, pomegranate)
- Afternoon: 10 g gum; 4.5 g insects (two locusts, five waxmoth larvae)

## 5 Conclusions

Re-assessing the diet following modification has provided more information about food palatability, and highlighted that these changes in the diet content had succeeded in improving the nutrient composition of the diet. Altering the relative proportions of different foods in the diet has also altered the amount of certain foods consumed. Modifying the diet has:

1. Increased the amount of high-protein items, pellets and gum consumed per tamarin
2. Increased the levels of vitamin E
3. Increased dietary protein levels
4. Highlighted further food preferences, which can be used to increase palatability of the diet.

Further study on the feeding ecology of pied tamarins in the wild is needed to establish a diet for captive tamarins that is truly representative of their needs. Captive and wild callitrichid diets vary enormously, but although the actual wild food items can generally not be replicated in captivity, the nutrients can. Formulating robust conclusions concerning food preference is extremely difficult, as palatability varies both between individuals, and over time. The pied tamarin diet and the health of the pied tamarins at Jersey Zoo is continually being monitored, and trials of gluten-free and lactose-free diets are currently being assessed, in order to try to establish a diet that is both nutritious and palatable. Wasting and diarrhoea are still re-occurring problems in the population, and it is hoped that improving nutritional status will go some way in improving the health of this endangered primate in captivity.

## Acknowledgements

Thanks go to all the staff and volunteers of the Mammal Department that cooperated with this study while data were being collected, particularly Austin Brown, Mark Brayshaw, Will Masefield, Begona Sastre, and also to Eluned Price for advice and comments during the study and write up of the report.

## Products mentioned in the text

**Primate Pellets:** pelleted food, manufactured by Special Diets Services, P.O. Box 705, Witham, Essex, CM8 3AD, UK.

**Baby Cereal:** fortified mixture of seven cereals, manufactured by Milupa, White Horse Business Park, Trowbridge, Wiltshire, BA14 0XB, UK.

**Yakult:** Fermented skimmed milk drink, manufactured by Yakult, 12-16 Telford Way, London, W3 7XS, UK.

## References

Albers, N.; Behm, G.; Dressler, D.; Klaus, W.; Küther, K.; Lindner, H. (1984): *Vitamins in animal nutrition*. Arbeitsgemeinschaft für Wirkstoffe in der Tierernährung e. V. (AWT).

Allen, M. E.; Oftedal, O. T. (1996): Essential nutrients in mammalian diets. In: *Wild mammals in captivity. Principles and techniques.* (D. G. Kleiman, M. E. Allen, K. V. Thompson, S. Lumpkin, eds.). Chicago: University of Chicago Press, pp. 148–157.

Barnard, D.; Knapka, J.; Renquist, D. (1988): The apparent reversal of a wasting syndrome by nutritional intervention in *Saguinus mystax*. *Laboratory Animal Science* 38: 282–288.

Coates, M. E. (1972): The nutrition of laboratory animals. In: *The UFAW Handbook* (UFAW, ed.). 4th Edition. UFAW, pp. 26–46.

Crook, G. (1989): A nutritional reversal of marmoset wasting syndrome. *Australian Primatology* 4: 21.

de Boer, L. (2000): Pied Tamarin (*Saguinus bicolor bicolor*) EEP Annual Report 1998. In: *EEP Yearbook 1998/99 including Proceedings of the 16th EAZA Conference, Basal, 1999* (F. Rietkerk, B. Hiddinga, K. Brouwer, S. Smits, eds.). EAZA Executive Office, Amsterdam, pp. 127–128.

Egler, S. G. (1992): Feeding ecology of *Saguinus bicolor bicolor* (Callitrichidae: Primates) in a relict forest in Manaus, Brazilian Amazonia. *Folia Primatologica* 59: 61–76.

Egler, S. G. (1993): First field study of the pied tamarin, *Saguinus bicolor bicolor. Neotropical Primates* 1(2): 13–14.

Flurer, C. I. (1988): Coprophagy in marmosets due to insufficient protein (amino acid) intake. *Laboratory Animals* 22: 330–331.

Flurer, CI.; Zucker, H. (1985): Long-term experiments with low dietary protein levels in Callitrichidae. *Primates* 26: 479–490.

Foster, K. J.; Feistner, A. T. C.; Wormell, D. (2001): Food intake and the nutrient composition of pied tamarin diets at Jersey Zoo. In: *Proceedings of the Third Annual Symposium on Zoo Research* (S. Wehnelt, C. Hudson, eds.). Federation of Zoological Gardens of Great Britain and Ireland.

Gore, M. N.; Brack, M.; Brandes, F.; Rensing, S.; Kaup, F-J. (1998): Callitrichidae as a model for gluten intolerance. Abstract no. 031, *Abstracts of the XVIIth Congress of the International Primatological Society. Antananarivo, Madagascar*: International Primatological Society.

Gore, M. A.; Brandes, F.; Kaup, F. J.; Lenzer, R.; Mothes, T.; Osman, A. A. (2001): Callitrichid nutrition and food sensitivity. *Journal of Medical Primatology* 30: 179–184.

Hilton-Taylor, C. (Compiler) (2000): *2000 IUCN Red List of Threatened Species.* Gland, Switzerland and Cambridge, UK: IUCN.

Heymann, E. W.; Smith, A. C. (1999): When to feed on gums: Temporal patterns of gummivory in wild tamarins, *Saguinus mystax* and *Saguinus fuscicollis* (Callitrichidae). *Zoo Biology* 18: 459–471.

Ialeggio, D. M.; Baker, A. J. (1995): Results of a preliminary survey into wasting marmoset syndrome in callitrichid collections. In: *Proceedings of the First Annual Conference of the Nutrition Advisory Groups of the American Zoo and Aquarium Association.* Ontario, Canada, pp. 148–158.

López, J.; Wormell, D.; Rodriguez, A. (In Press): Preliminary evaluation of the efficacy and safety of a UVB lamp used to prevent metabolic bone disease in pied tamarins *Saguinus bicolor* at Jersey Zoo. *Dodo* 37: 41–49.

Martin, D. P. (1986): Feeding and nutrition. In: *Zoo and wild animal medicine* (M. E. Fowler, ed.). 2nd Edition. Philadelphia: WB Saunders Co, pp. 661–663.

Meydani, M. (1995) : Vitamin E. *Lancet* 345: 170–175.

Mittermeier, R. A.; Stuart, S. N.; Groombridge, B. (1993): A revision of the IUCN list of threatened animals. *Neotropical Primates* 1(2): 1–2.

[NRC] National Research Council (1978): *Nutrient Requirements of Non-human Primates.* Washington, DC: National Academy Press.

Portman, O. W. (1970): Nutritional requirements (NRC) of non-human primates. In: *Feeding and nutrition of nonhuman primates* (R. S. Harris, ed.). New York: Academic Press, pp. 87–115.

Price, E. C.; Herron, S.; Wormell, D.; Brayshaw, M. (1999): Getting primates to eat pellets: The nutrition of New World monkeys at Jersey Zoo. *Dodo* 35: 57–66.

Robbins, C. T. (1993): *Wildlife feeding and nutrition.* 2nd ed. London, UK: Academic Press.

[WCS] Wildlife Conservation Society (1999): *Zootrition: Dietary Management Software.* Bronx, Wildlife Conservation Society.

Wormell, D. (2000): *Management guidelines for pied tamarins Saguinus bicolor bicolor.* Jersey UK: Durrell Wildlife Conservation Trust.

Wormell, D.; Brayshaw, M.; Price, E.; Herron, S. (1996): Pied tamarins *Saguinus bicolor bicolor* at the Jersey Wildlife Preservation Trust: Management, behaviour and reproduction. *Dodo, Journal of the Wildlife Preservation Trusts* 32: 76–97.

Wormell, D.; Brayshaw, M. (2000): The design and redevelopment of New World primate accommodation at Jersey Zoo: A naturalistic approach. *Dodo* 36: 9–1.

*K. Foster*[1], *D. Preece*[2]

# Nutrition of Iguanas at Jersey Zoo

**_Abstract_**

*The diet and nutritional requirements of three species of iguana were studied at Jersey Zoo in order to establish whether the diets were providing nutrients adequate for health and reproduction, and to try to formulate a clearer understanding of the requirements of these species. The diets were quantified for the rhinoceros iguana, Cyclura cornuta cornuta; Lesser Antilles iguana, Iguana delicatissima; and Utila Island iguana, Ctenosaura bakeri.*

*The diets were quantified by weighing the amount of food provided and remaining each day, allowing analysis of the nutrients consumed per group, and estimates per individual. The iguanas consumed diets that were high in fibre (20–30 %) and low in fat (2–6 %), which mirrors wild diets. The protein consumption by Iguana and Ctenosaura was within an acceptable range for these genera (20–26 %), although protein consumed by Cyclura exceeded the range for this genus (10–20 % recommended), which could cause health problems. The calcium to phosphorus ratio of Cyclura and Iguana diets exceeded the recommended minimum of 2 : 1, but the Ctenosaura diet required calcium supplementation to raise the Ca : P ratio to 2 : 1, to compensate for the inverse Ca : P of insects and the low calcium content of fruit.*

*A forage and leafy greens-based iguana diet appears to be contributing well to the husbandry regime, by providing a natural food source that contains a balance of nutrients necessary to maintain health and allow reproduction, as demonstrated by the successful hatching of a complete clutch of Iguana delicatissima eggs at Jersey Zoo in November 2000.*

**_Keywords_**

diet, health, nutrients, reproduction, reptile

[1] Research Department, Durrell Wildlife Conservation Trust, Les Augrès Manor, Trinity, Jersey, JE3 5BP, Channel Islands. Tel. 01534 860078; Fax. 01534 860001; Email: austinkatebrown@hotmail.com.

[2] Herpetology Department, Durrell Wildlife Conservation Trust, Jersey, UK.

# 1 Introduction

## 1.1 Background

Iguanas can be difficult to maintain and breed successfully in captivity due to their complex husbandry requirements. Nutrition is an important aspect of the captive management regime, playing an essential role in health, growth and reproduction (Cowan 1980; Andrews 1982; Duvall et al. 1982; Oftedal and Allen 1996). The properties of fibre, fat, protein, vitamins and minerals in relation to herbivorous and omnivorous reptiles, are shown in figure 1 (Information collated from: Murphy and Collins 1980; Jackson and Cooper 1981; Allen et al. 1989; Frye 1991a; Burgmann et al. 1993; Donoghue 1993 a,b; Frye and Townsend 1993; Oftedal and Allen 1996; Waters 1998).

A study was carried out at Jersey Zoo that focused on the diet and nutriational requirements of three species of iguana, to investigate whether the diets were providing nutrients adequate for health and reproduction, and to try to formulate a clearer understanding of the nutritional requirements of these species. The species studied were the rhinoceros iguana, *Cyclura cornuta cornuta*; Lesser Antilles iguana, *Iguana delicatissima;* and Utila Island iguana, *Ctenosaura bakeri.*

# 2 Animals and Methods

*Cyclura cornuta cornuta,* is native to the Dominican Republic and Haiti, and is classified as Vulnerable by IUCN (Hilton-Taylor 2000). It is predominantly a terrestrial forager, feeding on a variety of foliage, fruits and flowers. Some *Cyclura* species feed opportunistically on carrion and slow moving invertebrates, with animal matter comprising 2–3 % of the total volume of food consumed (Auffenberg 1982).

The Lesser Antilles iguana, *Iguana delicatissima,* is native to the Lesser Antilles, Dominica and the surrounding islands of the Caribbean, and is classified as Vulnerable by IUCN (Hilton-Taylor 2000). It is primarily an arboreal folivore, and the diet of the *Iguana* genus consists of foliage, fruits and flowers (Frye and Townsend 1993). *Iguana delicatissima* is considered to be a true herbivore and although some *Iguana* species are known to take animal matter in captivity, it is rarely a food source in the wild (Van Devender 1982).

The Utila Island iguana, *Ctenosaura bakeri,* is native to Utila Island off the coast of Honduras. It is not classified by the IUCN (Hilton-Taylor 2000). It is predominantly an arboreal species and the genus is omnivorous. Although the precise feeding habits of *Ctenosaura bakeri* are unknown, the diets of some *Ctenosaura* species consist of up to 75 % invertebrates and animal protein, such as eggs and small mammals (Frye and Townsend 1993).

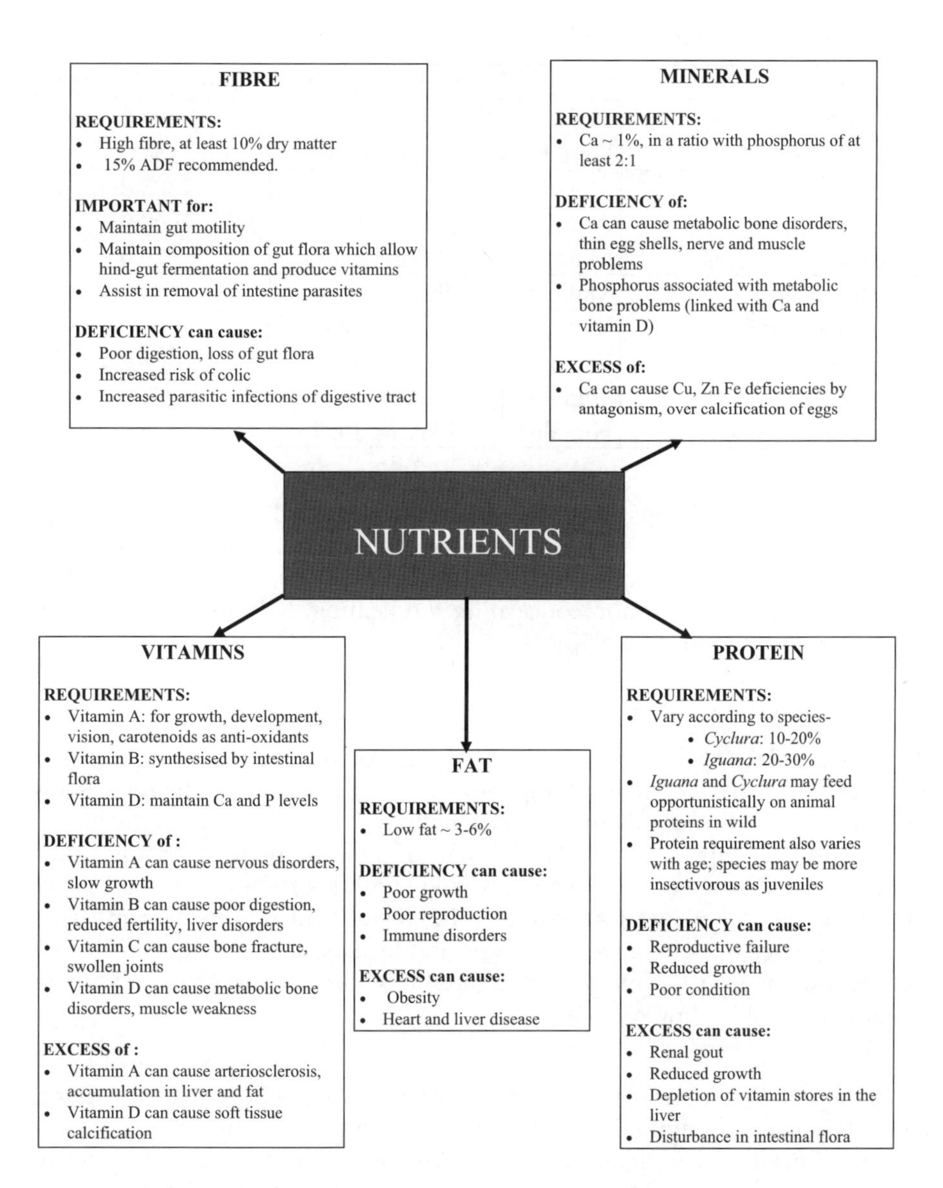


**Figure 1.** Key nutrients for herbivorous and omnivorous iguanas.

## 2.1 Housing

The details of the animals that were studied are given in table 1. The adult male and female *Iguana* and *Cyclura* were housed as a pair, the other individuals were housed separately.

All of the iguanas were housed in indoor heated enclosures, maintained by forced air central heating at 28–30 ºC during the day with hot spots of up to 35 ºC, and 22–24 ºC at night. Metal halide lamps provided ambient lighting.

**Table 1.** Details of species studied.

| Species | Sex | Date of Hatching | Body weight (g) |
|---|---|---|---|
| *Cyclura c. cornuta* | Male | 1964 (5 years) | 9500.0 |
| *Cyclura c. cornuta* | Female | Unknown | 4150.0 |
| *Iguana delicatissima* | Male | Unknown | 2800.0 |
| *Iguana delicatissima* | Female | Unknown | 2000.0 |
| *Iguana delicatissima* | Male | 2 May 1997 | 529.0 |
| *Ctenosaura bakeri* | Male | 1992 (2 years) | 683.0 |
| *Ctenosaura bakeri* | Male | 15 Aug. 1998 | 68.0 |
| *Ctenosaura bakeri* | Female | 15 Aug. 1998 | 68.0 |
| *Ctenosaura bakeri* | Female | 15 Aug. 1999 | 31.0 |
| *Ctenosaura bakeri* | Female | 15 Aug. 1999 | 26.0 |

Active UV™ heat lamps provided hot spots and UV light. The enclosures were sprayed daily to raise humidity levels. Humidity generally varied from 35 % to 65 %, although actual humidity levels were not recorded during this study. Detailed information concerning the heating, lighting and humidity regime is given in Brice (1995).

### 2.2 Current diet

*Iguana* and *Cyclura* were provided with 1–3 different food items per day, chosen from a variety of greens, forage and vegetables (table 2). The food items provided varied from day to day, seasonally, and depending upon availability at the Zoo's organic farm. The content of the *Ctenosaura* diet varied each day; on 3–4 days a week they were provided with 1–4 different items per day, from a variety of greens, forage and fruit; greens, fruit and mealworms were provided once or twice a week; crickets and locusts were provided 2–3 times per week. The insects were provided randomly throughout the day to mirror a more natural feeding regime.

Feed items were sprinkled with the dietary supplement Nutrobal (approximately 0.4 g per iguana per day) to provide extra vitamins and minerals, specifically calcium, and chopped cuttlebone was also provided. Adult females were provided with a vitamin $D_3$ supplement (Woodstock) once a week (0.035 ml, which contains approximately 400 IU of vitamin D). Greens and vegetables from the organic farm were provided unwashed, to provide additional minerals from the soil. Distributing food widely and providing whole forage items promoted foraging and provided behavioural enrichment, encouraging the iguanas to move around the enclosure and tear off pieces of foliage, a natural feeding behaviour.

### 2.3 Feeding Trials

Data were collected in June and July 2000, resulting in 21 days of data collection for each group. The iguanas were fed once a day at approximately

**Table 2.** The diet provided to three species of iguana at Jersey Zoo during the study (over 21 days).

| Food item | | | *Cyclura* | *Iguana* (adult) | *Iguana* (juvenile) | *Ctenosaura* |
|---|---|---|---|---|---|---|
| Fruit: | Apple | *Malus pumila* | | | | 4 |
| | Apricot | *Prunus armeniaca* | | | | 2 |
| | Papaya | *Carica papaya* | | | | 2 |
| | Pear | *Pyrus communis* | | | | 5 |
| Vegetables: | Carrot | *Daucus carota var. sativus* | 1 | 2 | | 5 |
| | French beans | *Phaseolus vulgaris* | 1 | 1 | | 2 |
| Greens: | Chicory | *Cichorium intybus* | 2 | 3 | | 4 |
| | Clover | *Trifolium pratense* | 1 | | 1 | 1 |
| | Dandelions | *Taraxacum officinale* | 1 | 1 | 4 | |
| | Komatsuna | *Brassica perviridis* | | 2 | | |
| | Mibuna | *Brassica rapa var. japonica* | 4 | 7 | 5 | |
| | Nasturtium | *Tropaeolum major* | | 3 | 3 | 1 |
| | Pak choi | *Brassica rapa var. chinensis* | 12 | 15 | 8 | 4 |
| | Red mustard | *Brassica juncea var. rugosa* | 1 | | 1 | |
| | Romaine | *Lactuca sativa var. longifolia* | 6 | 9 | | 2 |
| | Watercress | *Nasturtium officinale* | 2 | 1 | | 3 |
| Insects: | Cricket | *Acheta domesticus* | | | | 3 |
| | Locust | *Schistocerca gregaria* | | | | 3 |
| | Mealworm | *Tenebrio molitor* | | | | 3 |
| Forage: | Hazel | *Corylus avellana* | | 1 | 1 | |
| | Lime forage | *Tilia europaea* | 5 | 4 | 4 | |
| | Pseudo-acacia | *Acacia* spp. | 3 | 3 | 3 | 2 |

10:00 hrs. Each food item was weighed before being offered to the iguanas, using spring balances (accurate to 5 g) for the forage branches and electronic balances (accurate to 0.1 g for weights up to 600 g, to 1.0 g for weights up to 3 kg) for the greens, vegetables, fruits and insects. Control feeds consisted of portions of the foods being provided to the iguanas, and the weight change measured in the control feed was used to correct the food remains for changes in moisture content that was due to atmospheric conditions. The controls were put in place in each enclosure daily to take into account variations in temperature and humidity. The feed remains and controls were removed from the enclosures at 8:00 hrs the following morning and re-weighed, in order to calculate the amount of food that had been consumed per group, and an estimate per individual when the iguanas were housed in pairs. Behavioural observations of the iguanas feeding were also made *ad libitum*.

The database of food composition in Zootrition™ software (WCS 1999) was used to provide data on the nutrients present in the food items provided. The nutritional composition of food items varies according to production conditions, e. g. the soil in which plants are grown, and the diet on which mealworms and crickets are raised, will affect their composition. This is a source of error in the dietary analysis, but will still provide an approximation of the nutrient composition. The nutrient content of the diets consumed was calculated using Zootrition software. The diets offered were not analysed nutriationally, as much of the offered food consisted of inedible components, e. g. large branches of forage, for which no nutritional breakdown was available.

A Mann-Whitney U test (Siegel and Castellan 1998) was used to compare the amount of food consumed on days when different numbers of food items were provided.

The recommended nutrient levels in green iguana (*Iguana iguana*) diets in the Zootrition database (Allen and Oftedal 2001) were used for comparison to the diets consumed by the iguanas at Jersey Zoo.

## 3 Results

### 3.1 Food consumption

The diets consumed by the iguanas, and the average amount of food consumed per iguana per day, are given in table 3. Greens formed the largest component of the diets of *Cyclura* and *Iguana*; fruit formed the largest component of the *Ctenosaura* diet.

*Cyclura* consumed an average of 178.1 g on days when just one food item was provided, and an average of 260.2 g on days when two or more different items were provided (fresh weights), although this difference was not significant ($p = 0.17$). Intra-specific competition was observed between the male and female *Cyclura*, particularly when chopped food items such as runner beans and carrot were provided, and the male was observed preventing the female from approaching the food.

**Table 3.** Proportion of diets consumed and mean, minimum and maximum amount of food consumed per iguana per day (fresh weights)

| Nutrient | Unit | Cyclura (adult) | *Iguana* (adult) | *Iguana* (sub-adult) | *Ctenosaura* (adult) | *Ctenosaura* (juvenile) |
|---|---|---|---|---|---|---|
| Greens | % | 85.0 | 52.0 | 64.0 | 20.0 | 20.0 |
| Forage | % | 12.0 | 40.0 | 36.0 | 10.0 | 10.0 |
| Vegetables | % | 3.0 | 8.0 | — | 20.0 | 20.0 |
| Fruit | % | — | — | — | 43.0 | 43.0 |
| Insects | % | — | — | — | 7.0 | 7.0 |
| Mean consumed | g | 211.2 | 43.1 | 24.1 | 35.5 | 11.5 |
| Minimum consumed | g | 13.2 | 13.5 | 7.0 | 19.8 | 7.1 |
| Maximum consumed | g | 428.6 | 113.4 | 55.2 | 47.8 | 17.9 |

### 3.2 Nutrient composition

The nutrient composition of the diets that were consumed by each group is given in table 4. The diets consumed were high in total dietary fibre (forming 20 % to 29 % of the diet) and ADF (11 % to 23 %). The diets that were consumed were low in fat (below 6 %), which mirrors wild diets. The protein content of the diets consumed was between 21 % and 25 % for *Cyclura* and *Iguana*, and between 19 % and 26 % for *Ctenosaura*. The Ca : P of the diets consumed were 3 : 1 for *Cyclura*, 3.8 : 1 and 5.3 : 1 for *Iguana* adult and subadult respectively, and 1.7 : 1 and 2.2 : 1 for *Ctenosaura* adult and juvenile respectively. Calcium levels of *Cyclura* and *Iguana* diets were above the 1.1 % recommended for green iguanas, but the *Ctenosaura* diets contained calcium at below this level.

**Table 4.** Nutrient composition of the diets consumed (dry matter).

| Nutrient | Unit | Green iguana* | Cyclura (adult) | *Iguana* (adult) | *Iguana* (sub-adult) | *Ctenosaura* (adult) | *Ctenosaura* (juvenile) |
|---|---|---|---|---|---|---|---|
| Total dietary fibre | % | — | 25.0 | 29.4 | 24.3 | 21.8 | 19.9 |
| ADF | % | 15.0 | 20.1 | 39.1 | 17.8 | 15.7 | 21.4 |
| Crude fat | % | 3.0 | 3.11 | 2.57 | 3.05 | 3.73 | 5.5 |
| Crude protein | % | 26.0 | 24.7 | 21.8 | 21.6 | 19.8 | 25.8 |
| Riboflavin | mg/kg | — | 8.99 | 2.7 | 7.88 | 3.14 | 2.3 |
| Thiamin | mg/kg | — | 5.64 | 2.46 | 3.67 | 3.69 | 2.8 |
| Vitamin A | IU/g | — | 379.6 | 215.3 | 328.2 | 182.2 | 178.3 |
| Vitamin $B_6$ | mg/kg | — | 16.0 | 7.13 | 10.4 | 5.16 | 8.0 |
| Vitamin C | mg/kg | — | 4354.4 | 1125.8 | 3258.3 | 807.4 | 507.0 |
| Vitamin $D_3$ | IU/g | — | 0.35 | 1.01 | 1.27 | 0.55 | 2.4 |
| Vitamin E | mg/kg | — | 118.2 | 236.8 | 175.5 | 65.3 | 88.5 |
| Vitamin K | mg/kg | — | 0.12 | 0.34 | 0.42 | 0.18 | 0.80 |
| Ash | % | — | 11.0 | 7.54 | 9.4 | 5.95 | 6.5 |
| Calcium | % | 1.1 | 1.37 | 1.10 | 1.48 | 0.52 | 0.80 |
| Ca:P ratio | | 1.7:1 | 3.1:1 | 3.8:1 | 5.3:1 | 1.7:1 | 2.2:1 |
| Copper | mg/kg | 10.0 | 19.94 | 39.0 | 33.3 | 16.0 | 30.7 |
| Iodine | mg/kg | — | 0.14 | 0.34 | 0.47 | 0.19 | 0.80 |
| Iron | mg/kg | 100.0 | 115.4 | 49.8 | 129.9 | 53.7 | 87.1 |
| Magnesium | % | 0.15 | 0.22 | 0.07 | 0.15 | 0.13 | 0.10 |
| Manganese | mg/kg | 70.0 | 36.7 | 20.0 | 46.2 | 24.4 | 46.3 |
| Phosphorus | % | 0.65 | 0.44 | 0.26 | 0.28 | 0.30 | 0.40 |
| Potassium | % | 0.5 | 3.27 | 2.21 | 2.66 | 1.73 | 1.7 |
| Selenium | mg/kg | — | 0.08 | 0.06 | 0.07 | 0.13 | 0.2 |
| Sodium | % | — | 5.1 | 13.6 | 17.2 | 7.48 | 31.6 |
| Zinc | mg/kg | 80.0 | 27.9 | 29.1 | 37.6 | 46.0 | 103.3 |

* Green iguana recommended nutrients, Allen and Oftedal, 2001 (Zootrition database of recommended nutrients)

## 4 Discussion

The diets consumed by the iguanas were generally satisfactory in terms of essential nutrients, although data on the precise requirements of these species, particularly in terms of vitamins and minerals, are limited. Some nutrients were not present in the food breakdowns in the Zootrition database, therefore the diet analysis represents the minimum level of nutrients in the diet. For example, only 9 % of the food items provided included data for iodine content, therefore reducing the accuracy of the diet analysis.

The high fibre diet is essential for maintaining gut motility, the appropriate composition of micro-organisms in the gastro-intestinal tract, and the removal of intestinal parasites. All the iguanas consumed diets that exceeded the recommended minimum of 10 % fibre (Donoghue 1993a), and were within 20 % of the recommended 15 % ADF for green iguanas (Allen and Oftedal 2001). 50 % of data for ADF was missing in the food item analyses consumed by *Cyclura* and *Iguana*, and 31 % for *Ctenosaura*, which means that the actual ADF content of the diets consumed is likely to be different to the calculated value in the diet analyses.

The protein level in the diet that was consumed by *Cyclura* appears higher than necessary, which could cause health problems. 10–20 % protein may be more appropriate for this genus (Auffenburg 1982; Frye 1991b; Frye and Townsend 1993), so a reduction in protein content could be beneficial. However, much of the nitrogen content of forage will be unavailable as lignin, reducing the amount of nitrogen available for assimilation, particularly in forage items; lime forage contains approximately 20 % lignin (Zootrition, WCS 1999). Protein consumption by *Iguana* was within the recommended range of 15–30 % (Donoghue 1993a), but slightly below the 26 % of green iguanas (Allen and Oftedal 2001). Protein consumption by *Ctenosaura* varied with age, with the adult consuming 19.8 % protein and the average for the juvenile being 25.8 % ± 4.3. This pattern is also often apparent in omnivorous iguanas in the wild, with juveniles consuming a higher protein (more insectivorous) diet than the adults (Van Devender 1982).

The *Ctenosaura* diet contained a lower Ca : P than *Cyclura* and *Iguana* because of the inverse Ca : P of crickets and mealworms, and the low calcium content of fruit. The Ca : P of all the diets consumed were at or above the recommended green iguana recommendation of 1.7 : 1. However, the calcium content of the *Ctenosaura* diet was below that of the green iguana recommended level, so an increase in calcium could be beneficial to prevent metabolic bone disorders.

The fat levels in the diets consumed by *Cyclura* and *Iguana* contained the right level of fat compared to the recommendations for green iguanas. *Ctenosaura* consumed fat at above this level (at 3.7 % and 5.5 % [± 0.9] by the adult and juveniles respectively). *Ctenosaura* are insectivorous, whereas green iguanas are herbivorous, therefore a higher fat consumption by *Ctenosaura* was expected.

The levels of vitamin A appear to be high in the diets consumed by all species, although the vitamin A content was actually represented by carotenoids (vitamin A precursors), which unlike retinol (the active form of the vitamin), are not toxic when present in excess as they are only converted as required (Albers et al. 1984; McDonald et al. 1988). Less than 1 % of the vitamin A in the diets consumed was retinol, supplied by the Nutrobal and insects, although the insect contribution to the vitamin A levels in the *Ctenosaura* diet was very small.

As already discussed, there will be inaccuracies in the diet composition due to the use of a database of food composition, rather than carrying out nutriational analysis of the actual food items provided. The availability of nutrients was also not assessed in this study. Nutrient availability depends upon the digestibility of food items, and the form in which the nutrients are present. For example, new leaves and twigs of forage contains fibre that is more easily assimilated, nutrients which are more readily available, less lignin and fewer secondary compounds and toxins than older foliage (Milton 1979). Nutrient interactions can also affect the uptake of nutrients. For example, *Brassica* species contain a substance that inhibits the absorption of iodine, a mineral essential for the synthesis of thyroid hormone (Frye and Townsend 1993) making it difficult to assess accurate nutrient status from intake studies. However, despite these problems, the analysis has still provided a useful estimate of the nutritional content of the diets consumed by the iguanas.

## 5 Recommendations

The iguana feeding regime at Jersey Zoo was generally providing satisfactory levels of nutrients and behavioural enrichment, but the following list of recommendations may help to improve the diets further.

- Protein: Should be reduced for *Cyclura*, by providing forage items more frequently, as forage (e. g. hazel, lime, pseudo-acacia) is generally lower in protein than leafy green vegetables and legumes.
- Calcium: *Ctenosaura* may benefit from an increase in calcium levels, to counteract the inverse Ca : P of insects and most fruits. The proportion of high calcium containing foods, such as leafy greens and forage should be increased.
- Feed *Cyclura* one item per day to reduce over consumption that can lead to obesity, as this study showed an increase in food intake on days when more than one food item was provided.
- Scatter food more widely when chopped items are given to *Cyclura* to help to reduce male: female competition.
- Increase proportion of insects and animal matter in the diet of *Ctenosaura*, as these are natural food sources, although low calcium/ inverse Ca : P foods such as insects, should be balanced with high calcium-containing foods or supplements to prevent a calcium deficiency.

## 6 Conclusions

The organic farm at Jersey Zoo is providing a good source of greens, vegetables and forage, to allow the provision of well-balanced diets to the iguanas.

1. The diets consumed were high in fibre, essential for maintaining intestinal health.
2. Fat levels in the diet were low, which mirrors wild diets.
3. *Iguana* and *Ctenosaura* consumed protein within the range appropriate for these genera. Protein consumed by *Cyclura* was higher than necessary.
4. The diets consumed contained a Ca:P of at least 1.7:1, to mirror green iguana recommended levels.

The diet is proving to benefit the health and reproduction of these iguanas, as demonstrated by the successful hatching of a complete clutch of *Iguana delicatissima* eggs in November 2000. The information obtained on the current diet may prove useful to help further knowledge on the nutrients that these species require in order to breed successfully in captivity.

## Acknowledgements

Many thanks to Richard Gibson and Kevin Buley of the Herpetology Department at Jersey Zoo for their assistance and cooperation; and also Anna Feistner and Eluned Price for support and advice during the study and subsequent write up.

## Products mentioned in the text:

**Active UV ™:** UV heat lamps, manufactured by Wild Inside, Metamorph Enterprises, 132 Garden Street Suite 24, Santa Barbara, California.

**Nutrobal:** Vitamin and mineral supplement, manufactured by Vetark Animal Health, PO Box 60, Winchester, Hampshire, SO23 9XN, UK.

**Vitamin $D_3$:** Oily vitamin $D_3$ supplement for New World monkeys and reptiles, manufactured by Woodstock Nutritional Supplements, 61 Hempstead Lane, Potten End, Berkhamstead, Hertfordshire, HP4 2RZ, UK.

## References

Albers, N.; Behm, G.; Dressler, D.; Klaus, W.; Küther, K.; Lindner, H. (1984): *Vitamins in animal nutrition*. Arbeitsgemeinschaft für Wirkstoffe in der Tierernährung e.V. (AWT).

Allen, M. E.; Oftedal, O. T. (2001): Recommended levels of nutrients in green iguana diets. In: *Zootrition Dietary Management Software*, Version 2. Bronx, New York: Wildlife Conservation Society.

Allen, M. E.; Oftedal, O. T.; Werner, D. I. (1989: Nutritional studies with the Green Iguana. In: *Proceedings 8th Dr Scholl Conference on the Nutrition of Captive Wild Animals* (T. P. Meehan, M. E. Allen, eds.). Chicago: Lincoln Park Zoological Society, pp. 73–81.

Andrews, R. M. (1982): Patterns of growth in reptiles. In: *Biology of the reptilia*, volume 13D (C. Gans, F. H. Pough, eds.). London: Academic Press, pp. 273–320.

Auffenberg, W. (1982): Feeding strategies of the Caicos ground iguana, *Cyclura carinata*. In: *Iguanas of the world: Their behavior, ecology, and conservation* (G. M. Burghardt, A. S. Rand, eds.). Park Ridge: Noyes Publications, pp. 84–116.

Brice, S. (1995): A review of feeding and lighting requirements for captive herbivorous lizards: *Cyclura* and *Iguana*. *Dodo, Journal of the Wildlife Preservation Trusts* 31: 120–139.

Burgmann, P. M.; Mcfararlen, J.; Thiesenhausen, K. (1993): Causes of hypocalcemia and metabolic bone disease in *Iguana iguana*. *Journal of Small Exotic Animal Medicine* 2(2): 63–68.

Cowan, D. F. (1980): Adaptation, maladaptation and disease. In: *Reproductive biology and diseases of captive reptiles* (J. B. Murphy, J. T. Collins, eds.). Ohio: Society for the Study of Amphibians and Reptiles, pp. 191–196.

Donoghue, S. (1993a) : Leaping lizards! It's not easy to feed iguanas. *Veterinary Techniques* 14(5): 281–287.

Donoghue, S. (1993b): Supermarket savvy; Effective use of produce in diets for herbivorous lizards. *Reptile and Amphibian Magazine* May/June, 57–65.

Duvall, D.; Guillette, L. J.; Jones, R. E. (1982): Environmental control of reptilian reproductive cycles. In: *Biology of the reptilian* (C. Gans, F. H. Pough, eds.). Volume 13D. London: Academic Press, pp. 201–231.

Frye, F. L. (1991a): *A practical guide for feeding captive reptiles.* Malabar: Krieger Publishing Co.

Frye, F. L. (1991b): *Reptile care: An atlas of diseases and treatments*. Volume 1. Neptune City: TFH Publications Inc.

Frye, F. L.; Townsend, W. (1993): *Iguanas: A guide to their biology and captive care*. Malabar: Krieger Publishing Company.

Hilton-Taylor, C. (Compiler) (2000): *2000 IUCN Red List of Threatened Species*. IUCN, Gland, Switzerland and Cambridge, UK.

Jackson, O. F.; Cooper, J. E. (1981): Nutritional diseases. In: *Diseases of the reptilian* (J. E. Cooper, O. F. Jackson, eds.). London: Academic Press, pp. 410–428.

McDonald, P.; Edwards, R. A.; Greenhalgh, J. F. D. (1988): *Animal Nutrition*. Harlow, UK: Longman Scientific & Technical.

Milton, K. (1979): Factors influencing leaf choice by howler monkeys: A test of some hypotheses of food selection by generalist herbivores. *American Naturalist* 114: 362–378.

Murphy, J. B.; Collins, J.T. (eds.) (1980): *Reproductive biology and diseases of captive reptiles*. Ohio: Society for the Study of Amphibians and Reptiles.

Oftedal, O. T.; Allen, M. E. (1996): Nutrition as a major facet of reptile conservation. *Zoo Biology* 15: 491–497.

Siegel, S.; Castellan, N. J. Jr. (1988): *Non-parametric Statistics for the Behavioural Sciences*. New York: McGraw-Hill Inc.

Van Devender, R. W. (1982): Growth and ecology of spiny-tailed and green iguanas in Costa Rica, with comments on the evolution of herbivory and large body size. In: *Iguanas of the world: Their behavior, ecology, and conservation* (G. M. Burghardt, A. S. Rand, eds.). Park Ridge: Noyes Publications, pp. 162–183.

Waters, M. (1998): Case report: Metabolic bone disease in a green iguana (*Iguana iguana*). *CPD Veterinary Medicine* 1(2): 61–63.

Wildlife Conservation Society (1999): *Zootrition dietary management software*. Bronx, New York: Wildlife Conservation Society.

*R. Gisler[1], J.-M. Hatt[1], R.W. Mayes[2], M. Lechner-Doll[3], M. Clauss[4], A. Liesegang[5], M. Wanner[5]*

# The practical evaluation of a new digestive marker system in reptiles – *N*-alkanes in Galapagos giant tortoises (*geochelone nigra*)

**Abstract**

*The present study was undertaken to evaluate different aspects of digestive strategies in Galapagos giant tortoises (Geochelone nigra), kept at the Zoological Garden of Zurich, Switzerland. Two trials were conducted, using natural and synthetic n-alkanes as digestive markers. One trial was carried out to determine the mean retention time (MRT) of the digesta in the intestinal tract of the tortoises, and another trial was carried out to determine the following parameters: recovery rates of digestive markers, food composition, diet intake and apparent digestibility. The suitability of alkanes as digestive markers in herbivorous reptiles was evaluated.*

*With alkane $C_{36}$, the MRT of the solid digesta phase could be determined very well. Based on direct observations, food composition could reliably be estimated with the alkane method. The use of the double marker method as described by Dove and Mayes (1991) yielded trustworthy results for the estimation of diet intake. No coherence was found between the recovery rates of the alkanes and the length of the carbon chains, as it was found in other hindgut ferments as well. In comparison to direct observation the apparent digestibility was significantly underestimated with three different markers, but the lowest deviation was reached with alkane $C_{36}$.*

*The results of the current study clearly show that in herbivore tortoises, alkanes possess a great potential as digestive markers for studies of digestive physiology. Mainly in the wild, where total faecal collection is not possible, alkanes will be suitable markers for the determination of different parameters of digestive physiology.*

**Keywords**

*Reptiles, herbivore, hydrocarbons, digestion*

[1] Division of Zoo Animals and Exotic Pets, University of Zurich, 8057, Zurich, Switzerland. *Address for correspondence*: Jean-Michel Hatt, PD Dr. med. vet., M.Sc., Division of Zoo Animals and Exotic Pets, University of Zurich, Winterthurerstr. 260, 8057 Zurich, Switzerland, Email: Jean-Michel.Hatt@access.unizh.ch, Fax: +41 / 1 635 89 01; Tel. +41 / 1 635 83 42.

[2] Macaulay Land Use Research Institute, Craigiebuckler, Aberdeen AB15 8QH, UK.

[3] Institute of Zoo Biology and Wildlife Research, 10315 Berlin, Germany.

[4] Institute of Animal Physiology, Physiological Chemistry and Animal Nutrition, Ludwig-Maximilians-Universität, 80539 Munich, Germany.

[5] Institute of Animal Nutrition, University of Zurich, 8057 Zurich, Switzerland.

# 1 Introduction

The growing importance of reptiles as pets and in conservation programs has led to an increasing interest in their management and especially in their nutritional needs. At the Zoological Garden of Zurich, Switzerland, a study was undertaken to evaluate aspects of digestive strategies in Galapagos giant tortoises (*Geochelone nigra*) and the application of *n*-alkanes as digestive markers in these animals. For the first time *n*-alkanes, which are hydrocarbons with different numbers of carbon atoms, have been used in giant tortoises in order to evaluate their potential as digestive markers in herbivorous reptiles.

## 1.1 The use of digestive markers in reptiles: a general survey

In reptiles, many different marker systems have been used to determine different parameters of their digestive physiology, such as faecal output and digestive kinetics. For example water-insoluble dyes like Sudan III, Carmine red and Indigo carmine have been used, or feedstuff impregnated with one of them, and UV-fluorescent powder.

Small solids mainly of synthetic materials, such as plastic or rubber, were very often used for the estimation of the passage time of food particles. Studies were conducted in which polyacrylamide beads and other synthetic micro beads were used, as well as small pieces of vinyl, plastic rings and stripes, polyester tape, strips of plastic surveyors tape, little loops of polyester threads, and coloured glass beads.

Heavy metals and oxides from them may also be used in reptiles, whereby it is important to use metals which occur only in smallest traces in soil, mud and dirt, because it is a natural behaviour of many reptiles to ingest soil. Metallic markers that have been used in different reptile species are ytterbium-marked particles, chromium-mordant fibres and chromic oxide ($Cr_2O_3$).

Radiolabeled markers like ($^{14}C$)polyethylene glycol and ($^{3}H$)glycerol triether were used in reptiles as well.

For the estimation of the passage of the liquid digesta phase, water-soluble substances were used, mostly chelates of metals with ethylene-diamine tetraacetic acid (EDTA). In the past, polyethylene-glycerol (PEG) was often used, but it has now been replaced by the chelates cobalt-EDTA (Co-EDTA) and chromium-EDTA (Cr-EDTA), which are easy to analyse. Mainly Co-EDTA is used as a marker of the liquid digesta phase, since chromium is often simultaneously used as a marker of the solid phase.

As internal digestive markers, acid detergent lignin (ADL), acid insoluble ash (AIA) and manganese ($Mn^{2+}$) were used in reptiles.

The list of different marker systems applied to reptiles is quite long and could even go further. These markers were used in studies with different sorts of reptiles, as for example in different lizard species, iguanas, tortoises, turtles, and in alligators. With Galapagos giant tortoises markers like Carmine red and AIA were used.

However, it must be noted that most marker systems have been used in reptiles without thorough validation, which is a disadvantage for the comparison of the results obtained in different studies. Sometimes the data even are collected only in passing to other studies, and were listed only fragmentarily. A concentration on fewer but validated marker systems would be an important achievement.

The *n*-alkanes represent a marker system, with which different parameters of digestive physiology may be investigated. In the current study with Galapagos giant tortoises, these alkanes were used for the first time in a reptile species, with the aim to evaluate the alkanes as a valuable marker system and to establish them in the series of digestive markers in reptiles.

### 1.2 N-alkanes and their use as digestive markers until present day

*N*-alkanes are aliphatic, saturated hydrocarbons, which occur naturally in the lipophile, epicuticular wax layer of plants. These vegetal – or so-called "natural" – alkanes normally have an odd number of carbon atoms, and nonacosane ($C_{29}$) and hentriacontane ($C_{31}$) form the largest fraction. Alkanes with an even number of carbon atoms occur only in very small amounts in plants.

The method of using alkanes as markers in digestive studies has received considerable attention in the last fifteen years, due to the following properties: they are non-toxic; they show a high chemical stability against digestive processes in the gastrointestinal tracts of land-living warm-blooded animals; they are simple to analyse with gas chromatography – even at very low concentrations in the analysable material; and finally, their occurrence in plant waxes is general.

These properties of the alkanes raised the interest of scientists, to evaluate this marker system in different animal species. It was R. W. Mayes and his co-workers from the Macaulay Land Use Research Institute of Aberdeen, United Kingdom, who initiated research on the possible use of alkanes as digestive markers in ruminants.

In the meantime, several studies with alkanes have been carried out, mainly with domestic ruminants like sheep, goats and dairy cows, and the alkane method has gained increasing popularity. In more recent studies, alkanes also have been used in other animals – captive and free-ranging: in mammals like giraffes, horses, pigs, mountain hares and rabbits, in birds like chicken and pigeons and even in farmed fish species, the arctic char. Reviews on the method have been published (Dove and Mayes 1991; Dove and Mayes 1996).

The vegetal alkanes with their odd number of carbon atoms are used as internal markers; they are included in feedstuff which is normally eaten by the animals, like hay for example, which is rich in $C_{31}$. In addition, synthetic alkanes with a similar but even number of carbon atoms can be used as external markers. In particular octacosane ($C_{28}$), dotriacontane ($C_{32}$) and hexacontane ($C_{36}$) have been shown to be suitable as external markers, because they are quite cheap and their content in plant feedstuff is very low.

Synthetic alkanes can be offered to animals in diverse modes, coupled on different carrier substances, e. g. impregnated in shreddered paper, in gelatine capsules and controlled-release capsules (CR-capsules), impregnated in pellets or in feeding plants, or also they may be fed as a mixture of pulverized, synthetic alkanes with the feedstuff.

Natural and synthetic alkanes can be used together in the same trial. Considering they have very similar chemical structures, both can be analysed with gas chromatography at the same time.

In studies with alkanes, this marker system was used for the determination of very different parameters of digestive physiology. *N*-alkanes were used to estimate digestive kinetics, such as mean retention time (MRT) and digesta flow through the gastrointestinal tract. They have been used for the determination and quantification of food intake with the double marker method of Mayes et al. (1986). For that purpose two alkanes (one natural and one synthetic) are used, which differ in only one carbon atom, and which have a similar recovery rate, for example $C_{32}/C_{33}$ or $C_{31}/C_{32}$. Also the estimation of the composition of the food eaten by the animal can be carried out with *n*-alkanes, because of the alkane profile, which is characteristic for every plant species. Above all, this is of main interest in studies with animals grazing in the wild, because all other methods used in this context up to now have proven to be inadequate. Finally, estimation of the apparent digestibility of feedstuff and of different food components is possible with the alkane method as well.

### 1.3 N-alkanes in Galapagos giant tortoises: a description of the current study with emphasis on the practical aspects of the trials

The aim of the current study was the examination of the following parameters: digesta kinetics, food composition, food intake and apparent digestibility of the eaten feedstuff in adult and juvenile Galapagos giant tortoises.

Apart from *n*-alkanes, conventional markers were used, and a total faecal collection was performed as well. The results obtained with the alkane method were compared with the results obtained with the other methods.

In a first trial, the MRT's of the liquid and the solid phases of the digesta in the gastrointestinal tract of the giant tortoises were estimated. As marker for the liquid phase, Co-EDTA was used, and for the solid phase the alkane $C_{36}$ and chromium-mordant fibres were used.

In a second trial, the suitability of alkanes ($C_{28}$, $C_{32}$ and $C_{36}$) was compared with the conventional markers ADL and AIA for the determination of the apparent digestibility; besides this, a comparison between the alkane method and a total faecal collection was carried out for the determination of food intake and food composition.

## 2 Methods

### 2.1 Trial 1: Estimation of the MRT of the liquid and the solid digesta phases

According to Warner (1981), the MRT is the average time, during which single food particles of the eaten feedstuff remain in the gastrointestinal tract of an individual. For the determination of the MRT with the marker method, one or more markers are fed to the animals in a single dose and after this, faeces samples are collected at specific intervals during an adequate period of time in order to measure the appearance and disappearance of the marker in the faeces. This method is called "pulse dose / sample collection method" according to Warner (1981).

The trial was performed with four adult and four juvenile Galapagos giant tortoises of the Zoological Garden of Zurich, Switzerland. Age, sex and body mass (BM) of each of the animals are summarised in table 1. The single marker doses were estimated on the basis of the animal's BM, in order to feed each animal the same marker dose per kg BM.

**Table 1.** Age (years), sex and body masses (BM kg) of the adult and juvenile Galapagos giant tortoises used for the two trials.

| | Animal no. | Age (years) | Sex | BM (kg) in trial 1 | BM (kg) in trial 2 |
|---|---|---|---|---|---|
| Adults | 1 | ~ 60 | female | 99.5 | 99.5 |
| | 2 | ~ 40 | male | 135.0 | not used |
| | 3 | ~ 40 | male | 139.5 | not used |
| | 4 | ~ 40 | male | 207.0 | 207.5 |
| Juveniles | 5 | 8 | female | not used | 34.9 |
| | 6 | 7 | male | not used | 27.2 |
| | 7 | 7 | female | not used | 37.0 |
| | 8 | 5 | male | 12.5 | 14.6 |
| | 9 | 5 | female | 5.5 | 7.2 |
| | 10 | 4 | female | 7.6 | 9.5 |
| | 11 | 4 | female | 8.0 | 9.4 |

Two conventional digestive markers were used: Co-EDTA was used as marker for the liquid phase of the digesta. Tortoise pellets were used as carrier substance. The dose of Co-EDTA was 0.8 mg per kg BM. Cr-mordant fibres of a length of less than 2 mm were used as marker for the solid digesta phase. Each animal received 2 g of the fibres (equivalent to 20 mg chromium), which is a dose that has turned out to be enough in studies with free-ranging ruminants.

As a second marker for the solid phase, the even-chained alkane $C_{36}$ was chosen. The carrier for this marker were tortoise pellets as well; the production of these alkane-impregnated pellets was very simple: The pellet rations of each animal were prepared in ceramic bowels so that no pellet was laying on top of another. For an amount of 10 g pellets, 187.5 mg $C_{36}$ were dissolved in 3 ml *n*-hexane ($C_6$) at a temperature of 40 °C. After heating, the alkane-hexane solution was poured over the pellets immediately, taking care that the solution was uniformly spread and that the pellets wouldn't become too soggy. The pellets were shaken softly to facilitate the absorption of the alkane solution. Afterwards the pellets were spread on a tray and left under a ventilation outlet over night, until the hexane had evaporated.

150 g of tortoise pellets were labelled with $C_{36}$ in this manner, so that finally a concentration of 2300 ppm $C_{36}$ in the pellet dry matter (DM) was reached. The giant tortoises were fed 200 mg pellets per kg BM, and thus they received an alkane dose of 0.46 mg $C_{36}$ per kg BM.

The application of the markers to the giant tortoises turned out to work without any difficulties. Alkanes don't have any special taste, which could repel the animals. The marker-labelled pellets and the chromium-mordant fibres were fed individually and were taken voluntarily by the tortoises. For the juvenile giant tortoises, the pellets and the fibres were mixed to a small pile; for the adults, the markers, filled in hollowed tomatoes and kiwis, were offered with tweezers.

After the marker application, the faeces of the giant tortoises were collected daily for a period of 25 days and the exact defecating time was noted. It is important to fix the collecting period for long enough, so that ideally the decrease of the marker concentration can be followed to zero. Reptiles are poikilotherm animals, their metabolism depends on the environmental temperature and is slower than in mammals; therefore the digesta passage through the gastrointestinal tract of reptiles takes not only hours like in mammals, but several days. According a study of Liesegang et al. (2000), the MRT of Galapagos giant tortoises is about 18 days. The additional time of seven days was a factor of safety.

### 2.2 *Trial 2: Estimation of food composition, intake and apparent digestibility*

For the determination of recovery rates, food composition, intake and apparent digestibility, a daily or continual application of marker substance is needed, which leads to a constant marker excretion. It is to be noted that the period until a steady state of food particles and marker concentration in the gastrointestinal tract is reached, depends on the diet and the animal.

For this trial, nine Galapagos giant tortoises of the Zoological Garden of Zurich, Switzerland, were used and divided into two groups: two adults (nos. 1 and 4) and three juveniles (nos. 5, 6 and 7) were kept in a group and also fed together; four juveniles (nos. 8, 9, 10 and 11) were housed separately during feeding time to perform a total faecal collection with them (which is the exact gravimetric coverage of food intake and faecal mass). Age, sex and BM of each of the animals are summarised in table 1.

During the whole trial, the animals were fed a mixture of feedstuff consisting of four components, whose proportions always were constant: hay, apple, lettuce and alkane-labelled tortoise pellets.

Hay, as the major part of the mixture, considerably increases the content of crude fibres, which is of certain importance for herbivore reptiles as hindgut fermenters. Hay is rich in the natural alkanes $C_{29}$ and $C_{31}$ as well, and therefore should be detectable in the faeces. Apple and lettuce were added as taste carrier. Besides, the apple skin contains alkanes as well, which should be detectable too. Lettuce is advantageous because it has a satisfactory calcium/ phosphorus-relation; it contains itself no amounts of alkanes. Tortoise pellets are very suitable carriers for food markers without any content of alkanes, and the tortoises very well accept them. In this trial, the pellets were labelled with three different even-chained alkanes: $C_{28}$, $C_{32}$ and $C_{36}$. 16 kg tortoise pellets were grinded and newly formed with the alkanes in a pellet machine. 15 kg pellets with an alkane concentration of 1700 ppm of DM were produced.

The feeding phase of the trial endured for 25 days as it was in the first trial, in order to feed the tortoises with the mixture diet over a period of time, that lasted longer than the MRT of the food. In this way, a steady state of the mixture diet was attained.

After this, the faeces of the animals were collected twice daily and the time of defecation was noted. In the juvenile tortoises, which were kept individually, a total faecal collection was performed.

## 3 Results and discussion

The purpose of this paper is to focus on the practical side of the trials and to give only a short presentation of the results of this study, mainly from the point of view of the evaluation of the *n*-alkanes. The detailed data of the study will be published elsewhere (Hatt et al. submitted).

In both trials, the dose of the *n*-alkanes fed to the giant tortoises turned out to be high enough, so that they were detected in the faecal analysis. Both the manual and the mechanical production of alkane-labelled pellets are not only simple, but also efficient methods of marker application on carrier substances, and therefore they are recommended for future studies.

### 3.1 Results of trial 1

A typical pattern of marker excretion is presented by the adult tortoise no 2 (figure 1). Cr and $C_{36}$ were both excreted as a pulse, and the passage of both markers were so similar, that it is safe to say the chromium-mordant fibres and $C_{36}$ as well were representing the solid phase of the digesta. Co-EDTA reached a maximum of excretion earlier than Cr and $C_{36}$.

In the adult giant tortoises, a significant difference between the MRT's of the liquid phase (approximately 9 days) and the solid phase (approximately 12 days) was discovered; in the juveniles the MRT's of both phases lasted appro-

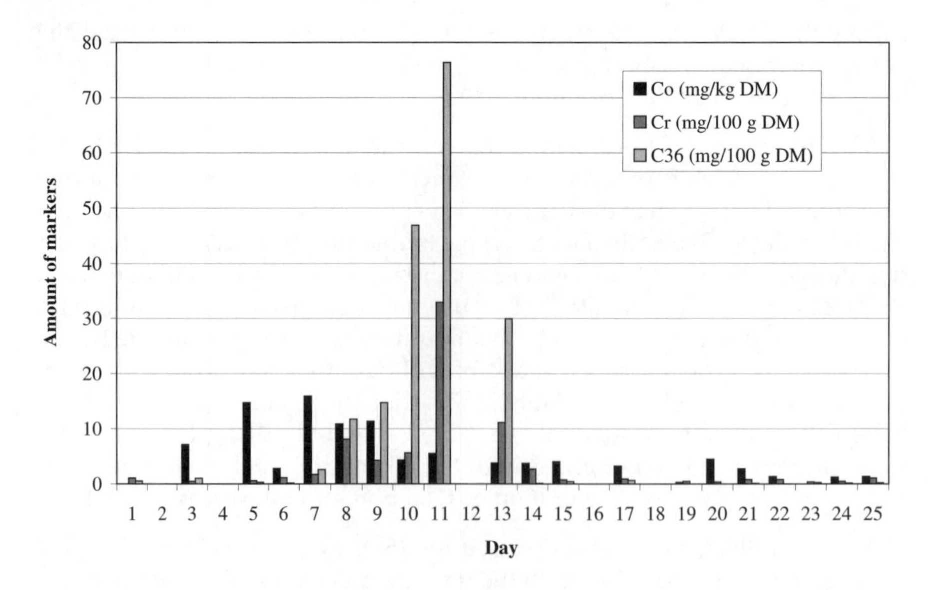


**Figure 1.** Amount of three digestive markers Co-EDTA (Co), Chromium (Cr) and alkane $C_{36}$ excreted by the adult Galapagos giant tortoise no 2. Co-EDTA represents the liquid digesta phase, Cr and $C_{36}$ represent the solid digesta phase.

ximately 9 days. The reason for the longer retention of the solid digesta phase in the adults is probably the nature of the given food: the juvenile giant tortoises were fed a mixture of finely chopped vegetables, whereas the adults received coarse pieces of food, which – due to the size – is suspected to have slowed down the gastrointestinal passage. In spite of the high differences of BM and stature of the adult and juvenile tortoises, and the longer intestinal tract of the adults, the MRT's of the liquid digesta phase did not differ between the two groups. Therefore the conclusion is that in Galapagos giant tortoises, BM and stature of an animal do not influence the MRT of digesta.

Apart from chromium-mordant fibres, which is a reliable marker for the solid digesta fraction, the synthetic alkane $C_{36}$ that has been used here for the first time in a reptile species, proved to be a suitable marker for determination of the passage of the solid digesta phase and therefore can be recommended for further kinetic studies with reptiles.

### *3.2 Results of trial 2*

The composition of the mixed food has been estimated very reliably with the alkane method, with the aid of the alkane profiles of the single components. The results obtained with the alkane method corresponded very well with the results obtained with the total faecal collection (table 2). For these estimations, it is important to choose diet components, which differ as much as possible from each other, so that a respective association becomes easy.

**Table 2.** Results of the food composition (% DM), obtained with the total faecal collection and the alkane method.

| | **Total faecal collection** | **Alkane method** |
|---|---|---|
| **Food composition** | % DM | % DM |
| Apple | 8[a] | 11[b] |
| Hay | 77[b] | 75[b] |
| Pellets | 15[b] | 14[b] |

[a,b] Different superscripts within the same line indicate significant differences ($p < 0.05$) by paired t-test.

Furthermore, an interesting observation was made: the three juvenile giant tortoises, kept in a group with the adults, were shown to successfully select for apples. This result coincides with personal observations during the study.

The obtained results clearly show that the use of alkanes is a reliable method for the determination of food composition. Therefore we conclude that *n*-alkanes have a potential for further studies in this field and for studies with animals in the wild as well.

With the four separately fed juvenile Galapagos giant tortoises a total faecal collection was performed and the recovery rates of the digestive markers were determined. The respective absolute recovery rates were for $C_{25}$ 0.67, $C_{27}$ 0.49, $C_{28}$ 0.86, $C_{29}$ 0.72, $C_{31}$ 0.91, $C_{32}$ 0.66, $C_{33}$ 1.08 and $C_{36}$ 0.70, for ADL 0.66 and for AIA 0.47.

This is an interesting discovery, because according to some authors (Mayes and Lamb 1984; Mayes et al. 1986; Dove and Mayes 1991; Hameleers et al. 1996) the recovery rate of alkanes in the faeces of domestic ruminants increases with increasing length of the carbon chains. This was not the case in the giant tortoises of this study, a finding that agrees with observations made in other hindgut fermenters like horses, ponies and pigs (Mayes et al. 1995) and mountain hares (Hulbert 1993), where recoveries did not correlate as well with chain length. Further studies should be directed on the recovery of *n*-alkanes in the faeces of tortoises.

By comparing the other markers ADL and AIA with the alkanes, the following recovery rates were found: $C_{36}$ had a recovery rate of 70 %, ADL had one of 66 % and AIA of 47 %. The most probable reason for these low recovery rates of the markers is absorption through the mucosa of the digestive tract of the giant tortoises. This phenomenon is described in the literature for all of the three digestibility markers: Mayes et al. (1986) postulated such absorption processes in sheep, causing a low recovery rate of *n*-alkanes. The fermentative microorganisms of the paunch flora are unable to break down or synthesize *n*-alkanes. There are also reports of ADL (Fahey and Jung 1983; van Soest 1994) and AIA (Kotb and Luckey 1972; Owens and Hanson 1992), which say that these markers would be partially digested and absorbed in the gastrointestinal tract of animals.

The estimation of food intake by the four juvenile giant tortoises individually kept was performed according to the double marker method of Mayes et al. (1986) with the alkane pair $C_{31}/C_{32}$, whose concentrations in the faeces showed similar orders of magnitude. Considering the relative recovery rates of the alkanes relative to $C_{31}$, the estimations yielded reliable results. The results are summarised in table 3. With these results, it can be noted that the alkane method is quite suitable to estimate food intake in herbivore tortoises.

The apparent digestibility of the organic matter (OM) was significantly underestimated with all of the three markers AIA (18.3 % OM), ADL (38.9 % OM) and $C_{36}$ (48.5 % OM) in comparison to the results of the total faecal collection (67.5 % OM). Nevertheless, the smallest deviation was observed with $C_{36}$. The reason for the underestimation of apparent digestibilities is the low recovery rates of the markers.

With the results obtained in trial 2, it becomes clear that the total faecal collection (the exact documentation of food intake, and the collection of the total faecal mass over a certain period of time) is now, as ever, the only safe method to determine precisely the apparent digestibility of the diet of Galapagos giant tortoises.

**Table 3.** Results of the intake (g DM), obtained with the total faecal collection and the alkane method.

| | **Total faecal collection** | **Alkane method** |
|---|---|---|
| **Intake** | g DM | g DM |
| | 16.7[c] | 17.7[c] (with RR)<br>24.5[d] (with AR) |

[c,d] Different superscripts within the same line indicate significant differences ($p < 0.05$) by Scheffé F-test.

### *3.2 A summary of the evaluation of the alkanes as digestive markers*

The results of the current study clearly show that in herbivore reptiles, alkanes possess a potential as digestive markers for the study of different aspects of digestive physiology, and through this increase the understanding concerning feeding and digestion of these animals.

In addition, compared with other marker systems, alkanes present many advantages concerning their characteristics as digestive markers, such as presence in plants which are naturally eaten by animals, easy application to the animals and harmlessness for them, readily detectable even at very low concentrations in the analysable material, and low costs.

## 4 Conclusions

A short summary of the evaluation of the *n*-alkanes as a digestive marker system is given below:

1. Synthetic alkanes are non-toxic and do not have any unpleasant taste, therefore they appeared to be ingested voluntarily by domestic herbivorous animals as well as by wild-living animals.

2. During the entire study, the Galapagos giant tortoises did not show any physical or psychological changes, which could have been caused by the alkanes. During the whole time, the animals gave a healthy impression and showed a good appetite. Pathological findings connected with their digestive tract e. g. diarrhoea or constipation, were not found.

3. For the current studies, a small amount of alkanes was used, but detection of the alkanes in the faeces was still possible. However in further studies, a higher dosage of alkanes is recommended, particularly because these markers are non-toxic for the animals. In order to find out if higher recovery rates will result, a higher dosage could be given.

4. The chemical preparation of the samples and the following analysis with gas chromatography are very simple. Natural and synthetic alkanes can be analysed in the same analytical passage.

5. Alkanes have been shown to be suitable markers for kinetic studies, in the estimation of the MRT with the "one pulse / sample collection"-method. Apart from $C_{36}$, further studies could use other synthetic alkanes and feedstuff with characteristic profiles of natural alkanes for the determination of single digesta phases and food particles of different sizes.

6. Estimation of the food composition with the alkane method was successful in the present study. Further studies are therefore encouraged to analyse quantitatively and qualitatively the food intake of herbivore reptiles kept in groups or living in their natural habitat. Seasonal or other preferences of different feedstuff could be detected.

7. Estimation of food intake using the alkanes succeeded; therefore this marker system is recommended for future works concerning this parameter.

8. Coupled with the low recovery rates and the determination of the apparent digestibility, future work should be based on the behaviour of these hydrocarbons in the gastrointestinal tract of the giant tortoises.

   It should be investigated whether the recovery rates vary between different studies or whether they remain at constant values. Besides, studies about the recovery rate of alkanes in relation to the length of the carbon chains would be of interest. If it would turn out that $C_{31}$ generally has the best recovery rate as in the current study, where it was 91 %, estimation of intake should be carried out with this alkane.

9. Estimation of the apparent digestibility using the alkane method produced results which resembled most of the observed values. This leads

to the conclusion that in field studies, where total faecal collection is not possible, $C_{36}$ can be used as a marker in order to at least get an idea about the magnitude of the digestibilities, or to compare different digestibilities (e. g. influenced by season).

10. For the exact determination of the apparent digestibility of a diet, attention must be paid to achieving to a homogenous mixing of the marker with the digesta. On that occasion, the mode, the period and the frequency respectively of the marker application, and the period of faeces collection as well play an important role. On the basis of kinetic studies, the behaviour of a marker substance in the digestive tract of an animal can be understood. Through that, the time period and the frequency interval of the marker application can be established to reach a constant excretion of the marker within the faeces.

    Considering the results of the current study, it would make sense in future research to increase the interval of the application of the alkanes and to prolong the faecal collection period respectively.

11. *n*-alkanes possess a great potential as markers for studies of digestive physiology with herbivore reptiles. Studies are recommended to further investigate the recovery of alkanes in tortoises and to study the application of the alkane method in other herbivorous reptile species both in captive and wild situations.

## Acknowledgements

We like to thank the following institutions for their financial allowance: Friends of Galapagos Islands, Switzerland; Schildkröten-Interessensgemeinschaft Schweiz (SIGS), Stiftung zum Wohle der Schildkröten; Commission of Zoo Biology, Zoological Garden Zurich. Further we like to thank Prof. Dr. Michael Kreuzer and his co-workers from the Institute of Animal Sciences, ETH Zurich for performing the analyses of alkane profiles.

## Products mentioned in text

**$C_{28}$:** synthetic alkane, Octacosan purum powder, Fluka Chemie AG, Buchs, Switzerland.

**$C_{32}$:** synthetic alkane, Dotriacontan purum powder, Fluka Chemie AG, Buchs, Switzerland.

**$C_{36}$:** synthetic alkane, Hexatriacontan purum powder, Fluka Chemie AG, Buchs, Switzerland.

n-**hexane ($C_6$)**: synthetic alkane, Hexane low in aromatic hydrocarbons, BDH, Chemie Brunschwig AG, Basel, Switzerland.

**Tortoise pellets:** Dorsval tortoise pellets®, Roswal AG, Zurich, Switzerland.

## References

Dove, H.; Mayes, R. W. (1991): The use of plant wax alkanes as marker substances in studies of the nutrition of herbivores: a review. *Australian Journal of Agricultural Research* 42: 913–952.

Dove, H.; Mayes, R. W. (1996): Plant wax components: a new approach to estimating intake and diet composition in herbivores. *Journal of Nutrition* 126: 13–26.

Fahey Jr., G. C.; Jung, H. G. (1983): Lignin as a marker in digestion studies: a review. *Journal of Animal Science* 57: 220–225.

Hameleers, A.; McNab, J.; Mayes, R. W. (1996): Use of saturated aliphatic hydrocarbons (alkanes) as markers in nutrition studies in chickens. *British Poultry Science* 37: 105–106.

Hatt, J.-M.; Gisler, R.; Mayes, R. W.; Lechner-Doll, M.; Clauss, M.; Liesegang, A.; Wanner, M. (submitted): The use of dosed and herbage *n*-alkanes as markers for the determination of intake, digestibility, mean retention time and diet selection in Galapagos tortoises (*Geochelone nigra*).

Hulbert, I. A. R. (1993): *The effect of upland afforestation on the ecology of lagomorphs with different feeding strategies*. [PhD Thesis]. Aberdeen: University of Aberdeen.

Kolb, A.R.; Luckey, T. D. (1972): Markers in nutrition. *Nutrition Abstracts and Reviews* 42(3): 813–839.

Liesegang, A.; Hatt, J.-M.; Forrer, R.; Wanner, M.; Isenbügel, E. (2000): Examination of the digestibility of Ca, Mg and P in four captive born juvenile Galapagos giant tortoises (*Geochelone [elephantopus] nigra*). In: *Zoo Animal Nutrition* (J. Nijboer, J.-M. Hatt, W. Kaumanns, A. Beijnen, U. Ganslosser, eds.). Fürth: Filander Verlag, pp. 45–49.

Mayes, R. W.; Lamb, C. S. (1984): The possible use of *n*-alkanes in herbage as indigestible faecal markers. *Proceedings of the Nutrition Society* 43: 39A.

Mayes, R. W.; Lamb, C. S.; Colgrove, P. M. (1986): The use of dosed and herbage *n*-alkanes as markers for the determination of herbage intake. *Journal of Agricultural Science* 107: 161–170.

Mayes, R. W.; Dove, H.; Chen, X. B.; Guada, J. A. (1995): Advances in the use of faecal and urinary markers for measuring diet composition, herbage intake and nutrient utilisation in herbivores. In: *Recent developments in the nutrition of herbivores* (M. Journet, E. Grenet, M.-H. Farce, M. Thériez, C. Demarquilly, eds.). Proceedings of the IVth International Symposium on the Nutrition of Herbivores, Paris, pp. 381–406.

Owens, F. N.; Hanson, C. F. (1992): Symposium: External and internal markers. External and internal markers for appraising site and extent of digestion in ruminants. *Journal of Dairy Science* 75: 2605–2617.

van Soest, P. J. (1994): *Nutritional ecology of the ruminant*. 2th ed. Ithaca: Cornell University Press, pp. 111–115.

Warner, A. C. I. (1981): Rate of passage of digesta through the gut of mammals and birds. *Nutritional Abstract Review Series* 51B: 789–820.

*J.-M. Hatt*[1]

# Markers in zoo animal nutrition with special emphasis on *n*-alkanes

**Abstract**

*Markers may allow to measure digestibility, intake, faecal output, digesta kinetics and even diet composition, without the use of total faecal collection and individual caging. Due to the fact that zoo animals are not tame (not domesticated) they are more difficult to handle, controlled feeding and sampling are complicated and may even be dangerous. Therefore markers have in the past played an important role in digestive studies in zoo animals. The present paper presents the frequently used internal (which are naturally present in feedstuffs) and external (which are mixed into the diet) marker systems used in zoo animal nutrition. Internal markers discussed are: lignin, acid (HCl)-insoluble ash, and manganese ($Mn^{2+}$). External markers discussed are: chromic oxide ($Cr_2O_3$), titaniumoxide ($TiO_2$), mordants such as of Cr and cerium, cobalt ethylnediamine tretra-acetic acid (Co-EDTA), plastic pieces and dyes. Their advantages but also problems are discussed. A new marker system in zoo animal nutrition, n-alkanes, is introduced, which may be used both as internal and external marker.*

**Keywords**

*digestibility, diet intake, ingesta kinetics, digestive physiology*

## 1 Introduction

Digestibility studies have traditionally been performed on live animals. Trials to measure digestibility *in vitro* have so far not been successful on a larger scale. Due to the fact that zoo animals are not tame they are more difficult to handle, controlled feeding and sampling are complicated and may even be dangerous. This is one of the main reasons why scientific digestibility studies in non-domestic animals and especially in zoo animals are rare compared to domestic animals.

Since total faecal collection, which is a reliable and commonly used technique in domestic animals, can only rarely be applied in zoo animals alternatives have been looked for in the past. The increasing need for digestibility studies

[1] Zurich Zoo and Division of Zoo Animals and Exotic Pets, University of Zurich, Winterthurerstrasse 260, CH – 8057 Zurich. Address for correspondence: Jean-Michel Hatt, PD Dr. med. vet., M.Sc., Division of Zoo Animals and Exotic Pets, University of Zurich, Winterthurerstr. 260, 8057 Zurich, Switzerland; Email: Jean-Michel.Hatt@access.unizh.ch, Fax: +41 / 1 635 89 01; Tel. +41 / 1 635 83 42

which are a prerequisite for understanding digestive strategies in zoo animals and hence are the basis for the correct feeding, has led to the search for alternatives. Inert marker systems have been found to be an important tool for such studies and they have been applied in several zoo animals. Markers allow measurements digestibility, intake, faecal output, digesta kinetics and even diet composition, without the use of total faecal collection and individual caging. However the uncritical use of markers may also be the source of important mistakes being made as to the interpretation of results (Bernard et al. 1995).

The present paper aims at presenting a selection of the frequently used internal (which are naturally present in feedstuffs) and external (which are mixed into the diet) marker systems used in zoo animal nutrition. Their advantages but also problems are discussed. Radioactive isotopes which are frequently used as markers in domestic animals will not be discussed. Their use in zoo animals is limited due to the hazard for the zoo personnel and public. A new marker system in zoo animal nutrition, *n*-alkanes, is presented, which may be used both as internal and external marker.

## 2 Internal markers

### 2.1 Lignin

An overview on the use of lignin has been published by Fahey and Jung (1983). This marker was probably one of the first to be used in non-domestic animals. Smith *et al.* 1956 used it in mule deer (*Odocoileus hemionus*). Table 1 gives an overview on the species in which lignin has been used. However, it should also be noted that in ruminants, lignin may undergo fermentation (Merchen 1988) and Kane *et al.* (1952) observed fluctuations in the excretion of lignin. Both can lead to low marker recoveries and result in erratic results. A further problem arises from the analysis because minor variations in the concentration of sulphuric acid will result in important inaccuracies in the measurement of lignin (Van Soest 1994). Ideally the lignin concentration in the diet should be above 5% on a dry matter basis. However most diets for zoo animals have a lower ratio. Lignin is not suitable for carnivores.

### 2.2 HCl-insoluble ash

Similar to lignin the acid (HCl)-insoluble ash has been widely used in herbivores and table 2 lists non-domestic species in which this marker has been used. However, a major disadvantage of this marker system is the possibility of contamination of faeces, resulting in an overestimation of digestibility. Minerals in the diet that are insoluble in acid may arise from two sources: biogenic mineral fractions in the forage and contamination from soil and dust (Van Soest, 1994). The latter has already been of concern in Aldabra tortoises (*Geochelone gigantea*) studied in the field (Hamilton & Coe 1982) but contamination may also result through the uptake of sand (geophagy) or stones (lithophagy) which has been described in several species of tortoises and ter-

**Table 1.** Non-domestic species in which lignin has been used as marker for the measurement of digestibility.

| Species | Scientific Name | Source |
|---|---|---|
| Mule deer | *Odocoileus hemionus* | Smith et al. (1956) |
| Bison | *Bison bison* | Hintz et al. (1976) |
| Lama | *Lama glama* | Hintz et al. (1976) |
| Persian gazelle | *Gazella s. subgutturosa* | Hintz et al. (1976) |
| Onager | *Equus hemionus* | Hintz et al. (1976) |
| Przewalski horse | *Equus caballus przewalskii* | Hintz et al. (1976) |
| Grévy-Zebra | *Equus grevyi* | Hintz et al. (1976) |
| 15 Species of Zoo-herbivores | | Ullrey et al.(1979) |
| Red deer | *Cervus elaphus* | Renecker and Hudson (1990) |
| Moose | *Alces alces* | Renecker and Hudson (1990) |
| Red-footed tortoise | *Geochelone carbonaria* | Bjorndal (1989) |
| Yellow-footed tortoise | *Geochelone denticulata* | Bjorndal (1989) |

**Table 2.** Non-domestic species in which HCl-insoluble ash has been used as marker for the measurement of digestibility.

| Species | Scientific Name | Source |
|---|---|---|
| Roe deer | *Capreolus capreolus* | Enders (1973) |
| Reindeer | *Rangifer tarandus* | Staaland et al. (1986) |
| Giraffe | *Giraffa cameopardalis* | Baer et al. (1985) |
| African elephant | *Loxodonta africana* | Spala et al. (1990) |
| Galapagos tortoise | *Geochelone nigra* | Liesegang et al. 2001 |

rapins (Gans and Gans 1978; Zwart 2000). The problem of contamination with the marker HCl-insoluble ash is less important in comparative studies under identical circumstances, as demonstrated in a study on calcium digestibility in Galapagos tortoises involving this marker (Liesegang et al. 2000).

### 2.3 Manganese ($Mn^{2+}$)

A marker system that has been used both in herbivores and carnivores is manganese. Published studies are listed in table 3. Although it appears that this marker could have a wide range of applications in zoo animals it has only been used infrequently. When used in carnivores it was mentioned by Fadely et al. (1990 ) that it is important that the prey is swallowed in one piece since the $Mn^{2+}$ content within the prey is variable. In cotton rats (*Sigmodon hispidus*) and Northern fur seals (*Callorhinus ursinus*) recovery rates of 95 % and 90 % were measured (Kaufman et al. 1976; Fadely et al. 1990).

**Table 3.** Non-domestic species in which manganese ($Mn^{2+}$) has been used as marker for the measurement of digestibility

| Species | Scientific Name | Source |
|---|---|---|
| Cotton rats | *Sigmodon hispidus* | Kaufman et al. (1976) |
| Howler monkeys | *Alouatta palliata* | Nagy and Milton (1979) |
| Three-toed sloths | *Bradypus variegatus* | Nagy and Montgomery (1980) |
| Northern fur seal | *Callorhinus ursinus* | Fadely et al. (1990) |
| Steller sea lions | *Eumetopias jubatus* | Rosen and Trites (2000) |
| Chuckwalla | *Sauromalus obesus* | Nagy (1977) |

## 3 External markers

### 3.1 Chromic oxide ($Cr_2O_3$) and titaniumoxide ($TiO_2$)

The external marker which probably has been used most often in digestive studies with zoo animals is $Cr_2O_3$, a powder which is fine, heavy and not readily soluble.

In their study with different zoo felids (see table 4) Barbiers et al. (1980) compared this marker system with the total faecal collection. For the apparent digestibility of crude energy, crude fat and organic matter they found a significant correlation of the two methods. However, for dry matter and crude protein the correlation was not significant.

A major disadvantage of this marker is that it tends to an uneven distribution in the digesta, which will result in fluctuation when excreted. In a study with captive Oryx antelopes (*Oryx leucoryx* and *Oryx beisa*) these fluctuation prevented the use of this marker system (Rusterholz 1984). Similar fluctuations were also noted in Northern fur seals (*Callorhinus ursinus*) (Fadely et al. 1990). In Asian elephants (*Elephas maximus*) Löhlein (1999) measured a recovery rate of 97 %, he dosed the marker twice daily to reduce fluctuations.

**Table 4.** Non-domestic species in which Chromic oxide ($Cr_2O_3$) has been used as marker for the measurement of digestibility.

| Species | Scientific Name | Source |
|---|---|---|
| Leopard | *Panthera pardus* | Barbiers et al. (1980) |
| Lion | *Panthera leo* | Barbiers et al. (1980) |
| Puma | *Felis concolor* | Barbiers et al. (1980) |
| Tiger | *Pathera tigris* | Barbiers et al. (1980) |
| Asian elephant | *Elephas maximus* | Löhlein (1999) |
| Several Primates Species | | Price (1993) |
| Several Lemur species | | Cabré-Vert and Feistner (1995) |
| American alligator | *Alligator mississipiensis* | Staton et al. (1990) |
| Green turtle | *Chelonia mydas* | Davenport and Scott (1993) |

Titanium dioxide ($TiO_2$) has been successfully investigated in New Zealand fur seals (*Arctocephalus forsteri*) and Australian sea lions (*Neophoca cinerea*) to measure TT (Bodley et al. 1999).

### 3.2 Mordants (Cr, Ce ect.) and Cobalt ethylenediamine tetra-acetic acid (Co-EDTA)

Mordants and Co-EDTA are marker which have been predominantly used in herbivores to measure digesta kinetics, such as transit time (TT) and mean retention time (MRT). A large survey on markers used for the estimation of TT was first published by Warner (1981). The longer food is retained in the gastrointestinal tract, the better it can undergo fermentation. Of major interest is the estimation of the liquid and particle phase of the digesta. Co-EDTA as developed by Udén et al. (1980) has shown to be an excellent marker for the liquid phase. However, it has to be noted, that certain diets (especially when a mineral mix is added) may contain high levels of Co, which can interfere with kinetic studies. Furthermore in the Malayan chevrotain (*Tragulus napu*) minor amounts of Co seem to cause diarrhoea (Bernard et al. 1994). In this species Cr-EDTA was used without problems. For the identification of the particle phase Cr-mordanted cell walls have successfully been used in domestic herbivores. Cr binds strongly to the fibre. However this strong binding results in a digestibility of the mordanted -fibres below 10 % in beef (Mader et al. 1984). Other mordants have been produced with Cerium (Ce) and the Lanthanoids (Lanthan [La] and Samarium [Sa]) but their use is limited.

Table 5 gives an overview of markers that have been used to measure liquid phase and particle phase kinetics in non-domestic species. In domestic birds Cr- and Ce-labelled rice, $Cr_2O_3$ and radio dense beads have been used to identify the particle phase (Branch and Cummings 1978; Udén et al. 1980; Ferrando et al. 1987). For the liquid phase Cr-EDTA and phenol red has been successfully applied (Gonalons et al. 1982; Vergara et al. 1989). However the vast majority of kinetic studies in birds has been performed with radioactive isotopes. (Björnhag 1989).

### 3.3 Other external markers

Particularly in zoo animals, a wide number of other external markers for the estimation digesta passage has been used, which are not commonly used in domestic species and therefore have not been thoroughly evaluated. Hence it may be questioned what phase of digesta was exactly measured. These markers have especially been used in reptiles and they include coloured glass beads (Troyer 1984; Waldschmidt et al. 1986; Troyer 1987), coloured vinyl-disks (Harwood 1979; Troyer 1984), stripes of plastic (Harlow et al. 1976; Ruppert 1980; Mautz and Nagy 1987; Van Damme et al. 1991; Bjorndal and Bolten 1992; Van Marken 1992; Meienberger et al. 1993; Spencer et al. 1998), stripes of polyester (Hailey 1998) and even coloured tissue papers (Hamilton and Coe 1982). In the giant panda (*Ailuropoda melanoleuca*) wheat kernels have been used to determine passage rate (Mainka et al. 1989).

**Table 5.** Marker systems that have been used in non-domestic species for the determination of digesta kinetics of particle and liquid phase (Co-EDTA = Cobalt ethylenediamine tetra-acetic acid; Ce = Cerium; Cr = Chromium; Sm = Samarium; Yb = Ytterbium)

| Species | Scientific name | Liquid phase marker | Particle phase marker | Source |
|---|---|---|---|---|
| **Artiodactyla** | | | | |
| Dromedary | *Camelus dromedarius* | Polyethylenglycole | Ce und Cr | Heller et al. 1986; Kayouli et al. 1993 |
| Lama | *Lama guanacoe f. glama* | Polyethylenglycole | Ce und Sm | Heller et al. 1986 |
| Red deer | *Cervus elaphus* | Co-EDTA | Cr | Renecker and Hudson 1990 |
| Moose | *Alces alces* | Co-EDTA | Cr | Renecker and Hudson 1990 |
| **Rodent** | | | | |
| Degu | *Octodon degus* | Co-EDTA | Cr | Sakaguchi and Ohmura 1992 |
| Leaf-eared mouse | *Phyllotis darwinii* | Co-EDTA | Cr | Sakaguchi and Ohmura 1992 |
| Nutria | *Mycastor coypus* | Co-EDTA | Cr | Sakaguchi and Nabata 1992 |
| Mara | *Dolicotis patagonum* | Co-EDTA | Cr | Sakaguchi et al. 1992 |
| Desert woodrat | *Neotoma lebida* | Co-EDTA | Cr | Sakaguchi et al. 2000 |
| **Marsupials** | | | | |
| Long-nosed bandicoot | *Perameles nasuata* | Co-EDTA | Cr | Moyle et al. 1995 |
| Greater glider | *Petauroides volans* | Co-EDTA | Cr | Foley and Hume 1987 |
| Brushtail possums | *Trichosurus vulpecula* | Co-EDTA | Cr | Sakaguchi and Hume 1990 |
| Ringtail possums | *Pseudocheirus peregrinus* | Co-EDTA | Cr for particles >0,3 mm Yb for particles <0,075 mm | Sakaguchi and Hume 1990 |
| **Primates** | | | | |
| Chimpanzee | *Pan troglodytes* | Co-EDTA | Cr | Milton and Demment 1988 |
| Gorilla | *Gorilla g. gorilla* | Co-EDTA | Cr | Caton 1999 |
| Orang-Utan | *Pongo pygmaeus* | Co-EDTA | Cr | Caton et al. 1999 |
| Several marmosett spp. | *Cebuella pygmea, Callithrix jacchus* | Co-EDTA | Cr | Caton and Hume 1996 |
| Several tamarin spp. | *Saguinus* spp. and *Leontopithecus* spp. | Co-EDTA | Cr | Caton and Hume 1996 |
| Several sifaka spp. | *Propithecus* spp. | Co-EDTA | Cr | Campbell et al. 1997 |
| **Reptiles** | | | | |
| Desert tortoise | *Gopherus agassizii* | Co-EDTA | Cr und Yb | Barboza 1995 |

Dyes have been used for the estimation of TT but also for the individual identification of faeces in animals that are kept in a group. Blue colour has been given to an orang-utan (*Pongo pygmaeus*) (Caton et al. 1999). The food colours Ponceau 4R (E 124) and Indigotin (E 132) were successfully investigated to individually identify faeces in a group of ruffed lemurs (*Varecia v. variegata*), lion-tailed macaques (*Macaca silenus*) and Malayan sun bear (*Ursus malayanus*) (Müller et al. 1999). Karasov *et al.* (1986) used Sudan III for the comparative estimation of transit time in two herbivorous lizards (*Disposaurus dorsalis* and *Sauromalus obesus*) and in two species of rodents (*Neotoma lepida* and *Mus musculus*). The concentration of marker in faeces was measured by spectrometry. Carmine red was used in Galapagos tortoises (*Geochelone nigra*) for the measurement of transit time (Liesegang et al. 2000).

## 4 *N*-Alkanes

*N*-Alkanes, which are hydrocarbons found in the epicuticular waxes of plants as mixtures of different carbon chain lengths, have received considerable attention in domestic animals in the last 15 years. They have been used to study different aspects of digestive strategies, such as digestibility, diet intake, food selection, and digesta kinetics in mammals and recently in birds (Dove and Mayes 1996; Hameleers and Mayes 1996). Comprehensive reviews on the alkane method in domestic ruminants have been published (Dove and Mayes 1991; Dove and Mayes 1996). A major advantage of the *n*-alkane technique is that it allows the estimation of digestibility and intake with the same marker system and therefore considerably reduces laboratory work. Whereas digestibility is estimated by the use of an odd-chain n-alkane, naturally present in plants, as internal marker, the method for estimating intake is based on the combined use of a natural odd-chain *n*-alkane and a dosed even-chain *n*-alkane. The low, but measurable, concentrations of the even-chain alkane normally present in the diet is taken account of in the intake calculation. According to the theory of this method, the reliability of intake estimates is not affected by the digestibility of the ration or the marker recoveries in the faeces if the recoveries are sufficiently similar between the natural and dosed alkanes (Dove and Mayes 1991). In domestic ruminants the combinations $C_{31}/C_{32}$ and $C_{32}/C_{33}$ have been the most reliable alkanes for this procedure. The *n*-alkanes have also been used as makers to estimate dietary proportions of different plant species or plant components (Dove and Coombe 1992; Malossini et al. 1994; Salt et al. 1994; Dove and Moore 1995). Since different plant species tend to have differing mixtures of odd-chain alkanes (chain lengths in the range 21 to 35 carbon atoms) diet composition can be estimated from the patterns of alkanes in the faeces and in the dietary components. Similarly, the dietary proportions of different component feedstuffs can be estimated by having them labelled with separate synthetic *n*-alkanes (usually even-chain) (Hatt, in press).

A further application of *n*-alkanes as markers for digesta kinetic studies has been demonstrated in recent studies in ruminants (Mayes et al. 1997; Hatt et al. 1998).

Most research has been conducted with sheep and cattle (Dove and Mayes 1996). But the alkane method has also been applied to non-domestic ruminants and non-ruminant species, such as: the giraffe (*Giraffa camelopardalis*) (Hatt et al. 1998; Clauss 1998), pigs and horses (Mayes et al. 1995; Ordakowski et al. 2001), mountain hares (*Lepus timidus*) (Hulbert 1993) and rabbits (Letso 1996). Gudmundsson and Halldorsdottír (1995) successfully used synthetic alkanes incorporated into diets in order to estimate dietary intake and digestibility in farmed fish. In birds, *n*-alkanes have been evaluated in chickens (Hameleers and Mayes 1996) and feral pigeons (*Columba livia*) (Hatt et al. 2001). Recently alkanes have also been successfully used in a reptile species, the Galapagos tortoise (Hatt, submitted).

## 5 Conclusions

Marker systems play an important role in the study of digestive strategies in zoo animals. A wide variety of markers have been used in the past. However thorough validation has seldom occurred. Furthermore the markers may have been applied only to one or few species. It is difficult to compare these results. The concentration on fewer markers with a broader field of application appears warranted. The n-alkanes which have been successfully evaluated in mammals, birds and reptiles appear to fulfil the requirement for a digestive marker in zoo animals.

## References

Baer, D. J.; Oftedal, O. T.; Fahey G. C. (1985): Feed selection and digestibility by captive giraffe. *Zoo Biol.* 4: 57–64.

Barbiers, R. B.; Vosburgh, K.; Ullrey, D. E. (1980): Comparative digestibility studies in exotic felidae. *Ann. Proc. Amer. Assoc. Zoo Vets*, Washington. p. 31.

Barboza, P. S. (1995): Digesta passage and functional anatomy of the digestive tract in the desert tortoise (*Xerobates agassizii*). *J. Comp. Physiol.* 165B: 193–202.

Bernard, J. B.; De Bar, S. R.; Ullrey, D. E.; Schoeberl, B. J.; Stromberg, J.; Wolff, P. (1994): Fiber utilization in the larger Malayan chevrotain (*Tragulus napu*). *Ann. Proc. Amer. Assoc. Zoo Vets*, Pittsburgh, pp. 354–357.

Bernard, J. B.; Ullrey, D. E.; Wolff, P. L. (1995): Selecting appropriate markers for digestibility studies. *Proc. Nutr. Adv. Group Conf.* 1995, Toronto, pp. 203–206.

Bjorndal, K. A. (1989): Flexibility of digestive responses in two generalist herbivores, the tortoises *Geochelone carbonaria* and *Geochelone denticulata*. *Oecologia* 78: 317–321.

Bjorndal, K.A.; Bolten, A.B. (1992): Body size and digestive efficiency in a herbivorous freshwater turtle: advantages of small bite size. *Physiol. Zool.* 65: 1028–1039.

Björnhag, G. (1989): Transport of water and food particles through the avian caeca and colon. *J. Exp. Zool. Suppl.* 3: 32–37.

Bodley, K.B.; Mercer, J.R.; Bryden, M.M. (1999): Rate of passage of digesta through the alimentary tract of the New Zealand fur seal (*Arctocephalus forsteri*) and the Australian sea lion (*Neophoca cinerea*). *Aust. J. Zool.* 47: 193–198.

Branch, J.; Cummings, J.H. (1978): Comparison of radio-opaque pellets and chromium sesquioxide as inert markers in studies requiring accurate fecal collections. *Gut* 19: 371–376.

Cabré-Vert, N.; Feistner, A.T.C. (1995): Comparative gut passage time in captive lemurs. *Dodo* 31: 76–81.

Campbell, J.L.; Eisemann, J.H.; Glander, K.L.; Crissey, S.D. (1997): Digestive efficiency and passage rate in two propithecus species fed a captive diet. *Proceedings of the Second Conference of the Nutrition Advisory Group*, 1997, Fort Worth, p. nn.

Caton, J.-M. (1999): A preliminary report on the digestive strategy of the Western lowland gorilla. *Austral. Primatol.* 13: 2–7.

Caton, J.-M.; Hume, I.D. (1996): The digestive strategies of marmosets and tamarins. *Proceedings of the First Comparative Nutrition Society Symposium*, Leesburg, pp. 18–20.

Caton, J.-M.; Hume, I.D.; Hill, D.M.; Harper, P. (1999): Digesta retention in the gastro-intestinal tract of the orang-utan (*Pongo pygmaeus*). *Primates* 40: 551–558.

Clauss, M. (1998): *Feeding giraffe (Giraffa camelopardalis)* [MSc Thesis]. London: University of London.

Davenport, J.; Scott, C.R. (1993): Individuality of growth, appetite, metabolic rate and assimilation of nutrients in young green turtles (*Chelonia mydas* L.). *Herpetol. J.* 3: 26–31.

Dove, H.; Coombe, J.B. (1992): A comparison of methods for estimating supplement intake and diet digestibility in sheep. *Proc. Austral. Soc. Anim. Prod.* 19: 239–241.

Dove, H.; Mayes, R.W. (1991): The use of plant wax alkanes as marker substances in studies of the nutrition of herbivores: a review. *Aust. J. Agric. Res.* 42: 913–952.

Dove, H.; Mayes, R.W. (1996): Plant wax components: a new approach to estimating intake and diet composition in herbivores. *J. Nutr.* 126: 13–26.

Dove, H.; Moore, A.D. (1995): Using a least-squares optimization procedure to estimate botanical composition based on alkanes of plant cuticular wax. *Aust. J. Agric. Res.* 46: 1535–1544.

Enders, H. (1973): *Ein Beitrag zu Verdaulichkeitsbestimmungen von Futterrationen nach dem Indikatorverfahren mit Hilfe von Chromoxid bzw. der HCl-unlöslichen Restasche* [Dr.med.vet. Thesis]. München: Tierärztliche Fakultät.

Fadely, B.S.; Worthy, G.A.J.; Costa, D.P. (1990): Assimilation efficiency of northern fur seals determined using dietary manganese. *J. Wildl. Manage.* 54: 246–251.

Fahey, G.C.; Jung, H.G. (1983): Lignin as a marker in digestion studies: a review. *J. Anim. Sci.* 57: 220–225.

Ferrando, C.; Vergara, P.; Jimenez, M.; Gonalons, E. (1987): Study on the rate of passage of food with chromium-mordanted plant cells in chickens (*Gallus gallus*). *Q. J. Exp. Physiol.* 72: 251–259.

Foley, W.J.; Hume, I.D. (1987): Passage of digesta markers in two species of arboreal folivorous marsupials – the greater glider (*Petauroides volans*) and the brushtail possum (*Trichosurus vulpecula*). *Physiol. Zool.* 60: 103–113.

Gans, C.; Gans, K.A. (1978): *Biology of the Reptilia.* London: Academic Press.

Gonalons, E.; Rial, R.; Turk, J.A. (1982): Phenol red as indicator of digestive tract motility in chickens. *Poult. Sci.* 61: 581–583.

Gudmundsson, O.; Halldorsdottír, K. (1995): The use of n-alkanes as markers for the determination of intake and digestibility of fish feed. *J. Appl. Ichthyol.* 11: 354–358.

Hailey, A. (1998): The specific dynamic action of the omnivorous tortoise *Kinixys spekii* in relation to diet, feeding pattern and gut passage. *Physiol. Zool.* 71: 57–66.

Hameleers, A.; Mayes, R.W. (1996): The use of n-alkanes to estimate herbage intake and diet composition by dairy cows offered a perennial rye-grass/ white clover mixture. *Grass Forage Sci.* 53: 164–169.

Hamilton, J.; Coe, M. (1982): Feeding, digestion and assimilation of a population of giant tortoises (*Geochelone gigantea* Schweigger) on Aldabra atoll. *J. Arid Environ.* 5: 127–144.

Harlow, H.J.; Hillman, S.S.; Hofman, M. (1976): The effects of temperature on digestive efficiency in the herbivorous lizard *Dipsosaurus dorsalis*. *J. Comp. Physiol.* 111: 16–20.

Harwood, R.H. (1979): The effect of temperature on the digestive efficiency of three species of lizards, *Cnemidophorus tigris*, *Gerrhonotus multicarinatus* and *Sceloporus occidentalis*. *Comp. Biochem. Physiol.* 63A: 417–433.

Hatt, J.-M.; Lechner-Doll, M.; Mayes, R.W. (1998): The use of n-alkanes as markers for the determination of digestive strategies of captive giraffes (*Giraffa camelopardalis*). *Zoo Biol.* 17: 295–309.

Hatt, J.-M.; Mayes, R.W.; Clauss, M.; Lechner-Doll, M. (2001): Use of artificially applied n-alkanes as markers for the estimation of digestibility, diet composition and intake in feral pigeons (*Columba livia*). *Anim. Feed Sci. Technol.* 94: 65–76.

Heller, R.; Lechner, M.; Weyreter, H.; von Engelhardt, W. (1986): Forestomach fluid volume and retention time of fluid and particles in the gastrointestinal tract of the camel. *Journal of Veterinary Medicine* A 33: 396–399.

Hintz, H. F.; Sedgewick, C. J.; Schryver, H. F. (1976): Some observations on digestion of a pelleted diet by ruminants and non-ruminants. *IZY* 17: 54–56.

Hulbert, I. A. R. (1993): *The effect of upland afforestation on the ecology of lagomorphs with different feeding strategies* [PhD Thesis]: University of Aberdeen.

Kane, E. A.; Jacobson, W. C.; Moore, L. A. (1952): Diurnal variations in the excretion of chromium oxide and lignin. *J. Nutr.* 47: 263–273.

Karasov, W. H.; Petrossian, E.; Rosenberg, L.; Diamond, J. M. (1986): How do food passage rate and assimilation differ between herbivorous lizards and nonruminant mammals? *J. Comp. Physiol.* 156B: 599–609.

Kaufman, D. W.; O'Farrell, M. J.; Kaufman, G. A.; Fuller, S. E. (1976): Digestibility and elemental assimilation in cotton rats. *Acta Theriol.* 21: 147–156.

Kayouli, C.; Jouany, J. P.; Demeyer, D. I.; Taoueb, H.; Dardillat, C. (1993): Comparative studies on the degradation and mean retention time of solid and liquid phases in the forestomach of dromedaries and sheep fed on low-quality roughages from Tunisia. *Anim. Feed Sci. Technol.* 40: 343–355.

Letso, M. (1996): *A study of the use of n-alkanes to determine dietary intake and digestibility in grazing rabbits* [MSc Thesis]. Aberdeen: University of Aberdeen.

Liesegang, A.; Hatt, J.-M.; Forrer, R.; Wanner, M.; Isenbügel, E. (2000): Examination of the digestibility of Ca, Mg and P in four captive born juvenile Galapagos giant tortoises (*Geochelone [elephantopus] nigra*). In: J. Nijboer, J.-M. Hatt, W. Kaumanns, A. Beijnen, U. Ganslosser, eds.: *Zoo Animal Nutrition*. Fürth: Filander Verlag, pp. 45–49.

Liesegang, A.; Hatt, J.-M.; Nijboer, J.; Forrer, R.; Wanner, M.; Isenbügel, E. (2001): Influence of different dietary calcium levels on the digestibility of Ca, Mg and P in captive-born juvenile Galapagos giant tortoises (*Geochelone nigra*). *Zoo Biol.* 20: 367–374.

Löhlein, W. (1999): *Untersuchungen zur Verdaulichkeit von Futtermitteln beim asiatischen Elefanten* (*Elephas maximus*) [Dr.med.vet. Thesis]. München: Ludwig-Maximilians-Universität.

Mader, T. L.; Teeter, R. G.; Horn, G. W. (1984): Comparison of forage labeling techniques for conducting passage rate studies. *J. Anim. Sci.* 58: 208–212.

Mainka, S. A.; Guanlu, Z.; Mao, L. (1989): Utilization of a bamboo, sugar cane, and gruel diet by two juvenile giant pandas (*Ailuropoda melanoleuca*). *J. Zoo Wildl. Med.* 20: 39–44.

Malossini, F.; Bovolenta, S.; Piasentier, E.; Valentinotti, M. (1994): Variability of n-alkane content in a natural pasture and in faeces of grazing dairy cows. *Anim. Feed Sci. Technol.* 50: 113–122.

Mautz, W.J.; Nagy, K.A. (1987): Ontogenic changes in diet, field metabolic rate, and water flux in the herbivorous lizard *Dipsosaurus dorsalis*. *Physiol. Zool.* 60: 640–658.

Mayes, R.W.; Dove, H.; Chen, X.B.; Guada, J.A. (1995): Advances in the use of faecal and urinary markers for measuring diet composition, herbage intake and nutrient utilisation in herbivores. In: M. Joumet, E. Grenet, M.-H. Farce, M. Thériez, C. Demarquilly, eds.: *Recent developments in the nutrition of herbivores.* Paris: IVth International Symposium on the Nutrition of Herbivores, pp. 381–406.

Mayes, R.W.; Giraldez, J.; Lamb, C.S. (1997): Estimation of gastrointestinal passage rates of different plant components in ruminants using isotopically, labelled plant wax hydrocarbons or sprayed even chained *n*-alkanes. *Proc. Nutr. Soc.* 56: 187A.

Meienberger, C.; Wallis, I.R.; Nagy, K.A. (1993): Food intake rate and body mass influence transit time and digestibility in the desert tortoise (*Xerobates agassizii*). *Physiol. Zool.* 66: 847–862.

Merchen, N.R. (1988): Digestion, absorption and excretion in ruminants. In: D.C. Church, ed.: *The ruminant animal: digestive physiology and nutrition.* Englewood Cliffs: Prentice-Hall, pp. 172–201.

Milton, K.; Demment, M. (1988): Digestion and passage kinetics of chimpanzees fed high and low quality fibre diets and comparison with human diets. *J. Nutr.* 118: 1082–1088.

Moyle, D.I.; Hume, I.D.; Hill, D.M. (1995): Digestive performance and selective digesta retention in the long-nosed bandicoot, *Perameles nasuata*, a small omnivorous marsupial. *J. Comp. Physiol.* 164B: 552–560.

Müller, N.; Schwitzer, C.; Kaumanns, W.; Husung, A. (1999): On the application of different substances for individual marking of feces and measuring digesta passage rates in mammals. *EEP Research Group Newsletter* 6: 10–11.

Nagy, K.A. (1977): Cellulose digestion and nutrient assimilation in *Sauromalus obesus*, a plant-eating lizard. *Copiea* 1977: 355–362.

Nagy, K.A.; Milton, K. (1979): Aspects of diet quality, nutrient assimilation and water balance in wild howler monkeys (*Alouatta palliata*). *Oecologia* 39: 249–258.

Nagy, K.A.; Montgomery, G.G. (1980): Field metabolic rate, water flux, and food consumption in three-toed sloths (*Bradypus variegatus*). *J. Mamm.* 61: 465–472.

Ordakowski, A.L.; Kronfeld, D.S.; Holland, J.L.; Hargreaves, B.J.; Gay, L.S.; Harris, P.A.; Dove, H.; Sklan, D. (2001): Alkanes as internal markers to estimate digestibility of hay or hay plus concetrate diets in horses. *J. Anim. Sci.* 79: 1516–1522.

Price, E.C. (1993): Measuring gut passage time in small New World monkeys. *Anim. Welf.* 2: 47–52.

Renecker, L.A.; Hudson, R.J. (1990): Digestive kinetics of moose (*Alces alces*), Wapiti (*Cervus elaphus*) and cattle. *Anim. Prod.* 50: 51–61.

Rosen, D.A.S.; Trites, A.W. (2000): Digestive efficiency and dry-matter digestibility in Steller sea lions fed herring, pollock, squid, and salmon. *Can. J. Zool.* 78: 234–239.

Ruppert, R.M. (1980): Comparative assimilation efficiencies of two lizards. *Comp. Biochem. Physiol.* 67A: 491–496.

Rusterholz, M. (1984): *Nutrients as a factor in food selection by captive wild herbivores* [Phil. II Thesis]. Zürich: University of Zürich.

Sakaguchi, E.; Hume, I.D. (1990): Digesta retention and fibre digestion in brushtail possums, ringtail possums and rabbits. *Comp. Biochem. Physiol.* 96A: 351–354.

Sakaguchi, E.; Mangione, A.; Fournier, F.; Karasov, W.H. (2000): Coprophagy and digesta transit in desert woodrats (*Neotoma lepida*). In: C.L. KirkBaer, ed.: *Proceedings of the Third Comparative Nutrition Society Symposium*, Pacific Grove, pp. 187–193.

Sakaguchi, E.; Nabata, A. (1992): Comparison of fibre digestion and digesta retention time between nutrias (*Myocastor coypus*) and guinea-pigs (*Cavia porcellus*). *Comp. Biochem. Physiol.* 103A: 601–604.

Sakaguchi, E.; Nippashi, K.; Endoh, G. (1992): Digesta retention and fibre digestion in maras (*Dolicotis patagonum*) and guinea-pigs. *Comp. Biochem. Physiol.* 101A: 867–870.

Sakaguchi, E.; Ohmura, S. (1992): Fibre digestion and digesta retention time in guinea-pigs (*Cavia porcellus*), degus (*Octodon degus*) and leaf-eared mice (*Phyllotis darwini*). *Comp. Biochem. Physiol.* 103A: 787–791.

Salt, C.A.; Mayes, R.W.; Colgrove, P.M.; Lamb, C.S. (1994): The effects of season and diet composition on radiocaesium intake by sheep grazing on heather moorland. *J. Appl. Ecol.* 31: 125–136.

Smith, A.D.; Turner, R.B.; Harris, G.A. (1956): The apparent digestibility of lignin by mule deer. *J. Range Manage.* 9: 142–145.

Spala, P.; Vahala, J.; Hradecky, P. (1990): Lameness in young African elephants (*Loxodonta africana*) caused by inadequate nutrition. *Zool. Garten* 60: 244–247.

Spencer, R.J.; Thompson, M.B.; Hume, I.D. (1998): The diet and digestive energetics of an Australian short-necked turtle, *Emydura macquarii*. *Comp. Biochem. Physiol.* 121A: 341–349.

Staaland, H.; Hove, K.; White, R.G. (1986): Mineral absorption in relation to nutritional ecology of reindeer. *Rangifer Special Issue* No. 1: 279–287.

Staton, M.A.; Edwards, H.M., Jr.; Brisbin, I.L., Jr.; Joanen, T.; McNease, L. (1990): Protein and energy relationships in the diet of the American alligator (*Alligator mississipiensis*). *J. Nutr.* 120: 775–785.

Troyer, K. (1984): Structure and function of the digestive tract of a herbivorous lizard *Iguana iguana*. *Physiol. Zool.* 57: 1–8.

Troyer, K. (1987): Small differences in daytime body temperature affect digestion of natural food in a herbivorous lizard (*Iguana iguana*). *Comp. Biochem. Physiol.* 87A: 623–626.

Udén, P.; Colucci, P.E.; Van Soest, P.J. (1980): Investigations on chromium, cerium and cobalt as markers in digesta rate of passage studies. *J. Sci. Food Agric.* 31: 625–632.

Ullrey, D.E.; Robinson, P.T.; Whetter, P.A. (1979): Comparative digestibility studies with zoo herbivores. *Ann. Proc. Amer. Assoc. Zoo Vets*, Denver, pp. 120–121a.

Van Damme, R.; Bauwens, D.; Verheyen, R.F. (1991): The thermal dependence of feeding behaviour, food consumption and gut passage time in lizard *Lacerta vivipara* Jacquin. *Funct. Ecol.* 5: 507–517.

Van Marken, W.D. (1992): Digestion in an ectothermic herbivore, the green iguana (*Iguana iguana*): effect of food composition and body temperature. *Physiol. Zool.* 65: 649–673.

Van Soest, P.J. (1994): *Nutritional ecology of the ruminant.* Ithaca: Comstock Publishing Associates.

Vergara, P.; Ferrando, C.; Jimenez, M.; Fernandez, E.; Gonalons, E. (1989): Factors determining gastrointestinal transit time of several markers in the domestic fowl. *Q. J. Exp. Physiol.* 74: 867–874.

Waldschmidt, S.R.; Jones, S.M.; Porter, W.P. (1986): The effect of body temperature and feeding regime on activity, passage time, and digestive coefficient in the lizard *Uta stansburiana*. *Physiol. Zool.* 59: 376–383.

Warner, A.C.I. (1981): Rate of passage of digesta through the gut of mammals and birds. *Nutr. Abstr. Rev.* Series 51B: 789–820.

Zwart, P. (2000): Nutrition of Chelonians. In: J. Nijboer, J.-M. Hatt, W. Kaumanns, A. Beijnen, U. Ganslosser, eds.: *Zoo Animal Nutrition*. Fürth: Filander Verlag, pp. 33–44.

*J. Hummel[1,2], L. Kolter[1]*

# Passage rate and digestion in captive okapi (*Okapia johnstoni*)

***Abstract***

*Passage rate of ingesta, and organic matter and fibre digestibility was measured in 2 male okapis. Co-EDTA and chromium-mordanted fibres (fibre length < 2 mm) were used as markers for the fluid and particle phase of ingesta. Resulting mean retention times (MRT´s) were 36 h for fluid and 47 h for particle phase calculated after Thielemanns et al. (1978) and 34 h for the fluid and 48 h for the particle phase by using the model of Grovum and Williams (1973). The resulting mean ratio of* $MRT_{particle\ phase}/MRT_{fluid\ phase}$ *was 1,35 and 1,40, respectively. NDF digestibility was found to be 47 % in these animals. The rather low* $MRT_{particle\ phase}/MRT_{fluid\ phase}$ *ratio may be interpreted as the result of a generally low potential to retain particles in okapis, although comparison with data from studies in captivity or in the wild obviously have to be done very carefully.*

***Keywords***

*mean retention time; fibre digestibility; browser*

## 1 Introduction

### *1.1 Passage rate and nutritional ecology*

An important portion of the potentially available energy resources for herbivores is stored in the form of cellulose or hemicellulose in many ecosystems. These carbohydrates cannot be made available with the enzyme equipment of vertebrates. Even with the help of symbiotic microorganisms, these resources are only available if the microbes are given sufficient time for fermentation. An extension of fermentation time can be facilitated by large fermenting chambers in the digestive system like the rumen or the caecum or colon, were food and the attached microbes can be retained for considerable time.

Obviously, there are limits to the rule "the longer the retention time, the higher the overall energy yield": Some food components like lignin are not available even for symbiotic microbes, and a long retention may restrict food

[1] Zoo Cologne, Riehler Str. 173, 50735 Köln, Germany. Corresponding author: Jürgen Hummel, Isabellenstr. 18c, 50678 Köln, Tel.: ++49 221 20 53 577; Email: Juehummel@aol.com

[2] Institute of Animal Nutrition/University of Bonn.

intake. Therefore, each animal with fermenting capacity is confronted with a challenge concerning the passage rate of food through the digestive system: If the passage rate is too short, potentially available nutrients are lost, while a very long retention restricts the intake of fresh nutrients (Van Soest 1994).

The mammalian group known best for its fermenting chamber and capacity are the ruminants with about 155 species (Van Soest 1994). There is still discussion going on to what extent ruminants differ in physiological characteristics of their digestive system (Hofmann 1973, 1989; Gordon and Illius 1994; Robbins et al. 1995, Ditchkoff 2000).

The ratio of the mean retention time (MRT) of particles and of fluid in the forestomach, the selectivity factor ($MRT_{particle\ phase}/MRT_{fluid\ phase}$), has been used to classify ruminants (Lechner-Doll et al. 1990). Typically particles are retained longer than fluids in the forestomachs of all ruminants. Browsing ruminants feeding on a diet including high amounts of dicotyledonous plants like leaves of trees and shrubs or herbs are often reported to have a lower ability to retain particles in their forestomachs (Lechner-Doll et al. 1991; Clauss and Lechner-Doll 2001). There seems to be a less pronounced stratification in their rumen, their saliva production may be more pronounced and their rumen volumes tend to be smaller than those of grazing ruminants (Hofmann 1989). Higher concentrations of unsaturated fatty acids in the meat of browsers and relatively high amounts of glucose receptors in the small intestine of a browser (roe deer) have been interpreted as results of a faster rumen passage of ingesta (Rowell-Schäfer et al. 2001). For a further discussion of differences between browsers and grazers see Clauss et al. (this volume).

Despite still hypothetical differences of ruminant species/feeding types concerning particle retention ability, many other factors may influence ingesta retention and its measurement. Some of the most important should be mentioned here briefly.

### 1.2 Influence of food on passage rate

Particles are retained in the rumen due to their size and functional density in principle (Faichney 1986; Lechner-Doll et al. 1991; Kaske 1997). Factors like food intake or type of food obviously may have influence on retention time, too. Doubling of intake results in a decrease of 20–40 % in MRT; in part an enlargement of the rumen volume may compensate for the higher intake if given enough adaptation time (Kay 1987; Lechner-Doll et al. 1991). Offer and Dixon (2000) report mean retention times of ingesta to increase while the amount of concentrate is increased in a diet. Possible explanations may be the lower volume and higher digestibility of concentrates and a lower motility of the reticulorumen if high amounts of concentrate/unstructured food are fed.

### 1.3 Influence of methods

*Dosing/Sampling*: Passage rate can be quantified by dosing the animal once with a marker and by monitoring the concentration of marker in faeces over time. Especially the samples of the increase of the curve are important, since this rise may be rapid and since the highest changes in marker concentration between any samples occur during this period (see figure 1). Many researchers have used fistulated animals for measuring passage rate of marker from the rumen which gives the advantage of getting samples at defined intervals and independent of effects like daily defaecation rhythms of animals. The measurement of excretion of marker from the faeces is generally accepted as method and is obviously the only method which can be applied in a zoo environment.

*Marker*: The simplest method to measure passage rates may be to feed plastic particles or indigestible food particles to the animal and to retrieve and count them in the faeces. However, markers used for measuring passage rate are mostly analysed chemically. These markers typically consist of 2 components: While one component makes the marker behave like the chosen digesta fraction in the gastrointestinal tract (GIT), the other makes an easy analysation of the marker possible (typically metal ions or rare earth ions).

Markers for the fluid phase are well established and seem to behave in the same way as the part of digesta they should represent (Warner 1981). Often the strong ability of EDTA (Ethylenediamine tetraacetic acid) to build complexes with cations is used for that purpose (Cr-EDTA; Co-EDTA) (Udén et al. 1980). Another marker sometimes used for measuring fluid phase flow is polyethylene glycol.

Markers for the particle phase are more critical. They have to meet the following requirements: They should not be digestible (like any marker), the two components of the marker should be closely linked and they should behave as similarly as possible to the particle fraction they should represent. Concerning the latter respect, length and density of the marker are of special importance, since these features seem to be most important in determining passage from the rumen. Mordanted fibres (often chromium is used as mordant) are commonly used particle markers. While the two components show a strong linkage in this marker, density of the particles change if high amounts of chromium are bound in marker preparation (Ehle 1984). Van Soest et al. (1988) recommend chromium concentrations of < 2 % in the mordants, while only 8–10 % reduce digestibility to zero. Other frequently used markers are rare earth complexes, which have the disadvantage of a less strong linkage to the other component of the marker. Alkanes (Hatt et al. 1998) and $TiO_2$ (Rothfuss et al. 1997) have been used as passage rate marker, too. For a further discussion of markers see Hatt (this volume).

*Mathematical models*: Two important parameters of ingesta passage through the digestive tract are transit time (TT) and mean retention time (MRT). Transit time is the time of first occurance of marker in faeces; it is only of limited value, especially in animals with important fermenting chambers/ capacity. Measurement of MRT (the average time a marker stays in the digestive tract) is supposed to be the best way to characterize passage rate through the digestive tract (Hume 1995).

MRT can be calculated by cumulative integration of the marker excretion curve (Thielemanns et al. 1978) or by applying an equation of Grovum and Williams (1973). The latter is based on a two-compartment model, compartment 1 initially thought to be the reticulorumen and compartment 2 to be the caeco-colon. The application of this formula to the MRT of particles is sometimes critizised for mathematical insufficiencies (Lechner-Doll et al. 1991; Kaske 1997).

### 1.4 Passage rates of okapis

Like for most wild ruminants, not much is known about the digestive capacity of the okapi, a giraffe from the rainforests of the Kongo. Somehow unique in living in a rainforest as a large ruminant and depending completely on rainforest dicotyledonous foliage as forage (Hart and Hart 1989), the okapi may also be seen as a model for a browsing mid-sized ruminant (body weights of up to 300 kg for adult females). It is reported to be very selective, sometimes only taking leaf tips. Some efforts have already been made to evaluate existing diets and to design optimal diets for these animals in captivity, respectively (Crissey et al. 2000; Kanselaar et al. in prep.; Dierenfeld 1996); passage rates of fluids and particles in the gastrointestinal tract of this species have not been measured so far, although they may be interesting for a characterisation of the nutritional ecology of the okapi.

Data presented here can be viewed as a preliminary report of an ongoing PhD study, dealing with the foraging ecology and nutrition of the okapi.

## 2 Materials and methods

### 2.1 Animals and feeding

The study was done with two adult male okapis kept in a zoo (bodyweights app. 200 and 240 kg). The animals had access to an outdoor enclosure during the day. One of them was kept alone, the other shared its outdoor enclosure with a female. Over night (and during daily concentrate meals) all animals were separated. Lucerne hay of good quality (NDF: 380 g/kg; Crude protein 198 g/kg) was provided ad libitum during the whole day.

### 2.2 Marker preparation

Co-EDTA and Cr-mordanted fibres (< 2 mm) were used as markers, prepared according to Udén et al. (1980). Fibre length of the chromium mordanted lucerne fibre was determined by using fibres passing a sieve of 2 mm , but being retained by a sieve of 1 mm width. Concentration of chromium on the mordanted fibres was measured to be 4.5 %.

### 2.3 Marker dosing and sampling

The markers were fed to the animals as a pulse dose (mixed with squeezed banana) before they were provided with their usual food in the afternoon. Most of the marker was consumed in 15 minutes, leftovers were removed.

Faeces were sampled for 10 days after marker dosing. For the first 3 days samples were taken as often as possible, the next 4 days the sampling interval was every 4 hours, and for the last 3 days, faeces were collected every 8 hours. A time lapse video recorder was used to determine the exact time of faeces production during the night. To measure intake all offered food and all leftovers were weighed. Faecal output was measured by total collection.

Sampling of faeces was facilitated by the defaecation behaviour of okapis: Defaecation takes place while standing and is done in several single distinguishable small piles. Therefore, single defaecations could be separated easily from each other, and total collection was possible with an acceptable time effort.

### 2.4 Analysis

Dry matter content of samples was determined by oven-drying at 103 °C overnight. Samples were ashed at 560 °C for crude ash content or organic matter content, respectively (dry matter – crude ash = organic matter). NDF (neutral-detergent fibre), ADF (acid-detergent fibre) and ADL (acid detergent lignin) were analyzed according to Naumann and Bassler (1976). Hemicellulose and cellulose contents were calculated according to hemicellulose = NDF – ADF and cellulose = ADF – ADL.

Faeces sampled for passage rate determination were prepared according to Behrend (1999). Analysis for cobalt and chromium was done by atomic absorption spectroscopy.

### 2.5 Calculations

Digestibility of diet and nutrients was calculated with the formula

$$DI = \frac{(IN - FO)}{IN} \times 100$$

(*DI* = digestibility [%]; *IN* = daily intake [kg/d]; *FO* = faecal output [kg/d]).

Mean retention time calculation was done using 2 different approaches:

- according to Thielemanns et al. (1978) based on integration of the marker excretion curve using the equation

$$MRT = \frac{\sum c_i \times t_i \times dt}{\sum c_i \times dt}$$

($c_i$= marker concentration of sample i [mg/kg]; $t_i$= hours after marker dosing [h] and $dt$ = length of the interval represented by sample i [h])

- according to the two-compartment model of Grovum and Williams (1973) using the equation of the marker excretion curve

$$y = A \times e^{-k_1(t-TT)} - A \times e^{-k_2(t-TT)}$$

(A = constant; $k_1$ and $k_2$ = rate constants; t = hours after dosing [h]; TT = transit time or time between marker dosing and first appearance of marker in faeces [h]) to calculate constants A, $k_1$ and $k_2$ and transit time TT by nonlinear regression; MRT was calculated afterwards with the equation

$$MRT = \frac{1}{k_1} + \frac{1}{k_2} + TT$$

## 3 Results

During the trial, the animals consumed the diet summarized in table 1. Concentrate/roughage ratio differed considerably between the two individuals, as animal 1 selected a diet with a considerably lower concentrate/roughage ratio than animal 2.

**Table 1.** Intake of Okapis during the sampling period (feeds were weighed for 10 days).

| | Animal 1 (200 kg) | | Animal 2 (240 kg) | |
|---|---|---|---|---|
| **Intake [g DM/d]:** | | | | |
| Lucerne hay | 1615 | ± 340 | 1120 | ± 360 |
| Browse | 65 | ± 85 | 75 | ± 80 |
| Zoo concentrate | 895 | ± 245 | 1850 | ± 235 |
| Oats | 425 | ± 70 | 710 | ± 30 |
| Fruits/Vegetables/Bread | 130 | ± 45 | 130 | ± 45 |
| Total | 3130 | ± 400 | 3885 | ± 430 |
| Concentrate/Roughage Ratio (DM-basis) | 0.9 | | 2.3 | |

Apparent digestibility of organic matter and of different fibre fractions is given in table 2. It was on a comparable level for both animals, although digestibility of organic matter and of NDF was slightly higher in animal 2 (the animal with the higher concentrate intake), while digestibility of ADF was slightly higher in animal 1.

**Table 2.** Digestibility of the diet consumed by the animals; digestibilities of hemicellulose and cellulose result from calculating the respective concentrations in feeds and faeces by the equations hemicellulose = NDF - ADF and cellulose = ADF - ADL

| | Animal 1 | Animal 2 |
|---|---|---|
| Organic matter [%] | 71 | 74 |
| NDF [%] | 46 | 48 |
| Hemicellulose [%] | 56 | 60 |
| ADF [%] | 37 | 34 |
| Cellulose [%] | 51 | 47 |

Figure 1 shows the marker excretion curves of animal 1. Number of defaecations per day was 6.6 (±1.2) for animal 1 and 6.6 (± 0.7) for animal 2. The resulting MRT's are given in table 3. Animal 1 had higher retention times compared to animal 2 for both markers and for both methods. When applying the equation of Grovum and Willams (1973), the difference between the measured MRT's of the individuals was considerably smaller.

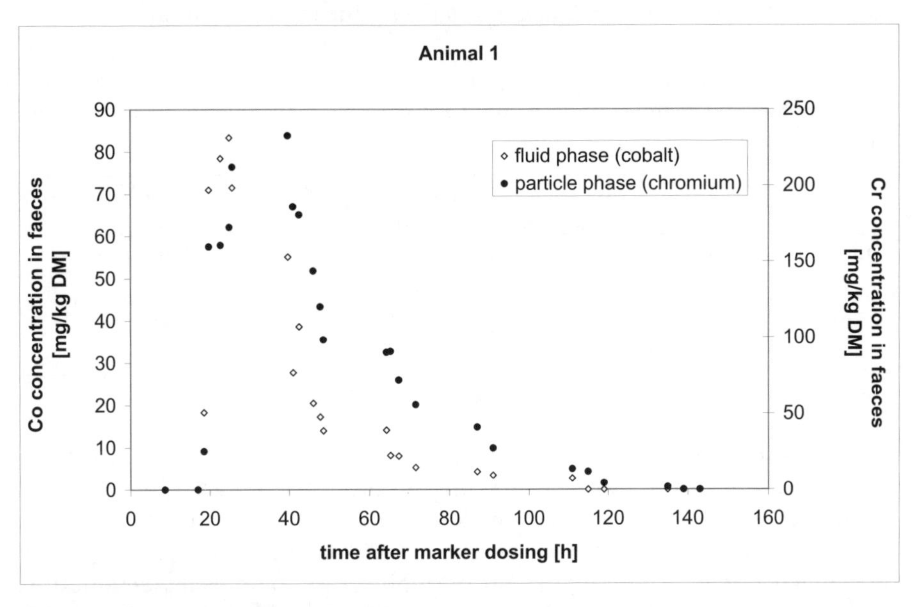


**Figure 1.** Marker excretion curves of animal 1.

## 4 Discussion

The resulting selectivity factors for particle retention in the GIT of the okapi of 1,26–1,43 seem to fit into the range of coefficients measured for browsing ruminants, possibly indicating a low ability to retain particles in the reticulorumen in this species. Clauss and Lechner-Doll (2001) give ranges of 1,14–1,80 for browsing and 1,56–3,80 for grazing ruminants (Data based on Co-EDTA and Cr-mordants with particle size < 2 mm as markers). Behrend (1999) found a $MRT_{particle\ phase}/MRT_{fluid\ phase}$ ratio of 1,30 for the roe deer (selecting for herbs and browse) and of 1,60 for the mouflon (foraging on grass) with the same markers. The values of the okapi would therefore be within the range of browsing ruminants concerning this physiological characteristic. Interestingly, the okapi had higher values than giraffes in another study using the same markers (Clauss 1998). Langer (1988) characterises the okapi as standing between the concentrate selecting and intermediate type in his classification.

Differences between ruminants of different feeding types have been found in data from studies working with fistulated animals measuring MRT of ingesta in the reticulorumen (Renecker and Hudson 1990; Lechner-Doll et al. 1990; Behrend 1999). This method produces higher differences between $MRT_{particle\ phase}$ and $MRT_{fluid\ phase}$ than the measurement from faeces. As the passage distal to the rumen is the same for particles and fluids (Faichney 1986), the additional time required for the passage of this part of the GIT reduces the quotient of the two MRT values (as $A/B$ will always be bigger than $(A+X)/(B+X)$ for any $A>B$ and $X>0$). Data based on marker excretion in faeces should therefore produce smaller, but still significant differences.

**Table 3.** Mean retention times of ingesta measured in the 2 animals; Method 1 is according to Thielemanns (1978), method 2 according to the model of Grovum and Williams (1973).

| | | $MRT_{fluid\ phase}$ [h] | $MRT_{particle\ phase}$ [h] | $MRT_{particle\ phase}/MRT_{fluid\ phase}$ |
|---|---|---|---|---|
| Animal 1 | Method 1 | 40,0 | 50,5 | 1,26 |
| | Method 2 | 34,9 | 48,6 | 1,39 |
| Animal 2 | Method 1 | 30,9 | 44,3 | 1,43 |
| | Method 2 | 33,0 | 46,6 | 1,41 |

From an evolutionary point of view, a strategy of faster passage of ingesta may be more useful for animals feeding on browse compared to ruminants feeding on grass: For any given phenological stage, browse contains higher levels of rather fast fermenting nutrients (cell solubles) and of completely unavailable nutrients (lignin) than grass, while grass contains higher amounts of slowly fermenting hemicelluloses and celluloses (Robbins 1993; Gordon and Illius 1994). A high selectivity of a species would be expected to have the same effect, independent of the botanical forage type.

Organic matter digestibility of the diet (71 and 74 %) was comparable to that measured in the wild if animals had access to many different food plant species (72 %) (Dierenfeld 1996). Digestibility of hemicellulose (58 %) and cellulose (49 %) was lower in this study compared to reports of other studies on okapis in captivity (digestibility coefficients of 69 % for hemicellulose and of 59 % for cellulose) and in the wild (digestibility coefficients of 77 % for hemicellulose and of 69 % for cellulose) (Crissey et al. 2000). NDF digestibility was not as low as the 23 % and 34 % reported in Prins et al. (1983) and Prins and Domhof (1984) for captive animals. The lower values of fibre digestibility found in captivity might be explained by a higher amount of easily available carbohydrates in the food of captive animals; a high amount of these carbohydrates is known to limit fibre digestibility (Kirchgessner 1997). The animal with the higher consumption of concentrate had a higher digestibility coefficient for hemicellulose, but not for cellulose in this study.

Comparison of data from different studies has to be done with caution as the influence of different variables may be considerable. For this reason, detailed information on body weights, food intake and type of diet are very important, although comparison of individual species on the basis of the ratio $MRT_{particle\ phase}/MRT_{fluid\ phase}$ is said to be rather robust concerning the latter influences (Lechner-Doll et al. 1991). Additionally, while drawing conclusions about feeding ecology from trials with captive animals, one has to keep in mind that zoo diets differ significantly from the natural forage of these animals. Detailed information on markers (particle size and density) are of importance, too. Although often impossible for practical reasons, inclusion of several species or variation of diets may help to achieve a higher comparability of results.

## 5 Conclusions

1. The presented data seem to support the hypothesis that ingesta flow of the okapi can be characterised by a rather low retention of particles in the reticulorumen or whole digestive system, respectively. The 2 animals in this study do not reach the extremely low selectivity factors measured for giraffe. The low sample size obviously does not allow a final evaluation.

2. Although measurement of retention time in zoo ruminants (or other animals) may have the shortcomings of measuring the retention of zoo diets and not of the natural forage, this kind of data may help in the understanding of different digestive strategies in ruminants.

3. Variables like food intake and concentrate/roughage ratio are of importance for resulting passage rates. To allow the highest possible comparability of studies, description of the used marker should be as detailed as possible (marker size and assumptions about density/amount of mordant). If possible, it is desirable to use different species and/or different diets in the same study.

## Acknowledgements

We would like to thank the zoos of Copenhagen, Rotterdam and Cologne for their cooperation in this ongoing project and the Institute of Animal Nutrition of the Agricultural Faculty, University of Bonn for constant support, advise and lab facilities.

The study is supported by a grant of the "Landesgraduiertenförderung Nordrhein-Westfalen".

## References

Behrend, A. (1999): *Kinetik des Ingestaflusses bei Rehen (Capreolus capreolus) und Mufflons (Ovis ammon musimon) im saisonalen Verlauf.* [Dissertation]. Berlin: Math.-Nat. Faculty Humboldt-University.

Clauss, M. (1998): *Feeding Giraffe (Giraffa camelopardalis).* [MSc Thesis]. London: Royal Veterinary College/Zoological Society of London.

Clauss, M.; Kienzle, E.; Hatt, J. M. (2003): Feeding practice in captive wild ruminants: peculiarities in the nutrition of browsers/concentrate selectors and intermediate feeders. A review. (this volume)

Clauss, M.; Lechner-Doll, M. (2001): Differences in selective reticulo-ruminal particle retention as a key factor in ruminant diversification. *Oecologia* 129: 321–327.

Crissey, S.; Dierenfeld, E. S.; Kanselaar, J.; Leus, K.; Nijboer, J. (2000): Feeding guidelines proposal for okapis – a joint European and North American project. In: *Zoo Animal Nutrition* (J. Nijboer, J.-M. Hatt, W. Kaumanns, A. Beijnen, U. Gansloßer, eds.). Fürth: Filander Verlag, pp. 257–270.

Dierenfeld, E. (1996): Nutrition session data and summary. In: *Proceedings of the Okapi Metapopulation Workshop*. White Oak Conservation Center Florida: White Oak Conservation Center. 13 p.

Ditchkoff, S. S. (2000): A decade since "diversification of ruminants": has our knowledge improved? *Oecologia* 125: 82–84.

Ehle, F. R. (1984): Influence of feed particle density on particulate passage from rumen of Holstein cows. *Journal of Dairy Science* 67: 693–697.

Faichney, G. J. (1986): The kinetics of particulate matter in the rumen. In: *Control of Digestion and Metabolism in Ruminants* (L. P. Milligan, W. L.Grovum, A. Dobson, eds.). Reston: Reston Publishing, pp. 173–195.

Gordon, I. J.; Illius, A. W. (1994): The functional significance of the browser-grazer dichotomy in African ruminants. *Oecologia* 98: 167–175.

Grovum, W. L.; Williams, V. J. (1973): Rate of passage of digesta in sheep: 4. Passage of marker through the alimentary tract and the biological relevance of rate-constants derived from the changes in concentration of marker in faeces. *British Journal of Nutrition* 30: 313–329.

Hart, J. A.; Hart, T. B. (1989): Ranging and feeding behaviour of okapi (*Okapia johnstoni*) in the Ituri Forest of Zaire: food limitation in a rain-forest herbivore? *Symposia of the Zoological Society London* 61: 31–50.

Hatt, J. M. (2003): Markers in zoo animal nutrition with special emphasis on n-alkanes. (this volume)

Hatt, J. M.; Lechner-Doll, M.; Mayes, B. (1998): The use of dosed and herbage *n*-alkanes as markers for the determination of digestive strategies of captive giraffe (*Giraffa camelopardalis*). *Zoo Biology* 17: 295–309.

Hofmann, R. R. (1973): *The ruminant stomach. Stomach structure and feeding habits of East African game ruminants*. East African Monographs in Biology. Nairobi: East African Literature Bureau.

Hofmann, R. R. (1989): Evolutionary steps of ecophysiological adaptation and diversification of ruminants: a comparative view of their digestive system. *Oecologia* 78: 443–457.

Hume, I. D. (1995): General concepts of nutrition and nutritional ecology. In: *Research and Captive Propagation* (U. Ganslosser, J. K. Hodges, W. Kaumanns, eds.). Fürth: Filander Verlag, pp. 90–98.

Kanselaar, J.; Nijboer, J.; Leus, K. (in prep.): Okapi (*Okapia johnstoni*) feeding in eight European zoos.

Kaske, M. (1997): Factors affecting digesta passage rate in cattle and sheep (in german). *Übersichten zur Tierernährung* 25: 1–40.

Kay, R. N. B. (1987): Comparative studies of food propulsion in ruminants. In: *Physiological and Pharmacological Aspects of the Reticulo-Rumen* (L. A. A. Ooms, A. D. Dgryse, A. S. J. P. A. M. van Miert, eds.). Dordrecht: Martin Nijhoff Publishers, pp. 155–170.

Kirchgessner, M. (1997): *Tierernährung*. 8th ed. Frankfurt (M): DLG Verlag.

Langer, P. (1988): *The mammalian herbivore stomach*. Stuttgart: Fischer Verlag.

Lechner-Doll, M.; Rutagwenda, T.; Schwartz, H. J.; Schultka, W.; v. Engelhardt, W. (1990): Seasonal changes of ingesta mean retention time and forestomach fluid volume in indigenous camels, cattle, sheep and goats grazing in a thornbush savannah pasture in Kenya. *Journal of Agricultural Science* 115: 409–420.

Lechner-Doll, M.; Kaske, M.; v. Engelhardt, W. (1991): Factors affecting the mean retention time of particles in the forestomach of ruminants and camelids. In: *Physiological Aspects of Digestion and Metabolism in Ruminants* (T. Tsuda, Y. Saaski, R. Kawashima, eds.). San Diego: Academic Press, pp. 455–482.

Naumann, C.; Bassler, R. (1976): *VDLUFA-Methodenbuch, Vol. III. Die chemische Untersuchung von Futtermitteln*. Darmstadt: VDLUFA-Verlag.

Offer, N. W.; Dixon, J. (2000): Factors affecting outflow rate from the reticulo-rumen. *Nutrition Abstracts and Reviews* Series B (Livestock Feeds and Feeding) 70: 833–844.

Prins, R. A.; Rooymanns, T. P.; Veldhuizen, M.; Domhof, M. A.; Cline-Theil, W. (1983): Extent of cell wall digestion in several species of wild ruminants kept in the zoo. *Der Zoologische Garten* 53: 393–403.

Prins, R. A.; Domhof, M. A. (1984): Feed intake and cell wall digestion by okapi (*Okapia johnstoni*) and giraffe (*Giraffa camelopardalis reticulata*) in the zoo. *Der Zoologische Garten* 54: 131–134.

Renecker, L. A.; Hudson, R. J. (1990): Digestive kinetics of moose (*Alces alces*), wapiti (*Cervus elaphus*) and cattle. *Animal Production* 50: 51–61.

Robbins, C. T. (1993): *Wildlife feeding and nutrition*. 2nd ed. New York: Academic Press.

Robbins, C. T.; Spalinger, D. E.; van Hoven, W. (1995): Adaptation of ruminants to browse and grass diets: are anatomical-based browser-grazer interpretations valid? *Oecologia* 103: 208–213.

Rothfuss, H.; Südekum, K. H.; Stangassinger, M. (1997): Ermittlung der Passage zweier Marker im Verdauungstrakt von Ochsen mit Hilfe unterschiedlicher Schätzverfahren: Einfluss des Ernährungsniveaus. *Archives of Animal Nutrition* 50: 283–300.

Rowell-Schäfer, A.; Lechner-Doll, M.; Hofmann, R. R.; Streich, W. J.; Güven, B.; Meyer, H. H. D. (2001): Metabolic evidence of a "rumen bypass" or a "ruminal escape" of nutrients in roe deer (*Capreolus capreolus*). *Comparative Biochemistry and Physiology* Part A 128: 289–298.

Thielemanns, M. F.; Francois, E.; Bodart, C.; Thewis, A. (1978): Mesure du transit gastrointestinal chez le porc à l'aide des radiolanthanides. Comparaison avec le mouton. *Ann. Biol. Anim. Bioch. Biophys.* 18: 237–247.

Udén, P.; Colucci, P. E.; van Soest, P. J. (1980): Investigation of chromium, cerium, and cobalt as markers in digesta. Rate of passage studies. *J. Sci. Food Agric.* 31: 625–632.

Van Soest, P. J. (1994): *Nutritional Ecology of the Ruminant.* 2nd ed. Ithaca: Cornell University Press.

Van Soest, P. J.; Sniffen, C. J.; Allen, M. S. (1988): Rumen dynamics. In: *Aspects of Digestive Physiology in Ruminants* (A. Dobson, M. A. Dobson, eds.). Ithaca: Cornell University Press, pp. 21–42.

Warner, A. C. I. (1981): Rate of passage of digesta through the gut of mammals and birds. *Nutrition Abstracts and Reviews* Series B (Livestock Feeds and Feeding) 51: 789–820.

G. P. J. Janssens[1], K. Vanhemelryck, M. Hesta, S. Millet, J. Debraekeleer, R. de Wilde

# Ration modelling for growing ostriches (*Struthio camelus*)

**Abstract**

*Due to the costly procedure of developing a de novo energy evaluation system, alternatives should be presented to estimate proper energy values in feedstuffs for certain animal species, like zoo animals or other species with low economic relevance. In the case of the ostrich, seven existing energy evaluation systems were tested for their feasibility for extrapolation to true metabolisable energy values (TMEo) for ostriches. The Dutch VEP net energy system for horses gave the best fit. In a pilot trial, two groups of 50 growing ostriches received rations differing in roughage/concentrates ratio. The ostriches' ad libitum intake of estimated TMEo was not influenced by the roughage/concentrates ratio and no differences in performance could be noted, giving preliminary evidence for the suitability of the extrapolation method to develop a reliable energy evaluation system.*

**Keywords**

*Ostriches, energy, modelling, growth, roughage, concentrates*

## 1 Introduction

In comparison to typical husbandry animals like pigs, cattle and poultry, nutritional requirements of the ostrich *Struthio camelus* have been scarcely investigated. Because of the time and finance-consuming character of metabolism trials, alternative methods are required to calculate a ration for growing ostriches.

Studies by Swart et al. (1993a, b, d) have shown the ability of growing ostriches for considerable fibre digestion. The use of roughages for ostriches is widespread but few data are known on the equilibrium between healthy growth and feed cost. It is hypothesised that the use of highly concentrated rations will lead to high growth rates and high feed utilisation efficiencies, but it also implies an elevated cost per unit of feed and is a predisposing factor in leg disorders. In zoos, lack of roughage can lead to behavioural anomalities like pica and cannibalism. The preferred nutrient and energy density of an ostrich

[1] Laboratory of Animal Nutrition, Ghent University, Heidestraat 19, B-9820 Merelbeke, Belgium; Tel.: +32 9 2647820, Fax: +32 9 2647848, E-Mail: geert.janssens@rug.ac.be.

ration will depend on the price ration of roughage, concentrates and the incidence of the problems mentioned above.

The present study was intended to demonstrate a model for ostrich ration calculation and to investigate the response of growing ostriches to two dietary roughage/concentrates ratios.

## 2 Methods

To develop a ration model, energy is the main factor of importance. Seven feedstuff matrices, developed at the Centraal Veevoederbureau (CVB 1999) in the Netherlands, were considered for testing their feasibility to derive true metabolisable energy values for ostriches (TMEo):

1. the net energy system for pigs : both the unit MJ $NE_{pigs}$/kg and the derived EW-unit were considered,
2. the metabolisable energy system for rabbits (MJ $ME_{rabbit}$/kg),
3. the metabolisable energy system for laying hens (MJ $ME_{hen}$ /kg),
4. the metabolisable energy system for poults (MJ $ME_{poult}$ /kg),
5. the metabolisable energy system for broiler chickens (MJ $ME_{broiler}$ /kg),
6. the net energy system for beef cattle (VEVI) and
7. the net energy system for horses (VEP).

The energy values presented in these matrices were obtained from metabolism trials in the respective species for a wide range of commonly used feedstuffs in husbandry animals. The EW values are easily obtained by dividing the respective $NE_{pigs}$ value by the $NE_{pigs}$ value of 1 kg barley and important for the curve fitting equation is that it is given as a figure with only two decimals. The VEVI and VEP value is the NE value for growth of 1 gram of barley in beef cattle and horses respectively.

These data were plotted against the limited number of experimentally obtained values of TMEo available in literature (Cilliers 1998; Cilliers et al. 1994 and 1999; Brand et al. 2000). The energy system with the best fit was chosen to estimate TMEo values in feedstuffs other than those in the regression analysis.

All statistics were performed with SPSS 10.0 (SPSS Inc., Chicago, Illinois).

The energy requirement, protein requirement and dry matter intake were estimated through body weight and growth rate, based on the formulae from several studies (Cilliers 1994; Degen et al. 1991; du Preez 1991; du Preez et al. 1990; Swart et al. 1993c) respectively. The model was constructed in Microsoft Excel. The model was tested by giving two rations, differing in their roughage/concentrate ratio to two groups of ostriches.

A group of ostriches, ranging from 19 to 73 kg of body weight and ranging from 162 to 232 days of age, were randomly divided into two groups of 50 birds, while maintaining a similar range in body weights in each group. They were housed in open air translucent plastic tunnels on straw bedding.

One group received a high roughage (HR) ration, whereas the other group received a low roughage ration (LR). During the first month, the HR ration consisted of grass silage, corn cob mix and concentrates in an as fed weight ration of 27:13:60, whereas the LR ration comprised grass silage, corn cob mix and concentrates in an as fed weight ratio of 35:18:47. During the second month of trial, grass silage and concentrates were given in a 36:64 ratio and a 61:39 ratio for the HR and the LR ration respectively. Due to the group housing, individual feed intakes could not be measured, but the total group feed intake was registered. Twenty birds out of each group were randomly taken and weighed at the start of the trial, two months later and at slaughter (four months later).

All feeds and feedstuffs were subjected to proximate analysis. These values were used to calculate the estimated true metabolisable energy ($TME_{ostrich}$) content, based on the formula for calculating the energy evaluation unit that was best fit for the TMEo extrapolation method.

# 3 Results

## *3.1 Modelling*

The fitted equations are shown in table 1. Linear regression analysis revealed that the VEP energy system for horses represented the best fit with the experimental TMEo values. The VEVI energy system for beef cattle is almost as good. The poultry energy evaluation systems were least suitable for estimating energy values for ostriches.

**Table 1.** Fitted equations for estimating TMEo from existing matrices.

| Energy unit | $R^2$ | equation | P-value |
|---|---|---|---|
| EW ($NE_{pig}$) | 0.911 | TMEo = 1.980+12.117x | < 0.001 |
| MJ $NE_{pig}$ /kg | 0.951 | TMEo = 4.443+1.092x | < 0.001 |
| MJ $ME_{rabbit}$ /kg | 0.932 | TMEo = 3.254+0.868x | < 0.001 |
| MJ $ME_{hen}$ /kg | 0.802 | TMEo = 5.738+0.786x | 0.003 |
| MJ $ME_{poult}$ /kg | 0.736 | TMEo = 5.864+0.797x | 0.010 |
| MJ $ME_{broiler}$ /kg | 0.684 | TMEo = 7.050+0.788x | 0.042 |
| VEVI ($NE_{beef}$) | 0.985 | TMEo = 4.418+0.008329x | < 0.001 |
| VEP ($NE_{horse}$) | 0.986 | TMEo = 6.076+0.008078x | < 0.001 |

## *3.2 Growth*

The roughage/concentrate ratio did not affect growth rate: 301±103 g in high roughage diet versus 301±115 g in the low roughage diet. Hence, to describe the growth characteristics of the ostriches in the trial, data were pooled over the treatment groups.

Regression analysis of the initial weight (at start of the trial) against age resulted in the formula:

$$W_1 = -18 \pm 15 + 0.318 \pm 0.074 \text{ A} \quad (R^2 = 0.397 \text{ and } p < 0.001)$$

where $W_1$ = initial weight (kg) and A = age at the start of the trial (days)

The estimated linear relationship between body weight at the end of the trial and age is :

$$W_2 = 23 \pm 17 + 0.202 \pm 0.086 \text{ A} \quad (R^2 = 0.164 \text{ and } p = 0.027)$$

where $W_2$ = body weight at the end of the trial (kg) and A = age at the start of the trial (days).

The linear regression of growth in function of age gave the following equation:

$$\text{Growth } (g/d) = 678 \pm 156 - 1.9 \pm 0.8 \text{ A} \quad (R^2 = 0.171 \text{ and } p = 0.023)$$

with A = age at the start of the trial (days).

The estimated linear relationship between initial body weight and body weight at the end of the trial is :

$$W_2 = 24 \pm 4 + 0.87 \pm 0.10 \, W_1 \quad (R^2 = 0.735 \text{ and } p < 0.001)$$

where $W_1$ = initial weight (kg) and $W_2$ = body weight at the end of the trial (kg).

### 3.3 Feed and energy intake

The animals in the LR group ingested 180 kg per animal in the first month and 331 kg per animal in the second month, whereas for the HR group this was 204 and 406 kg respectively. In the first month rations, the estimated TMEo levels were 13.92 and 12.59 MJ/kg for LR and HR respectively. In the second month, the LR feed contained 14.02 MJ/kg and the HR feed contained 11.20 MJ/kg.

When looking at the average daily TMEo intake per animal, this was fairly similar between the groups: 34.2 and 35.1 MJ for LR and HR respectively during the first month and 34.5 and 33.9 MJ for LR and HR during the second month. Over the total trial period, energy intakes were 34.7 and 34.3 MJ TMEo per animal per day.

Feeding the low concentrate ration saved about 818 € over the total trial, or 0.04 € per animal per day, for the same growth performance when compared to the high concentrate ration.

## 4 Discussion

The considerable fermentative digestion in the ostrich hindgut and caeca differentiates the ostrich from commercial poultry species as chicken or turkey and has greater similarities with the digestive system of the horse. This is reflected in the linear regression models presented above. Poultry energy systems – although based on metabolisable energy – are not feasible for estimating metabolisable energy values for ostriches, most likely because of the considerable fermentative capacity of the ostrich and the scarceness of poultry metabolisable energy values in fibrous feedstuffs. In contrast, net energy systems for herbivorous mammal species seem to be far more appropriate to derive a fairly accurate energy evaluation system for ostriches from. In the present study, the Dutch VEP horse energy system came out as the best fitting database, followed by the VEVI net energy system for beef cattle.

The animal trial demonstrated that the ostriches adjusted their intake level to the energy density in the diet to maintain a constant level of metabolisable energy intake. This resulted in similar growth rates in animals on diets with a differing roughage/concentrate ratio. Evidently, further research is necessary to validate the extrapolated energy evaluation system for ostrich feedstuffs and to gather data to calculate energy demands, but the present data indicate that the system can be used successfully to optimise feeding costs and to make energy supply more accurate.

## 5 Conclusions

Net energy evaluation systems for herbivorous species – like the Dutch VEP system for horses – are suitable for estimating true metabolisable energy levels in feedstuffs for ostriches. The technique of extrapolating existing energy evaluation systems for agricultural animal species to other species is of practical importance because it makes a cheap and fast method to obtain a fairly accurate energy evaluation system for animal species that are of less economical importance.

## Acknowledgements

We would like to thank Peter Vermeir and Biostruis Ltd. for the use of their facilities and birds and Herman De Rycke for the analytical work.

## References

Brand, T. S.; De Brabander, L.; Van Schalkwyk, S. J.; Pfister, B.; Hayes, J. P. (2000): The true metabolisable energy content of canola oilcake meal and full-fat canola seed for ostriches (*Struthio camelus*). *Br. Poult. Sci.* 41: 201–203.

Cilliers, S. C. (1994): Evaluation of feedstuffs and the metabolisable energy and amino acid requirements for maintenance and growth in ostriches (*Struthio camelus*). [Diss.] Stellenbosch: University of Stellenbosch.

Cilliers, S. C.; Hayes, J. P.; Maritz, J. S.; Chwalibog, A.; du Preez, J. J. (1994): True and apparent metabolizable energy values of lucerne and yellow maize in adult roosters and mature ostriches (*Struthio camelus*). *Anim. Prod.* 59: 309–313.

Cilliers, S. C.; Hayes, J. P.; Sales, J.; Chwalibog, A.; du Preez, J. J. (1998): The additivity of TMEn values of various ingredients in a complete diet for ostriches and adult roosters. *Anim. Feed Sci. Tech.* 71: 369–373.

[CVB] Centraal Veevoederbureau (1999): Verkorte Tabel Voedernormen Landbouwhuisdieren en Voederwaarde Veevoeders, CVB-reeks nr. 26. Lelystad: CVB.

Degen, A. A.; Kam, M.; Rosenstrauch, A.; Plavnik, I. (1991): Growth rate, total body water volume, dry-matter intake and water consumption of domesticated ostriches (*Struthio camelus*). *Anim. Prod.* 52: 225–232.

Du Preez, J. J.; Jarvis, M. J. F.; Capatos, D.; de Kock, J. (1990): Amino acid and energy requirements of ostriches predicted from recently obtained growth curves and carcass analyses. *Proc. 29th Ann. Congress S. Afr. Soc. Anim. Prod.*, p. L 3.5.

Du Preez, J. J. (1991): Ostrich nutrition and management. In: *Recent advances in animal nutrition in Australia* (D. J. Farell, ed.). Armidale: Dep. Biochemistry, Microbiology and Nutrition, University of New England.

Swart, D.; Mackie, R. I.; Hayes, J. P. (1993a): Fermentative digestion in the ostrich (*Struthio camelus var. domesticus*), a large avian species that utilizes cellulose. *S. Afr. J. Anim. Sci.* 23: 127–135.

Swart, D.; Mackie, R. I.; Hayes, J. P. (1993b): Influence of live mass, rate of digestion on energy metabolism and fibre digestion in the ostrich (*Struthio camelus var. domesticus*). *S. Afr. J. Anim. Sci.* 23: 119–126.

Swart, D.; Siebrits, F. K.; Hayes, J. P. (1993c): Growth, feed intake and body composition of ostriches (*Struthio camelus*) between 10 and 30 kg live mass. *S. Afr. J. Anim. Sci.* 23: 142–150.

Swart, D.; Siebrits, F. K.; Hayes, J. P. (1993d): Utilization of metabolizable energy by ostrich (*Struthio camelus*) chicks at two different concentrations of dietary energy and crude fibre originating from Lucerne. *S. Afr. J. Anim. Sci.* 23: 136–141.

*B. Kiefer[1], U. Ganslosser[2], P. Kretzschmar[2], E. Kienzle[1]*

# Food selection and food quality in territorial males of a free-ranging population of white rhinoceros (*Ceratotherium simum simum*) in South Africa

***Abstract***

*As part of a larger, multi-disciplinary approach to white rhino (Ceratotherum simum simum) behaviour, ecology and nutrition, a study was conducted on the foraging and ranging behaviour of three territorial males on a game ranch in Northern Transvaal, South Africa. Animal tracks representing the distance covered between midnight and early morning were followed, feeding sites identified, ingested grass species determined, and quantitative samples of ingested grass taken. Grass samples and additional grass and hay samples fed to white rhino at a German zoo were analysed for nutrient content. Food selection of free-ranging rhinos did not correspond to the frequency of occurrence of the individual grass species in their territory as determined by transect plots. The nutrient content of the diets selected by the three animals were very similar. There was no evident correlation between the distance travelled between feeding sites and the nutrient composition of selected diets. The mineral contents of the natural forages were noticeably lower than those of the zoo forages. This is in accord with similar reports from the literature on mineral contents of African and European forages. The relevance of this finding for captive mineral supplementation regimes should be further investigated.*

***Keywords***

*megaherbivore, grass analyses, minerals, protein*

## 1 Introduction

Food selection in free-ranging animals poses some serious difficulties for adaptive behaviour: Balancing multiple nutrients and minerals, according to the organism's current physiological needs, and avoiding toxic and anti-nutrient contents. This led to the concept of the nutritional niche, a multi-facetted set of environmental adaptations as dynamic as the ecological niche itself (Hume 1995). Optimal foraging theory as outlined e. g. by Stephens and

[1] Institute of Animal Physiology, Physiological Chemistry and Animal Nutrition, Faculty of Veterinary Science, Ludwig-Maximilians-Universität, Veterinär Str. 13, 80539 München, Germany, (breitmaulnashorn@gmx.de); FAX: ++49/89/21803208 (corresponding author).

[2] Zoological Institute I, Friedrich-Alexander University of Erlangen-Nürnberg, Staudtstr. 5, 91058 Erlangen, Germany.

Krebs (1986) allows predictions about the way an animal copes with this task. Profound knowledge of these decisions and adaptations in free-ranging animals is an important precondition for a better nutrition of zoo-animals. As part of a larger, multi-disciplinary approach to white rhino (*Ceratotherium simum simum*) behaviour, ecology and nutrition, a study was conducted on the foraging and ranging behaviour of territorial males. The present publication aims to outline the foraging behaviour, and analyse nutrient, energy and mineral content of the selected diet.

## 2 Methods

This project consisted of two parts, a field study on free-ranging animals and a feeding trail with captive white rhinos.

### *2.1 Field study*

The field study was conducted during February and March 1999 on a private game farm in South Africa (Northwest Transvaal). The vegetation of two territories of male white rhinos (animals A and G) was analysed by transect measurements. A total of 143 transect plots were placed in a distance of 0.8 minutes longitude and 0.8 minutes latitude to each other over the study area. At each plot all grass species were recorded, which allowed an analysis of the frequency of their occurrence. The frequency of occurrence of grass species within a territory was calculated from the number of transect plots it was present in relation to the total number of plots To characterise the habitat of a male territory, measurements on transect plots located within the territory established by Kretzschmar (2003) were used.

The tracks of three territorial males (A, B, G) were followed with the aid of an experienced tracker and the distance the animal walked was measured using a GPS. It usually represents the time from midnight until the late morning.

At each feeding site along the track, all plant species were identified and recorded. Afterwards they were classified into six classes of grazing value (depending on production of grazeable plant material) and into three classes of palatability (depending on nutritive value, fibre content, unpalatable chemical substances and moisture content) according to Van Oudtshoorn (1992). Grass next to the feeding site was collected in the same quantity and the same height as grass had been removed at the feeding site by the animal. Because different parts of grass have different chemical compositions (Field 1976), this technique was necessary to conduct an accurate investigation of the nutritive value of the rhino's food in their natural habitat. The grass samples from one track were pooled for nutritional analyses. Each rhino was tracked twice (A1, A2, B1, B2, G1 ,G2).

### *2.2 Captive study*

The second part of the project involved feeding trials with five white rhinos at the zoo of Erfurt, Germany. The rhinos were fed grass and hay. Each diet was given for a period of 15 days and food samples were collected daily. All samples were pooled for each diet.

### 2.3 Analyses

All food samples were subjected to nutritional analyses of the crude nutrients by Weender Analysis (Naumann and Bassler 1988), and of the cell wall constituents (Van Soest 1967) and the gross energy (bomb calorimetry). In all forage samples the macroelements and in the grass samples from Africa also the trace elements were analysed. Phosphorus levels were determined by a colorimetric method, potassium, calcium and sodium by flame photometry, chlorine by using an electronic Eppendorf Chloridmeter and magnesium, copper, zinc and iron by atomic absorption spectrophotometry.

## 3 Results

The rhinos were followed over a distance of 890–5180 m. Between 6–26 feeding sites were found per track and on average there was a distance of 148–518 m between the feeding sites. An average between 74 g and 483 g grass (fresh weight) was eaten per feeding site (table 1).

**Table 1.** Tracking data: length of the tracking distance in meter (m), number of feeding sites and amounts of the ingested grass (g) of fresh weight.

| animal | track | tracking distance (m) | feeding sites per track (n) | average tracking dist. per feeding site (m) | grass samples fresh weight (g) | average grass amount (g) per feeding site |
|---|---|---|---|---|---|---|
| A | A 1 | 4230 | 26 | 163 | 1930 | 74 |
| | A 2 | 890 | 6 | 148 | 2900 | 483 |
| B | B 1 | 2230 | 14 | 159 | 4250 | 304 |
| | B 2 | 1700 | 9 | 189 | 2870 | 319 |
| G | G 1 | 3010 | 8 | 376 | 1940 | 243 |
| | G 2 | 5180 | 10 | 518 | 2120 | 212 |

It is noticeable that track A1 with the lowest grass intake per feeding site (Table 1) contains the highest concentration of crude protein (table 3).

A total of 13 grass species were recognised as rhino food on all six tracks. At the feeding sites ($n = 73$), mostly only one grass species was eaten ($n = 45$), often two ($n = 21$) and rarely three ($n = 3$) or four ($n = 4$).

The frequencies with which the different grass species were eaten were not equal between the males. The food selection of the rhinos did not correspond to the frequency of occurrence of the individual plant species in their territory (table 2).

**Table 2.** Frequency of feeding (total number) and frequency of occurrence (in percent) of the grass species and their classification by Van Oudthoorn (1992) in the territories of animal A and G.

| | | | ANIMAL A | | ANIMAL G | |
|---|---|---|---|---|---|---|
| Grass species | graz. value | palatability | frequency of feeding | frequency of occurence | frequency of feeding | frequency of occurence |
| *Aristida spp.* | very low | unpalatable | 5 | 79 | 1 | 74 |
| *Brachiaria nigropedata* | very high | very palatable | 7 | 9 | – | 15 |
| *Digitaria eriantha* | high | palatable | 2 | 12 | 4 | 63 |
| *Enneapogon cenchroides* | medium | palatable | 3 | 3 | 5 | 15 |
| *Enneapogon scoparius* | very low | palatable | 2 | 39 | – | 41 |
| *Eragrostis rigidor* | low | unpalatable | – | 93 | 6 | 89 |
| *Heteropogon contortus* | medium | palatable | 4 | 15 | 1 | 19 |
| *Melinis repens* | low | palatable | 8 | 57 | – | 63 |
| *Panicum coloratum* | very high | palatable | 2 | 21 | 2 | 22 |
| *Panicum maximum* | very high | very palatable | – | 39 | 2 | 56 |
| *Schmidtia pappophoroides* | high | palatable | 2 | 94 | – | 67 |
| *Tragus berteronianus* | low | palatable | 5 | 79 | – | 44 |
| *Urochloa mosambicensis* | high | palatable | 4 | 61 | 1 | 48 |

The contents of the organic matter (OM), crude fat (CFat), crude fibre (CF), nitrogen free extracts (NfE), gross energy (GE), neutral detergent fibre (NDF), lignin (ADL) and most of the minerals of the samples from the tracks are very similar (table 3 and 4), although they consisted of three to ten different grass

**Table 3.** Composition of dry matter (DM as percent of fresh weight) and organic matter (OM), crude fat (CFat), crude fibre (CF), crude protein (CP), nitrogen free extracts (NfE), acid detergent lignin (ADL) and neutral detergent fibre (NDF) in percent of DM and the gross energy (GE) in MJ per kg DM of the grass samples from the feeding tracks.

| Track | DM (% FW) | OM (% DM) | CFat (% DM) | CF (% DM) | CP (% DM) | NfE (% DM) | GE (MJ/kg DM) | ADL (% DM) | NDF (% DM) |
|---|---|---|---|---|---|---|---|---|---|
| A 1 | 48.1 | 91.8 | 1.1 | 35.8 | 6.5 | 48.4 | 18.3 | 6.3 | 74.7 |
| A 2 | 65.4 | 92.2 | 1.1 | 37.1 | 4.1 | 49.9 | 18.4 | 6.6 | 75.4 |
| B 1 | 49.4 | 90.9 | 0.9 | 34.9 | 5.6 | 49.4 | 18.1 | 6.2 | 73.5 |
| B 2 | 64.9 | 92.0 | 1.0 | 34.9 | 4.2 | 51.9 | 18.3 | 7.5 | 75.1 |
| G 1 | 55.3 | 90.9 | 1.4 | 35.2 | 3.5 | 50.8 | 18.2 | 6.7 | 73.3 |
| G 2 | 68.0 | 92.6 | 1.1 | 35.4 | 4.1 | 52.0 | 18.6 | 7.5 | 75.7 |
| mean | 58.5 | 91.7 | 1.1 | 35.6 | 4.7 | 50.4 | 18.3 | 6.8 | 74.6 |
| SD | 8.7 | 0.7 | 0.2 | 0.8 | 1.1 | 1.4 | 0.2 | 0.6 | 1.0 |

species. Only the crude protein (CP) and dry matter (DM) content showed differences (table 3).

**Table 4.** Mineral content of the grass samples from the feeding tracks in dry matter.

| Track | Ca (g/kg) | P (g/kg) | Ca : P | Na (g/kg) | Cl (g/kg) | K (g/kg) | Mg (mg/kg) | Cu (mg/kg) | Fe (mg/kg) | Zn (mg/kg) |
|---|---|---|---|---|---|---|---|---|---|---|
| A 1 | 2.3 | 1.1 | 2.2 | 0.3 | 3.9 | 10.8 | 1086 | 6 | 156 | 25 |
| A 2 | 2.7 | 1.0 | 2.8 | 0.3 | 1.5 | 7.0 | 542 | 4 | 213 | 18 |
| B 1 | 2.2 | 1.2 | 1.9 | 0.2 | 3.0 | 9.9 | 1071 | 4 | 209 | 35 |
| B 2 | 1.9 | 1.0 | 2.0 | 0.3 | 4.3 | 7.1 | 566 | 4 | 220 | 27 |
| G 1 | 3.7 | 1.0 | 3.6 | 0.2 | 3.4 | 8.8 | 748 | 4 | 172 | 16 |
| G 2 | 1.8 | 1.0 | 1.8 | 0.4 | 4.9 | 7.4 | 947 | 4 | 91 | 16 |
| mean | 2.4 | 1.0 | 2.4 | 0.3 | 3.5 | 8.5 | 827 | 4 | 177 | 23 |
| SD | 0.7 | 0.1 | - | 0.1 | 1.2 | 1.6 | 243. 7 | 1 | 49 | 8 |

The mineral contents of the natural forage from the field study were noticeably lower than those of the forages of the zoo study (table 5). Other results of nutrient analyses of the zoo diets are published elsewhere (Kiefer et al. 2002).

**Table 5.** Average mineral contents of the grass samples from the field study and of the two forages from the zoo study.

| Forage composition | Ca (g/kg DM) | P (g/kg DM) | Ca : P | Na (g/kg DM) | Cl (g/kg DM) | K (g/kg DM) | Mg (g/kg DM) |
|---|---|---|---|---|---|---|---|
| Grass field | 2.44 | 1.03 | 2.36 | 0.27 | 3.5 | 8.5 | 0.83 |
| Grass zoo | 5.97 | 2.33 | 2.56 | 3.81 | 4.66 | 12.17 | 2.08 |
| Hay zoo | 5.87 | 1.93 | 3.04 | 2.49 | 11.42 | 22.62 | 1.36 |

## 4 Discussion

To investigate diet selection behaviour of animals, it is necessary to know what components are available to the animal (Stephens and Krebs 1986, Manly and McDonald 1993). Adult male white rhinos are strictly territorial (Owen-Smith 1973). The grass species composition of the diet selected by a territorial animal must be compared to the grass species composition of the home range of this animal for a usage-availability study (Johnson 1980). The results from of the investigated males show that the frequency of ingesting a plant species does not correspond to its frequency of occurrence (table 2). For instance, *Brachiaria nigropedata* (Black-footed signal grass) was chosen seven times for foraging at track A1 (the second most common food resource for animal A) even though it is not common in its territory (occurring only at 9 % of all transect points). Noticeably, this grass has a very high grazing value and a very high palatability value according to Van Oudthoorn (1992). The high proportion of this grass species in the sample A1 may be responsible for the high protein content of this sample (Table 3). It is possible that this animal was selecting his food plants for high protein content on this track (CP 6.5 % DM). The sample A1 also contained a high level of moisture (48 % DM) and a low level of lignin (ADL 6.3 % DM). All three features indicate a relatively young vegetation stage and high nutritive value of this grass sample.

The low amount of grass taken per feeding site and the high overall protein content of the ingested forage at track A1 could indicate that the animal ate less at the feeding sites but more selective for protein. Regarding all six feeding tracks, however, the relationship between the amount of grass taken per feeding site and protein content is not evident. For more detailed conclusions, a broader sample size is necessary. One could assume an overall compromise in selectivity: in a short-term perspective, an animal might select for high protein content. In a more long-term perspective, a balance between all nutritive demands (energy, nutrients, minerals, avoidance of anti-nutrients) might result in sufficient levels of all nutrients.

Malcolm (1981) noted that in addition to selection of protein and energy, large ungulates also appear to be able to select for minerals such as sodium and calcium. Comparing the concentrations of the nutritional components of the grass samples between the tracks, most of them show similar values (table 3 and 4). Ben-Sahar (1993) and Ben-Sahar and Malcolm (1992), determined the chemical composition (N, P, K, Ca, Mg, Fe, Zn, Cu, moisture, fibre) of ten different grass species in an area of South Africa near to our study site. Ben-Sahar (1993) supported the statement of Georgiadis and McNaughton (1990) that some grass species were characterised by high levels of a particular element and no single species accumulated high levels of all nutrients. The ranges of nutritive values between the tracks of this study are smaller than the ranges of nutritive values between the ten different grass species (Ben-Sahar 1993), because our track samples always consisted of several grass species.

The amounts of the macroelements in the South African grass are notably lower than in the forage of the zoo study (table 5). This situation persists if the concentrations of all measured elements (marco and trace elements) from South African grass are compared to the conventional amounts for German forage published by the German Agriculture Society (DLG 1973, 1995). Tropical forages are of lower quality than temperate ones and often chronically deficient in mineral elements (McDowell 1985). The mean amounts of the minerals calcium (2.4 g/kg DM) and phosphorus (1 g/kg DM) in the South African grass are half of the amounts of these minerals in the forage from the zoo study (Table 5). Dietary calcium to phosphorus ratios ranging from 1 : 1 and 2 : 1 are best for proper absorption and metabolism, even though higher ratios can be handled (Robbins 1993). In the field study the ratios range between 1.9 and 3.6 and in the zoo study between 2.6 and 3, so no health problems due to the dietary calcium to phosphorus ratios should be expected. Ben-Sahar (1993) found similarly low values of Ca (1.7–4.0 g/kg DM) and P (4.0–0.9 g/kg DM) in the ten South African grass species. Grass from the Serengeti National Park in Tanzania, also showed low amounts of Ca (3.4–4.1 g/kg DM) and P (2.8–4.2 g/kg DM) (McNaughton 1988). The concentration of sodium in African grass with an average of 0.3 g/kg DM was ten times lower than the German forages (table 5). The chlorine level was also lower in South African grass. Musalia et al. (1989) also found low sodium levels (0.2 g/kg DM) in grass commonly consumed by goats in western Kenya; the authors expect this to be a limiting factor of animal production in this area. The low sodium content of many plants could be an important defence that could reduce animal populations (Robbins 1993). Ungulates in Africa tend to meet their sodium requirements by geophagia at salt licks, at eroded termite mounts, or by consuming brackish water (Jarman 1972, McNaughton 1988), and white rhinos are no exception (Owen-Smith 1973 and 1988). At the game farm from this investigation salt licks were offered to all animal but no consumption by rhinos was directly observed. Potassium content also was considerably lower in the samples from South Africa compared to those from German (8.5 g/kg DM). Ben-Sahar (1993) reports potassium values of 4.8 to 14.9 g/kg DM in grass from South Africa. McNaughton (1988) presents, in grass from Kenya, values around 20 g/kg DM and Field (1976), for Uganda, values of eight different grass species between 2.7 and 28.4 g/kg DM. Magnesium content in South African grass samples, with a mean of 0.8 g/kg DM, is only about half the value common in grass in Germany (DLG 1995, Table 5). Musalia et al. (1989) and McNaughton (1988) found, for grasses from Kenya, about twice the amount of Mg than we did at our study site.

The results of our study demonstrate that white rhinos are capable of selecting not only at the level of feeding habitat (Owen-Smith 1973) but also at the level of particular of grass species. The difference in mineral content of the native forages and those used in a German captive feeding regime could suggest that a particular supplementation with marcominerals, e. g. calcium and phosphorus, is not as warranted as is commonly perceived within the zoo community.

## 5 Conclusions

1. Feeding tracks of male, territorial white rhino bulls on a game farm in South Africa varied considerably in length, amount of food taken, selectivity on the level of plant species.

2. Whereas one particularly long trail showed the animal to crop mostly small amounts of high-protein-content plants, all feeding trails taken together demonstrate an even distribution of nutrients, energy and minerals.

3. Mineral content of the plants consumed was considerably lower than that of plants fed to white rhino in a German zoo. This is in accord with similar reports from the literature on mineral contents of African and European forages. The relevance of this finding for captive mineral supplementation regimes should be further investigated.

## Acknowledgements

We want to thank DAAD and Zebra Foundation for their financial support.

## References


Ben-Sahar, R. (1993): Patterns of nutrient contents in grasses of a semi-arid savanna. *Afr. J. Ecol.* 31: 343–347.

Ben-Sahar, R.; Malcolm, J. C. (1992): The relationships between soil factors, grass nutrients and the foraging behaviour of wildebeest and zebra. *Oecologia* 90: 422–428.

DLG (1973): *Futterwerttabellen-Mineralstoffgehalte in Futtermitteln*. Arbeiten der DLG Bd. 62, Dokumentationsstelle der Universität Hohenheim, 2. Aufl. Frankfurt/Main, Germany: DLG-Verlag.

DLG (1995): *Futterwerttabellen für Pferde*. 3. Aufl., Frankfurt/Main, Germany: DLG-Verlag.

Field, C. R. (1976): Palatability factors and nutritive value of the food of buffaloes in Uganda. *E. Afr. Wildl.* J14: 181–201.

Georgiadis, N. J.; McNaughton, S. J. (1990): Elemental and fibre contents of savanna grasses: variation with grazing, soil type, season and species. *J. Appl. Ecol.* 27: 623–634.

Hume, J. D. (1995): General concepts of nutrition and nutritional ecology. In: *Resource and captive propagation* (U. Ganslosser, J. K. Hodges, W. Kaumanns, eds.). Fürth, Germany: Filander-Verlag, pp. 90–98.

Jarman, P. J. (1972): The use of drinking sites, wallows and salt licks by herbivores in the flooded Middle Zambezi Valley. *E. Afr. Wildl. J.* 10: 193–209.

Johnson, D. H. (1980): The comparison of usage and availability measurement for evaluating resource preference. *Ecology* 61: 65 71.

Kiefer, B.; Wichert, B.; Ganslosser, U.; Kretzschmar, P.; Kienzle, E. (2002): Digestibility trials in the zoo compared to field studies of white rhinoceros. *Proc. Int. Symp. Elephant and Rhino Res.*, June 7 11, 2001, Vienna, Schüling Verlag, pp. 190–195.

Kretzschmar, P. (2003): *Ecological, endocrinological and ethological investigations of female male choice in free-ranging white rhinoceros.* [Diss.] Zoological Institute I, Friedrich-Alexander University of Erlangen-Nürnberg, Germany.

Malcolm, C. (1981): Large herbivores and food quality. Symp. *Brit. Ecol. Soc.* 2: 345–368.

Manly, B. F. J.; McDonald, D. L. (1993): *Resource selection by animals: statistical design and analysis for field studies.* London: Chapman & Hall.

McDowell, L. R. (1985): *Nutrition of grazing ruminants in warm climates.* New York: Academic Press.

McNaughton, S. J. (1988): Mineral nutrition and spatial concentrations of African ungulates. *Nature* 334: 343–345.

Musalia, L. M.; Semenye, P. P.; Fitzhugh, H. A. (1989): Mineral status of dual-purpose goats and forage in western Kenya. *Small Rum. Res.* 2: 1–9.

Naumann, C.; Bassler, R, (eds.) (1988): *Die chemische Untersuchung von Futtermitteln. Band III Methodenbuch*. Darmstadt, Germany: Naumann-Neudamm.

Owen-Smith, N. (1973): *The behavioural ecology of the White Rhinoceros*. [Diss.] University of Wisconsin.

Owen-Smith, N. (1988): *Megaherbivores: The influence of very large body size on ecology*. Cambridge: Cambridge University Press.

Robbins, C. T. (1993): *Wildlife feeding and nutrition*. London/San Diego: Academic Press.

Stephens, D. W.; Krebs, J. (1986): *Foraging theory*. Princeton: Princeton University Press.

Van Oudtshoorn, F. P. (1992): *Guide to grasses of South Africa*. Cape Town, RSA: Briza Publikasies Cc.

Van Soest, P. J. (1967): Development of a comprehensive system of feed analysis and its application to forages. *J. Anim. Sci.* 26: 119–125.

*K. Leus[1], A.A. Macdonald[2], G. Goodall[2], S. Mitchell[2], A. Hartley[3], and L. Bauwens[1]*

# Cardiac glands with a difference – scanning electron microscopy of the cardiac gland region in the stomach of the babirusa (*Babyrousa babyrussa*), domestic pig (*Sus scrofa domestica*), white-lipped peccary (*Tayassu pecari*) and Bennett's wallaby (*Macropus rufogriseus*)


### Abstract

*The stomach of the babirusa differs from that of other pigs (Leus et al. 1999, Agungpriyono et al. 2000): it is larger and possesses a large diverticulum ventriculi, the gastric glands are confined to a small section at the end of the corpus ventriculi, the cardiac glands occupy a much larger surface area within the stomach (>70 % v. ~30 % in the domestic pig) and there are some variations in the distribution of endocrine cells. It was hypothesised that the babirusa is a non-ruminant foregut fermenting frugivore/concentrate selector (Leus et al. 1999). Scanning electron microscopy of very freshly fixed cardiac gland tissue from the stomachs of nine babirusa revealed that the surface of the whole of the cardiac gland region was characterised by a honeycomb pattern (Leus et al. 2002). At higher magnification the walls appeared to be almost entirely composed of bacteria. No histological study of the stomach of the babirusa or of those of other foregut fermenters with larger areas of cardiac glands has drawn attention to anything like this honeycomb structure. We therefore investigated fresh tissues from domestic pigs (Sus scrofa domestica), white-lipped peccaries (Tayassu pecari) and Bennett's wallabies (Macropus rufogriseus). The 'honey-comb' appearance of the luminal surface of the cardiac gland region of the babirusa stomach was not found in the equivalent regions of the stomachs of the other species. The possibility remains that this structure is a feature unique to the babirusa. Possible hypotheses regarding its function include surface enlargement to increase attachment space and*



[1] Centre for Research and Conservation, Royal Zoological Society of Antwerp, Koningin Astridplein 26, 2018 Antwerp, Belgium; Tel. +32 3 202 45 80; Fax. +32 3 202 45 47; e-mail: kristin.leus@zooantwerpen.be (corresponding author).

[2] Department of Preclinical Veterinary Sciences, Royal (Dick) School of Veterinary Studies, The University of Edinburgh, Summerhall, Edinburgh EH9 1QH, Scotland, UK.

[3] Institute of Zoology, Zoological Society of London, Whipsnade Wild Animal Park, Dunstable, Beds LU6 2LF, UK.

*retention time of bacteria in a stomach without strong compartmentalisation and/or to increase the area for absorption of fermentation products. The explanation may be of direct consequence to the feeding requirements of babirusa in zoos, which in turn may be an important factor for the success of its conservation breeding program.*

***Keywords***

*histology, bacteria, forestomach, fermentation*

## 1 Introduction

The stomach of the babirusa (*Babyrousa babyrussa*) differs from that of other pigs in several aspects (Leus et al. 1999, Agungpriyono et al. 2000): it is larger in size and possesses a voluminous *diverticulum ventriculi*; the gastric glands are confined to a small section at the end of the *corpus ventriculi*; the cardiac glands occupy a significantly larger surface area within the stomach (> 70 % *v.* ~ 30 % in the domestic pig (*Sus scrofa domestica*)) (figure 1) and there are some variations in the distribution of endocrine cells (further studies are necessary to determine the significance of the latter). The pH in the lumen of the cardiac gland region was deemed suitable for the survival of the numerous micro-organisms found therein. These organisms are likely to play a role in bacterial fermentation of plant structural compounds by means of enzymes which the mammalian host is unable to produce itself.

What little is known about the diet and digestion of babirusa in the wild and in captivity has been reviewed in Leus (1996), Leus (2000) and Leus et al. (in press). In the wild, babirusa appear to have a preference for fruits and seeds but to also consume leaves, grass, invertebrates and smaller vertebrates. They are less able to root with the nose in compact soil.

The above findings, together with a survey of the diets fed in captivity and the results of digestibility studies carried out on babirusa in zoos, strongly suggest that the babirusa is a non-ruminant foregut fermenting frugivore/concentrate selector.

Previous studies of the stomach, which concentrated on the gross anatomical and light microscopic structure, largely made use of museum material or specimens not collected immediately after death (Langer 1973, 1988, Leus et al. 1999). More recently, we have been able to obtain stomach tissues from nine babirusa that were euthanised for veterinary reasons not related to the gastro-intestinal tract. This more immediate fixation of tissues permitted investigations of the gastric mucosa using scanning electron microscopy. The granular honey-comb pattern we found covering the cardiac gland region of the babirusa (Leus et al. 2001, 2002) prompted us to carry out additional comparative studies of fresh tissues from an initial limited selection of other animals that have larger areas of cardiac or mucogenic glands in their stomachs: the domestic pig, the white-lipped peccary (*Tayassu pecari*) and the Bennett's wallaby (*Macropus rufogriseus*) (figure 1).

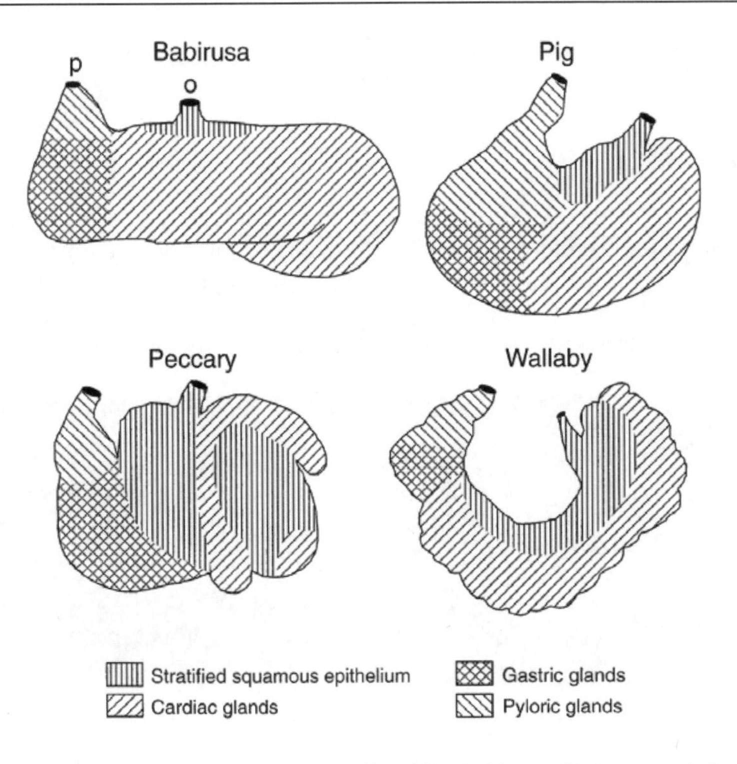


**Figure 1.** Schematic diagrams of the stomachs of the babirusa (*Babyrousa babyrussa*) (from Leus et al. 1999), the domestic pig (*Sus scrofa domestica*), the white-lipped peccary (*Tayassu sp.*) and the Bennett's wallaby (*Macropus rufogriseus*) indicating the distribution of the cardiac gland epithelium. [O = oesophagus; P = pylorus]

## 2 Materials and Methods

Stomachs from nine babirusa in five zoological collections were used for this study. Details of the animals and the fixation materials employed are contained in Leus et al. (2002). Stomachs from three domestic pigs were obtained fresh from the slaughter house. Tissues from two white-lipped peccaries and five Bennett's wallabies were obtained from zoological gardens during autopsy immediately after death. All of these animals were euthanised for reasons not related to the gastrointestinal system. Samples were initially fixed either in Bouin's fluid or 3 % gluteraldehyde. Those fixed in the former were kept in the fluid for 24 h only, after which they were stored in 70 % alcohol. For scanning electron microscopy all specimens were placed in a solution of 3 % gluteraldehyde in 0.1 M sodium cacodylate buffer (pH = 7.3) overnight and then immersed in 2 % guanidine hydrochloride and 2 % tannic acid for a second night (Murakami et al. 1977). They were subsequently post fixed in 2 % osmium tetroxide in distilled water for 8 hours. Dehydration in graded acetones was followed by critical point drying using carbon dioxide (Cohen 1979). After they were mounted on aluminium stubs, the specimens were sputter coated with 20 μm gold/palladium (Echlin 1975) and viewed in a Phillips 505 scanning electron microscope.

## 3 Results

The luminal cardiac gland region of the babirusa was typically characterised by a honey-comb pattern (figure 2). The walls of the honey-comb had a very granular appearance at low magnification. At higher magnification these walls appeared to be almost entirely composed of a bacterial microflora. The glandular tissue of the mucosa was situated underneath the honey-comb layer.

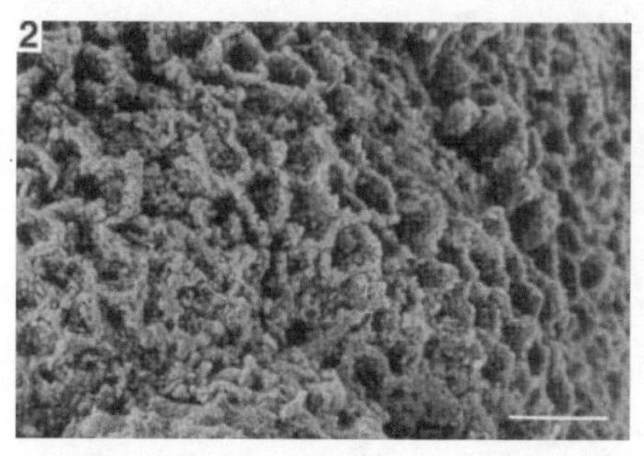


**Figure 2.** Scanning electron micrograph of the cardiac gland region of the stomach of the babirusa (*Babyrousa babyrussa*). The surface of the "honey-comb cells" has a granular appearance. The glandular epithelium underlies the honey-comb layer. Scale bar = 1 mm.

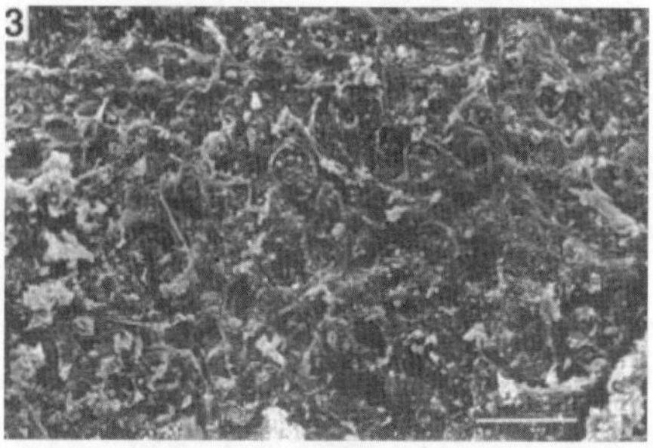

**Figure 3.** Scanning electron micrograph of the cardiac gland region of the stomach of the domestic pig (*Sus scrofa domestica*) Scale bar = 1 mm.

In the domestic pig the cardiac gland region had the appearance shown in figure 3. The mucosal surface could be seen partially covered with mucus, ingesta and bacteria. The openings to the gastric pits appeared as round dark depressions on the luminal surface.

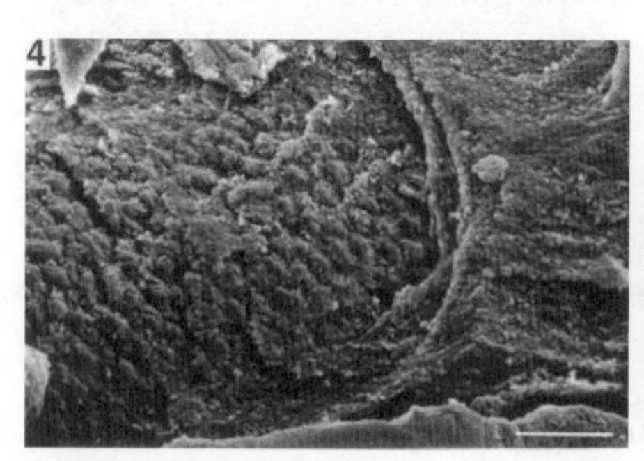


**Figure 4.** Scanning electron micrograph of the cardiac gland region of the stomach of the white-lipped peccary (*Tayassu pecari*) Scale bar = 1 mm.

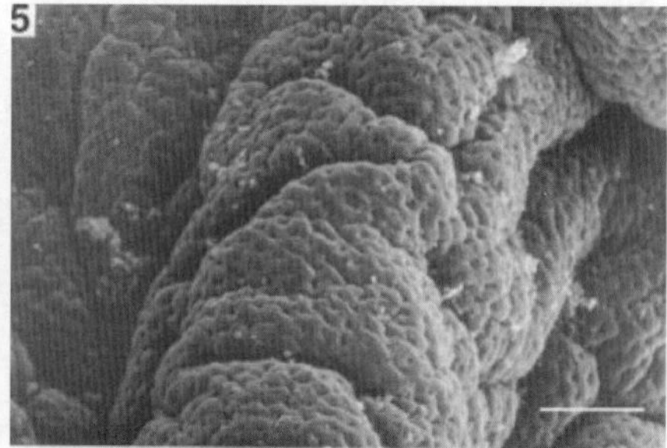


**Figure 5.** Scanning electron micrograph of the cardiac gland region of the stomach of the Bennett's wallaby (*Macropus rufrogriseus*) Scale bar = 1 mm.

The cardiac gland region of the peccary was covered in an amorphous layer of mucus. The underlying luminal surface of the epithelium was dimpled in appearance, thereby reflecting the location of the gastric pits and grooves (figure 4).

The mucosal surface of the cardiac gland region in the stomach of the Bennett's wallaby is illustrated in figure 5. The openings to the gastric pits appeared as dark invaginations between ridges on the luminal surface.

## 4 Discussion

The 'honey-comb' appearance of the luminal surface of the cardiac gland region of the babirusa stomach was not found in the equivalent regions of the stomachs of the domestic pig, white-lipped peccary or the Bennett's wallaby.

In the babirusa, light microscopy and electron microscopy have shown that the 'honey-comb' has a cellular infrastructure built on top of the epithelial ridges between the cardiac pits (Leus et al. 2002). This structure is very delicate, which may explain why it was not detected in previous studies of babirusa stomachs collected 90 minutes or longer after death (Leus et al. 1999).

Two questions can be posed: 1) is the honey-comb structure a feature unique to the babirusa, 2) what may be the function of this structure? A literature review revealed no reference to a microscopic honey-comb structure on the surface of the cardiac gland area of other wild pigs and non-ruminant forestomach fermenters. To eliminate the possibility that this was due to the fragile structure having been lost due to tissue autolysis, or the method of fixation or processing of the tissues, fresh stomachs of the domestic pig, white-lipped peccary and the Bennett's wallaby were also investigated.

Information on the gross and microscopic anatomy of the stomach of the closest relatives of the babirusa, the other wild pigs, is rare (Macdonald 1991, Leus and Macdonald 1997), but suggests that there is little difference with the anatomy of the stomach of the domestic pig. Scanning electron micrographs of the luminal surface of the cardiac gland region of the stomachs of the domestic pigs investigated as part of this study, revealed that the surface and gastric pits are lined by epithelial cells as described in the literature, without the additional overlying honey-comb infrastructure seen in the babirusa. Further studies are required to show if among the Suidae, the honey-comb structure is a feature unique to the babirusa. In any case, the proportion of the stomach surface covered by cardiac glands is much smaller in the stomach of the domestic pig (about 30 %) compared to that of the babirusa (> 70 %) (Leus et al. 1999). Furthermore, what little fermentation may take place in the cardiac gland region of the stomach of the domestic pig is of minor importance in the digestive processes of this species (Keys and DeBarthe 1974).

In contrast, forestomach fermentation has been shown to be an important aspect of diet digestion in the closest relatives of the pigs, the peccaries (Tayassuidae) (Shively et al. 1985; Lochmiller et al. 1989). In the peccary stomach, fermentation takes place in the gastric pouch and its two blind sacs, lined by a combination of cornified epithelium and cardiac glands (Langer 1978, 1979, Shively et al. 1985, Lochmiller et al. 1989). Nevertheless, scanning electron micrographs of the cardiac gland region failed to reveal the typical honey-comb layer which was so apparent in the babirusa.

The presence of significant areas of cardiac or other mucogenic glands in regions of the stomach where fermentation takes place is not unique to the babirusa or the peccaries. It also occurs in the Bradypodidae and Megalonychidae (sloths) and the Camelidae (Langer 1988, Stevens and Hume 1995). However, only two groups of animals share with the babirusa the possession of an enlarged region of the stomach lined almost exclusively with cardiac glands: the colobine monkeys (colobus monkeys and langurs) and macropod marsupials (kangaroos and wallabies) (Kunh 1968, Gemmel 1977, Langer 1988, Stevens and Hume 1995). For both these groups, forestomach fermentation is a crucial step in the digestive process (Moir 1965, Bauchop and Martucci 1968, Ohwaki et al. 1974, Bauchop 1978, Kay and Davies 1994). In the macropod marsupial stomach, fermentation takes place in the forestomach (itself composed of a sacciform and a tubiform region) lined with stratified squamous epithelium and cardiac glands (Langer et al. 1980, Langer 1988, Stevens and Hume 1995). The present study did not detect a honeycomb layer overlying the surface epithelium of the cardiac gland region of the stomach of the Bennett's wallaby. The Bennett's wallaby was selected for this initial stage of the comparative research because it shows a large amount of cardiac glands in the stomach and because the species occurs in captivity in large numbers in Europe. This made it more likely that fresh tissue from euthanised animals would become available within a short frame of time. However, further research is needed to investigate the absence or presence of the honeycomb structure in the stomachs of other kangaroos and wallabies, specifically those with relatively less grass and more grass roots, leaves and fruits in their diet, e. g. *Macropus agilis* or *Thylogale* sp. Also the stomachs of the colobine monkeys remain to be investigated.

At present the possibility remains that the honey-comb layer in the cardiac gland region of the babirusa stomach is a feature unique to this species. Until further studies are carried out we can only speculate on the function and significance of this structure. The honey-comb layer is potentially a unique adaptation of the babirusa for surface enlargement in order to increase attachment space and retention time of bacteria in a stomach without strong compartmentalisation. At the same time it may increase the area for absorption of fermentation products. All this may be of direct consequence for the feeding requirements of babirusa in zoological gardens, which in turn, may be a key factor for the success of its conservation breeding program.

## 5 Conclusions

1. The bacteria-filled 'honey-comb' layer at the luminal surface of the cardiac gland region of the babirusa stomach was not found in the equivalent

regions of the stomachs of the domestic pig, White-lipped peccary or the Bennett's wallaby.

2. The possibility remains that the honey-comb layer in the cardiac gland region of the babirusa stomach is a feature unique to this species.
3. Further studies are needed to investigate the function of this structure and the possible consequences for the feeding requirements of babirusa in captivity.

## Acknowledgements

We would like to thank Dr Francis Vercammen and Dr Walter De Meurichy of the Royal Zoological Society of Antwerp, the staff of the Whipsnade Wild Animal Park and the Department of Preclinical Veterinary Sciences of the University of Edinburgh for their help with the collection of the samples. The study was financially supported by the Development Trust of the University of Edinburgh. The Centre for Research and Conservation of the Royal Zoological Society of Antwerp gratefully acknowledges the structural support of the Flemish Government.

## References

Agunpriyono, S.; Macdonald, A. A.; Leus, K. Y. G.; Kitamura, N.; Adnyane, I. K. M.; Goodall, G. P.; Hondo, E.; Yamada, J. (2000): Immunohistochemical study on the distribution of endocrine cells in the gastrointestinal tract of the babirusa, *Babyrousa babyrussa* (Suidae). *Anat. Histol. Embryol.* 29: 173–178.

Bauchop, T. (1978): Digestion of leaves in vertebrate arboreal folivores. In: *The ecology of arboreal folivores* (G. Montgomery, ed.). Washington DC: Smithsonian Institution Press, pp. 193–204.

Bauchop, T.; Martucci, R. W. (1968): Ruminant-like digestion of the langur monkey. *Science* 161: 698–700.

Cohen, A. L. (1979): Critical point drying principles and procedures. *Scanning Electron Microscopy* 2: 303–323.

Echlin, P. (1975): Sputter coating techniques for scanning electron microscopy. *Scanning Electron Microscopy* 2: 217–224.

Gemmel, R. T.; Engelhardt, W. V. (1977): The structure of the cells lining the stomach of the tammar wallaby (*Macropus eugenii*). *J. Anat.* 123: 723–733.

Kay, R. N. B.; Davies, A. G. (1994): Digestive physiology. In: *Colobine monkeys, their ecology, behaviour and evolution* (A. G. Davies, J. F. Oates, eds.). Cambridge: Cambridge University Press, pp. 229–249.

Keys, J. E.; DeBarthe, J. V. (1974): Cellulose and hemicellulose digestibility in the stomach, small intestine and large intestine of swine. *J. Anim. Sci.* 39: 53–56.

Kunh, H. J. (1968): Zur Kenntnis von Bau und Funktion des Magens der Schlankaffen (Colobidae). *Folia Primatol.* 2: 193–221.

Langer, P. (1973): Vergleichend-anatomische Untersuchungen am Magen der Artiodactyla (Owen 1848). I. Teil: Untersuchungen am Magen der Nonruminantia (Suiformes). *Gegenbaurs morph. Jahrb.* 119: 514–561.

Langer, P. (1978): Anatomy of the stomach of the collared peccary, *Dicotyles tajacu* (L. 1758) (Artiodactyla: Mammalia). *Z. Säugetierk.* 43: 1–64.

Langer, P. (1979): Adaptational significance of the forestomach of the collared peccary, *Dicotyles tajacu* (L. 1758) (Mammalia: Artiodactyla). *Mammalia* 43: 235–245.

Langer, P. (1988): *The mammalian herbivore stomach, comparative anatomy, function and evolution*. Stuttgart: Gustav Fischer.

Langer, P.; Dellow, D. W.; Hume, I. D. (1980): Stomach structure and function in three species of macropodine marsupials. *Austr. J. Zool.* 28: 1–18.

Leus, K. (1996): The habitat and diet of the Sulawesi babirusa (*Babyrousa babyrussa celebensis*). In: *Population and habitat viability assessment workshop for the babirusa (Babyrousa babyrussa): Report* (J. Manansang, A. A. Macdonald, P. Miller, U. Seal, eds.). Apple Valley, MN: Conservation Breeding Specialist Group (SSC/IUCN), pp. 121–134.

Leus, K. (2000): Feeding babirusa (*Babyrousa babyrussa*) in captivity. In: *Zoo Animal Nutrition* (J. Nijboer, J.-M. Hatt, W. Kaumanns, A. Beijnen, U. Gansloßer, eds.). Fürth: Filander Verlag, pp. 237–250.

Leus, K.; Macdonald, A. A. (1997): From babirusa (*Babyrousa babyrussa*) to domestic pig: the nutrition of swine. *Proc. Nutr. Soc.* 56: 1001–1012.

Leus, K.; Goodall, G. P.; Macdonald, A. A. (1999): Anatomy and histology of the babirusa (*Babyrousa babyrussa*) stomach. CR Acad Sci Paris, *Sciences de la vie / Life Sciences* 322: 1081–1092.

Leus, K.; Morgan, C. A.; Dierenfeld, E. S. (in press): Nutrition. In: *babirusa (Babyrousa babyrussa) husbandry manual* (M. Fischer, edr.). St Louis, St Louis Zoological Park.

Leus, K.; Macdonald, A. A.; Goodall, G. P.; Veitch, D.; Mitchell, S.; Bauwens, L. (2001): Cardiac glands with a difference – electron microscopy of the cardiac gland region of the babirusa (*Babyrousa babyrussa*) stomach. In: *Abstract Book Second European Zoo Nutrition Conference* (A. L. Fidgett, ed.). Hampshire, UK: Marwell Zoological Park.

Leus, K.; Macdonald, A. A.; Goodall, G.; Mitchell, S.; Bauwens, L. (2002): Light and electron microscopy of the cardiac gland region of the stomach of the babirusa (*Babyrousa babyrussa* – Suidae, Mammalia). *Anatomy and Embryology* (Submitted for publication).

Lochmiller, R. L.; Hellgren, E. C.; Gallagher, J. F.; Varner, W.; Grant, W. E. (1989): Volatile fatty acids in the gastrointestinal tract of the collared peccary (*Tayassu tajacu*). *J. Mamm.* 70: 189–191.

Macdonald, A. A. (1991): Comparative study of the functional soft tissue anatomy in pigs and peccaries. *Bongo* 18: 273–282.

Moir, R. J. (1965): The comparative physiology of ruminant-like animals: In: *Physiology of digestion in the ruminant stomach* (R. W. Dougherty, R. S. Allen, W. Burroughs, N. L. Jacobson, A. D. McGilliard, eds.). London: Butterworths, pp. 1–15.

Murakami, T.; Yamamoto, K.; Itoshisha, T.; Irino, S. (1977): Modified tannin-osmium conductive staining method for non-conductive S.E.M. specimens. *Arch. Histol. Cytol.* 40: 35–40.

Ohwaki, H.; Hungate, R. E.; Lotter, L.; Hofmann, R. R.; Maloiy, G. (1974): Stomach fermentation in East African colobus monkeys in their natural state. *Appl. Microbiol.* 27: 713–723.

Shively, C. L.; Whiting, F. M.; Swingle, R. S.; Brown, W. H.; Sowls, L. K. (1985): Some aspects of the nutritional biology of the collared peccary. *J. Wild Manage.* 49: 729–732.

Stevens, C. E.; Hume, I. D. (1995): *Comparative physiology of the vertebrate digestive system.* 2nd ed. Cambridge: Cambridge University Press.

*A. Liesegang*[1], *K. Baumgartner*[2]

# Metabolic bone disease in juvenile Morelet's crocodile (*Crocodylus moreletii*) caused by nutritional deficiencies

**Abstract**

*Calcium and phosphorus are very important minerals in reptile nutrition, but many diets in zoos are still not sufficiently balanced. To achieve optimal growth, including a healthy skeleton, a well-balanced supply with these minerals and also vitamin D is the prerequisite. The present case report is intended to share our experiences.*

*In Nürnberg Zoo, three Morelet's crocodiles hatched for the first time in a European zoo in December 1999. The animals had an average weight of 31.9 g. They had access to artificial UV light (UVA, B and C). The dietary management proved to be difficult, because no data on dietary requirements exist for this species. The animals were x-rayed after 3½ months with an average body weight of 125.8 g because one had a broken leg. Radiography revealed severe signs of metabolic bone disease in all three crocodiles. The animal with the fracture was treated with a T-buster-splint bandage. In addition, the diet was enriched with mineral and vitamin supplements (0.2 g of Korvimin®ZVT was mixed with 2 ml of water; 0.3 ml of this solution was administered to each animal per day). After 6 weeks radiography revealed a healed fracture and a physiological ossification in all animals. At this time the crocodiles had an average weight of 445.3 g and a length of 528.3 mm.*

*In conclusion, this case report demonstrates a quick recovery of crocodiles with metabolic bone disease following diet supplementation with minerals and vitamins. A diet consisting of crickets especially in combination with meat always requires supplementation due to a low Ca : P ratio.*

**Keywords**

*Metabolic bone disease, Ca:P ratio, crocodile*

[1] Institute of Animal Nutrition, Zürich. *Correspondence to*: Dr. med. vet. Annette Liesegang, Institute of Animal Nutrition, Veterinary Faculty, University of Zurich, Winterthurerstr. 260, 8057 Zurich, Switzerland, Tel. +41-1-635 88 23, Fax. +41-1-635 89 32.

[2] Nürnberg Zoo, Nürnberg, Germany.

## 1 Introduction

The Morelet's crocodile (*Crocodylus moreletii*) is a relatively little known species from the Atlantic coast of Mexico and northern Central America. It's length rarely exceeds 3 m and it has a characteristic broad snout. These animals primarily live in freshwater habitats, particularly marshes, swamps, ponds and lagoons, but in some areas this species can be found in brackish water areas. Juveniles utilise dense cover. Adults are known to aestivate in burrows during the adverse conditions associated with the dry season. Juvenile animals consume invertebrates in and around the water as well as small vertebrates, usually small fish. As they grow larger their diets include a greater variety of prey such as reptiles, fish, aquatic snails, birds and mammals. Before the onset of rainy season, 20 to 45 eggs are laid in a mound nest near the water (Platt and Montanucci 1993). Population of Morelet's crocodile were greatly reduced in many areas due to uncontrolled hide hunting, mainly in the 1940s and 1950s (Abercrombie et al. 1980; Campbell 1972; Hunt and Tamarack 1992). They are seldomly held in zoos and scientific data nutritional requirements are scarce. No data on nutritional requirements or diets for this species in zoos exists. Usually they are fed like other carnivorous reptiles such as lizards. The presented case report is intended to share the experiences made at Nürnberg Zoo.

## 2 Animals

In Nürnberg Zoo, three Morelet's crocodiles (*Crocodylus moreletii*) hatched for the first time in a European zoo in December 1999. The animals had an average weight of 31.9 g. They were housed in a 60 × 35 cm terrarium and had access to artificial UV light (Ultra Lux lamp, 30–60 cm distance, 3 times/week for 10 minutes, bulbs are changed according to the manufacturer's recommendation every 6 months) after hatching until they were transferred to a bigger terrarium (200 × 80 cm) at the age of 3 months. In the bigger terrarium, they daily had access to a mixed light lamp (with a UV light component) for 8 hours (Philips MLR 180 W, 230–240 V). This lamp was fixed at a distance of 100–140 cm against the water basin, where the crocodiles mainly stayed during the day. The dietary management proved to be difficult. Firstly feeding recommendations are not found in the literature and secondly it was a challenge to feed anything at all to the freshly hatched crocodiles. The diet constisted of crickets and once or twice a week of baby mice. No supplementation was given. Occasionally the animals received chicks, small fish and fresh meat strips. The mineral contents and Ca : P ratios of the crickets and meat fed are listed in table 1. After 3½ months with an average body weight of 125.8 g, the animals were x-rayed, because one had a broken leg. Radiography revealed severe signs of metabolic bone disease in all three animals. The animal with the fracture was treated with a T-buster-splint bandage. In addition, the diet was enriched with mineral and vitamin supplements (0.2 g of Korvimin® ZVT was mixed with 2 ml of water; 0.3 ml of this solution was administered to each animal per day (238.4 mg/kg body weight)) (Köhler 1996). After 6 weeks radiography revealed a healed fracture and a physiological ossification in all animals. The dose of Korvimin® ZVT was increased according to body weight. The crocodiles had an average length of 528.3 mm and a weight of 445.3 g.

**Table 1.** Mineral content in % DM of the used feedstuffs.

| | **Ca** | **P** | **Ca:P ratio** |
|---|---|---|---|
| Crickets | 0.47 | 0.96 | 0.49 : 1 |
| Mice | 1.89 | 1.8 | 1 : 1 |
| Meat | 0.1 | 0.17 | 0.59 : 1 |
| Chick | 1.16 | 0.88 | 1.3 : 1 |
| Fish | 0.076 | 0.88 | 0.08 : 1 |

The animals are now 2 years old and were transferred to Luxemburg (Parc Merveilleux). They are healthy and have an average weight of 2010 g and average body length of 866 cm. The supplementation of Korvimin®ZVT was continued and adapted to size.

**Table 2.** Mineral content and Vitamin D content of Korvimin ZVT®.

| Ingredient | Unit | |
|---|---|---|
| Calcium | % | 15 |
| Phosphorus | % | 10 |
| Vitamin D | I.E./kg | 200 000 |

## 3 Discussion and conclusions

Previous studies have described that Ca and P play an important role in the nutrition of reptiles (Allen 1989; Allen et al. 1993). When a diet contains too much P in relation to Ca, the body makes every effort to re-establish a normal Ca : P ratio in the blood. Ca is first removed from blood plasma and than from existing calcified tissues, particularly bone (Frye 1997). Growing animals require sufficient vitamin D (Vitamin D3: 50–100 I.E./kg BW/week) and calcium with a Ca : P ratio of a least 1 : 1 (Zentek and Dennert 1997). Other sources suggest much higher calcium ratios in the diet for other reptiles (Donoghue and Langenberg 1994). Crickets have an average calcium content of 0.47 % and a Ca : P ratio of 0.49 (Dennert 1997). In young tortoises, the nutrient requirement of Vitamin D3 is related to the Ca : P ratio in the diet (Zwart 2000). Exact data on nutrient requirements of vitamin D3 in reptiles are still lacking, but extrapolations are made based on higher verterbrates (Zentek and Dennert 1997). Considering the possibilites, crickets proved to be the most appropriate food for our animals next to small fishes which were not well accepted at the beginning. In their natural habitat growing Morelet's crocodiles also eat insects, as well as small fish, and worms. Considering the small size of the young reptiles, crickets fulfil practical feeding purposes and these reptiles tended to hunt them which is a positive effect for natural behaviour.

In conclusion this case report demonstrates a quick recovery of crocodiles with metabolic bone disease following dietary supplementation with minerals and vitamins. A diet consisting of crickets especially in combination with meat always requires supplementation since the Ca content and the Ca : P ratio are too low. This case report shows how important dietary management is and that the recording and evaluation of diets for zoo animals should be done precisely.

## Products mentioned in the text

**KorviminZVT** Mineral supplementation, manufactured by WDT, Germany

**Osram Ultra-Vitalux** UV bulb, 300 Watt, manufactured by OSRAM GmbH, München, Germany

**Philips MLR,** 180 W, 230–240 V, mixed light bulb, manufactured by Philips Electronics, N.V., U.S.A.

## References

Abercrombie, C. L.; Davidson, D.; Hope, C.; Scott, D. E. (1980): Status of Morelet's crocodile (*Crocodylus moreletii*) in Belize. *Biol. Conserv.* 17: 103–113.

Allen, M. E.; Oftedal, O. T.; Ullrey, D. E. (1993): Effect of dietary calcium concentration on mineral composition of fox geckos (*Hamidactylus garnoti*) and cuban tree frogs (*Ostepilus septentrionalis*). *J. Zoo Wildlife med.* 2: 118–128.

Allen, M. E. (1989): Nutritional aspects of insectivory. [Diss.]. Lansing: Michigan State University.

Campbell, H. W. (1972): Preliminary report: status investigation of Morelet's crocodile in Mexico. *Zoologica* 57(3): 135–136.

Dennert, C. (1997): Investigations on feeding practices and commercial food for herbivores lizards and chelonians. [Diss.]. Hannover: University of Hannover.

Donoghue, S.; Langenberg, J. (1994): Clinical nutrition of exotic pets. *Austr. Vet. J.* 71: 337–341.

Frye, F. (1997): The importance of calcium in relation to phoshorus, especially in foliovorous reptiles. *Proc. Nutr. Soc.* 56: 1105–1117.

Hunt, R. H.; Tamarack, J. (1992): Cox Lagoon: A preserve for *Crocodylus moreletii* in Belize. In: *Crocodiles, Proceedings of the 11th Working Meeting of the CSG*. IUCN – The World Conservation Union, Gland, Switzerland. Vol. 1, pp. 183–191.

Köhler, G. (1996): *Krankheiten der Reptilien und Amphibien*. Ulmer Verlag.

Platt, S.; Montanucci, R. R. (1993): *Nesting ecology, juvenile and subadult food habits, and status of Morelet's crocodile (Crocodylus moreletii) in Belize*. Unpubl. report to The Wildlife Conservation Society NYZS, New York.

Zentek, J.; Dennert, C. (1997): Fütterung von Reptilien: Praxis und Probleme. *Tierärztl. Prax.* 25: 684–688.

Zwart, P. (2000): Nutrition of chelonians. In: *Zoo Animal Nutrition* (J. Nijboer et al., eds.). Fürth: Filander, pp. 33–44.

*W. Loehlein[1], E. Kienzle[1], H. Wiesner[2], M. Clauss[1]*

# Investigations on the use of chromium oxide as an inert external marker in captive Asian elephants (*Elephas maximus*): passage and recovery rates

### *Abstract*

*Digestibility studies in zoo herbivores that are kept in groups are often confounded by the fact that the intake of hay, which is usually offered to the whole group, cannot be measured on an individual basis. This problem can be solved by using a double marker method with an internal and an external marker. In elephants, the internal marker lignin has repeatedly been used successfully; however, no external digestibility marker has been reliably established for this species.*

*Seven captive Asian elephants were fed 500 g of chromium oxide per animal as a pulse-dose. Faeces were collected in toto for 60 hours afterwards. The amount of faeces from each single defecation was weighed, and a representative subsample was taken for chromium analysis. All faeces defecated during night hours were treated as a single defecation unit. With the individual chromium concentrations and the total weights, the recoveries of the chromium marker could be calculated, and the passage rates for these animals were determined. Additionally, four animals in an elephant orphanage in Sri Lanka were fed the same amount of chromium oxide. For these animals, only the passage rates could be determined.*

*The average first marker appearance was 24 hours, and the average last marker excretion 54 hours after marker feeding. The average mean retention time for four adult animals was 31.7 ± 2.7 hours. On average, the elephants excreted 3.9 ± 1.2 kg faeces/ 100 kg of body mass per day. The average chromium oxide recovery was 97 %.*

*The results confirm that chromium oxide is a reliable external marker in Asian elephants. The passage rate data compares well with other data from the literature. Like perissodactyls, the elephant uses a digestive strategy of passing large amounts of low quality forage through its gut within a relatively short period of time.*

### *Keywords*

*mean retention time, digestive physiology, feeding trial*

[1] Institute of Animal Physiology, Physiological Chemistry and Animal Nutrition, Munich, Germany. Corresponding author: Wolfgang Loehlein, Dr. med. vet., Institute of Animal Physiology, Physiological Chemistry and Animal Nutrition, Veterinaerstr. 13, 80539 Munich, Germany, Tel.: ++49 89 2180 2554, Fax: ++49 89 2180 3208, Email: wolfgang@loehlein.de

[2] Zoological Garden "Hellabrunn", Munich, Germany

## 1 Introduction

Although a number of digestibility studies with elephants have been performed, the amount of data does not allow useful statistical testing. It was therefore intended to increase the existing data pool by means of a digestibility study with captive Asian elephants at the Zoological Garden of Munich.

However, in contrast to other studies, the actual situation did not allow – for both logistic and animal welfare considerations – a seperation of the animals for the complete recording of the individual food intake for the staple diet item, grass hay. This is a problem often faced in a zoo setting, and can often prevent intake and digestibility studies from being performed. If, however, it is only one diet item, as in this case, that is fed to the whole group, then one could use a double marker method with an internal marker within the feedstuffs and an external marker that is additionally applied for the calculation of the intake of this particular diet item.

The internal marker lignin has been repeatedly used successfully in elephants (Ullrey et al. 1979, Reichard et al. 1982, Fujikara et al. 1989); however, no external marker has been established in this species. As a pilot study for consecutive digestibility studies, we therefore intended to test chromium oxide, which is probably the external marker that had the most widespread applications in many animal species (Kotb and Luckey 1972), by means of a passage rate and recovery trial.

## 2 Methods

The feeding trial at Munich Zoo was performed in November 1996. Seven captive elephants were used, of which 2 were juvenile, 1 subadult and 4 adult animals. For a detailed list of all animals that participated in the experiment including age and gender see table 1. The body weight (BW) of these animals

**Table 1.** Passage and recovery rates of captive Asian elephants fed chromium oxide as an inert, external marker. MRT = mean retention time. Body weights estimated (see Methods).

| Location | Animal | Age (years) | Sex | Body weight (kg) | first marker appearance (h) | last marker excretion (h) | MRT (h) | Marker recovery rate (%) |
|---|---|---|---|---|---|---|---|---|
| Munich Zoo | Gajendra | 4 | m | 888 | 14.0 | 43.8 | 21.8 | 95.5 |
| Munich Zoo | Mangala | 4 | f | 1067 | 15.0 | 43.0 | 21.4 | 98.9 |
| Munich Zoo | Panang | 8 | f | 2200 | 26.8 | 55.3 | 32.0 | 92.0 |
| Munich Zoo | Kathi | 31 | f | 3217 | 26.5 | 53.8 | — | — |
| Munich Zoo | Steffi | 27 | f | 3177 | 22.0 | 55.0 | 28.1 | 103.1 |
| Munich Zoo | Tina | 38 | f | 4013 | 21.0 | 56.8 | 32.1 | 97.6 |
| Munich Zoo | Dirndl | 32 | f | — | 26.8 | 58.5 | 34.6 | 95.8 |
| Sri Lanka | Sandaly | 4 | f | — | 14.5 | 42.0 | — | — |
| Sri Lanka | Esella | 5 | m | — | 17.0 | 45.0 | — | — |
| Sri Lanka | Jagura | 25 | m | — | 24.3 | 57.0 | — | — |
| Sri Lanka | Kandula | 17 | m | — | 21.8 | 54.3 | — | — |

was estimated after measuring the individual thorax girth using the method described by Hile et al. (1997). The animals were fed a diet of grass hay, straw, fruits, vegetables, oats, bread and a mineral supplement.

Blank faecal samples were gathered a day prior to marker application from each animal. The animals were fed 500 g of chromium oxide per animal as a pulse dose. Each animal received the chromium oxide hidden in a whole loaf of bread, which was swallowed *in toto* by each animal. The complete marker ingestion was guaranteed by the presence of the elephant keepers, who ensured that the elephants would not manipulate the breads with their trunks or spit them out. Faeces were collected *in toto* for 60 hours afterwards. The amount of faeces from each single defecation was weighed and a representative subsample was taken for chromium and dry matter analysis. The subsample always represented 10 % of the whole defecated portion after mixing with a concrete mixer. All faeces defecated during night hours were treated as a single defecation unit.

The dry matter content of the subsamples was determined by drying them at 103 °C to constant weight. Chromium oxide was determined photometrically after sample treatment with perchloric acid and sodiumhydroxide according to Petry and Rapp (1970).

With the individual chromium concentrations and the total dry matter weights, the recoveries of the chromium marker were calculated. The mean retention times (MRT) for these animals were calculated according to Thielemans et al. (1978) as

$$MRT = \frac{\sum t_i C_i \mathrm{d}t_i}{\sum C_i \mathrm{d}t_i}$$

With $C_i$ = marker concentration in the faecal sample at time $t_i$ (hours after marker administration) and $\mathrm{d}t_i$ = the interval (hours) of the respective sample

$$\mathrm{d}t_i = \frac{(t_{i+1} - t_i) + (t_i - t_{i-1})}{2}$$

Additionally, in July 1997 four animals (see table 1) in an elephant orphanage in Pinawela, Sri Lanka, were fed the same marker amount. These animals received a diet of native forages consisting of *Artocarpus heterophyllus*, *Artocarpus altilis*, *Cocos nucifera*, *Caryota urens*. For these animals, only the passage rates could be determined, as total faecal collection was not feasible.

Data is generally presented as means ± standard deviations (SD).

## 3 Results

The elephants excreted an average of 3.9 ± 1.2 kg faeces/100 kg BW/day. With an average faeceal dry matter content of 20.7 ± 1.5 %, this represented a faecal dry matter excretion of 0.8 ± 0.2 kg/100 kg BW/day.

The results of the passage and recovery calculations are presented in table 1. The first marker appearance in the faeces occured after 23.9 ± 1.1 hours after marker application in the adult elephants; marker excretion was complete after 54.4 ± 2.5 hours. In the four juvenile elephants, the first marker appearance occured after 15.1 ± 1.3 hours; marker excretion was complete in these animals after 43.0 ± 1.5 hours. The average mean retention time for the four adult elephants was 31.7 ± 2.7 hours. There were no distinctive differences in passage rate parameters between the Munich and the Sri Lanka elephants, in spite of the different feeding regime.

The average chromium oxide recovery was 97.1 % ± 3.7. In one case, the calculated recovery exceeded 100 %.

## 4 Discussion

The high marker recoveries for chromium oxide indicate that this substance can be used as a reliable inert, external marker in elephants. A prerogative for this reliability, however, is a meticulous sampling regime with thorough mixing of faeces before a subsample for analysis is taken. The pulse-dose technique used in this study does not allow the evaluation of potentially irregular excretion patterns of chromium oxide when it is fed in steady state as a digestibility marker. Such irregularities have been reported with chromium oxide in several animals (Kotb and Luckey 1972), and therefore, for the use as a digestibility marker, it is generally recommended that the daily marker dose be divided into at least two sub-doses throughout the day. In our study, the excretion curves for chromium oxide in the adult animals followed, for the individual defecations available for sampling, the usual passage rate pattern (figure 1), which could be interpreted as an indication for a regular marker passage without marker cumulation or segregation within the digestive tract. It should be noted, however, that the sampling regime of this study did not allow to isolate the defecation with the peak marker excretion, which occurred during night hours (figure 1).

Other studies have achieved calculated chromium oxide recoveries of more than 100 % (e. g. Kane et al. 1950, Sharpe and Robinson 1970). Such results indicate that a complete, homogenous mixture of the collected faeces was not achieved and the taken subsample contained a higher marker proportion than the whole defecation unit. As an ideal marker would have a theoretical recovery rate of exactly 100 %, deviations from this value – in both directions – reflect difficulties in sample generation.

The passage rates determined in this study are in accordance with other reports on ingesta passage in elephants (table 2). The chromium oxide marker used in this study neither binds to other particles, nor is it dissolved in the fluid ingesta phase, and therefore moves through the gut as very fine particles at a pace of their own. Hackenberger (1987) showed that there is hardly any difference between the fluid and particle passage in elephants.

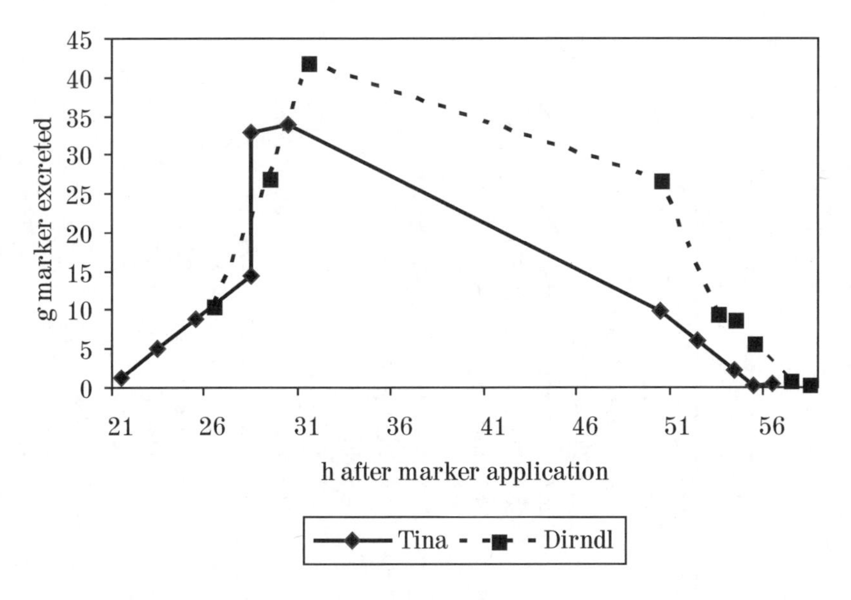


**Figure 1.** Excretion curves for chromium oxide in two captive Asian elephants. Only values from individual defaecations are presented. Peak marker excretions occurred during night hours when defaecations could not be differentiated. Marker excretion during the night amounted to 372.6 g in Tina and 346.6 g in Dirnd.

Despite a similar gastrointestinal (GIT) anatomy in elephants, equids, rhinoceroses and tapirs (Clemens and Maloiy 1982, Stevens and Hume 1995), the elephant has, in proportion to its body weight, a remarkably faster passage rate (table 3). The fact that the times of first and last marker appearance were similar in the zoo elephants of our study and the elephants in Sri Lanka fed on native forages suggests that the fast passage rates measured in zoos are not due to the nature of artifical diets *per se* but probably a general digestive feature of all elephants. The fast passage rate of the elephant, and the reportedly low digestibility coefficients achieved by this species (e. g. Tomat et al. 1999), are an exception to the classic concept for the influence of body size on digestive physiology: In general, larger animals have, relative to their energy requirements, more GIT volume than smaller animals, which means that they can afford to retain food longer, digest fibre more efficiently and therefore thrive on a "poor qualitiy" diet in the wild (e.g. Parra 1978, Demment and Van Soest 1985). Accordingly, Illius and Gordon (1992) determined a positive correlation between MRT and body weight for both hindgut and foregut fermenting herbivores. For hindgut fermenters, their equation is:

$$\text{MRT (hours)} = 9.4\ \text{BW(kg)}^{0.255}$$

According to this equation, the elephants of this study (BW range: 888 to 4013 kg) should have had a MRT range of 53.1–78.0 hours instead of the measured 21.8–34.6 hours. In a similar way it was demonstrated that the

**Table 2.** Passage rate data for elephants from the literature. T1 = first marker appearance; T2 = last marker excretion; MRT = mean retention time.

| Species | n | Age | Marker | Food | T1 (h) | T2 (h) | MRT (h) | Source |
|---|---|---|---|---|---|---|---|---|
| E. maximus | 1 | adult | pieces of rubber | hay | 21.0 | 54.5 | | Benedict (1936) |
| E. maximus | 2 | adult | brilliant green / basic fuchsin | | 20.3 | 65.8 | 32.7 | Gill (1960) |
| E. maximus | 1 | adult | fuchsin | grass hay | | | 50 | Foose (1982) |
| E. maximus | 1 | adult | fuchsin | alfalfa hay | | | 51 | Foose (1982) |
| E. maximus | 3 | adult | plastic O-rings | hay | | | 26.6 | Hackenberger and Atkinson (1982) |
| E. maximus | 37 | adult | plastic O-rings | timothy hay | 22.4 | | 26.6 | Hackenberger (1987) |
| E. maximus | 4 | adult | chromium oxide | grass hay / mixed feed | 23.9 | 54.5 | 31.7 | this study |
| | | | | | | | | |
| L. africana | 1 | adult | oranges | native forages | 11 | 19 | | Napier Bax and Sheldrick (1963) |
| L. africana | 1 | adult | beetroot | grass hay / straw | 21 | 46 | | Rees (1982) |
| L. africana | 3 | adult | fuchsin | grass hay | | | 50–54 | Foose (1982) |
| L. africana | 3 | adult | fuchsin | alfalfa hay | | | 38–48 | Foose (1982) |
| L. africana | 3 | adult | plastic O-rings | timothy hay / mixed feed | | | 22.8 | Hackenberger and Atkinson (1982) |
| L. africana | 15 | adult | plastic O-rings | timothy hay | 15.3 | | 19.2 | Hackenberger (1987) |
| L. africana | 3 | adult | plastic O-rings | timothy hay | | | 27.2 | Hackenberger (1987) |
| L. africana | 3 | adult | plastic O-rings | hay / mixed feed | | | 21.4 | Hackenberger (1987) |
| L. africana | 3 | adult | chromium mordanted hay | timothy hay | | | 26.0 | Hackenberger (1987) |
| L. africana | 3 | adult | chromium mordanted hay | timothy hay / mixed feed | | | 20.6 | Hackenberger (1987) |
| L. africana | 3 | adult | Co-EDTA | timothy hay | | | 25.0 | Hackenberger (1987) |
| L. africana | 3 | adult | Co-EDTA | timothy hay / mixed feed | | | 20.4 | Hackenberger (1987) |
| L. africana | 2 | juvenile | plastic tablets | native forages | 14 | 49 | | Monfort and Monfort (1979) |

**Table 3.** Comparative passage rate data for several groups of perossidactyla. T1 = first marker appearance; T2 = last marker excretion; MRT = mean retention time.

| Species | Food | T1 (h) | T2 (h) | MRT (h) | Source |
|---|---|---|---|---|---|
| Proboscidea | | | | | |
| *Elephas maximus* | zoo diet | 21–27 | 54–59 | 28–35 | this study |
| Perissodactyla | | | | | |
| Rhinocerotidae | | | | | |
| *Rhinoceros unicornis* | hay | | | 59–73 | Foose (1982) |
| *Diceros bicornis* | hay | | | 51–60 | Foose (1982) |
| *Ceratoterium simum* | hay | | | 60–65 | Foose (1982) |
| Tapiridae | | | | | |
| *Tapirus indicus* | zoo diet | 43 | 144 | | Honigmann (1936) |
| *Tapirus indicus* | hay | | | 42–48 | Foose (1982) |
| *Tapirus terrestris* | hay | | | 39–50 | Foose (1982) |
| Equidae | | | | | |
| *Equus grevyi* | hay | | | 40–45 | Foose (1982) |
| *Equus zebra* | hay | | | 43–44 | Foose (1982) |
| *Equus quagga* | hay | | | 36–46 | Foose (1982) |
| *Equus hemionus* | hay | | | 40–50 | Foose (1982) |
| *Equus caballus* | various diets | | | 28–33 | Hintz and Loy (1966) |
| *Equus caballus* | various diets | | | 38 | Van der Noot et al. (1967) |
| *Equus caballus* | various diets | | | 26–36 | Wolter et al. (1974) |
| *Equus caballus* | timothy hay | 7–11 | | 14–32 | Udén et al. (1982) |
| *Equus africanus f. asinus* | savanna pasture | | | 33 | Lechner–Doll et al. (1992) |

mean retention time measured in the largest extant ruminant, the giraffe, was much shorter than predicted by Illius and Gordon's equation for ruminants (Clauss 1998). The fact that in both hindgut fermenters and ruminants the largest representatives deviate from the general concept of increasing MRTs with increasing body size indicates the limitations of a theoretical approach that focuses on body size alone: While the approach explains why small animals have to ingest high quality food and have only a restricted potential for prolonged ingesta retention, it does not explain why large animals should not subsist on high quality forage, or pass their ingesta rather quickly. The theoretical question why the elephant does not make use of the digestive potential provided by its immense body size in terms of longer ingesta retention times and thus higher fibre digestibilities, but has chosen to employ a fast passage-low digestibility-strategy instead, remains to be answered.

## 5 Conclusions

1. The excellent recovery and the even distribution of chromium oxide in the faeces of captive Asian elephants suggests that chromium oxide can be reliably used as an inert, external marker in this species.

2. The fast passage rates obtained in this and other studies indicate that the elephant does not use the digestive potential theoretically provided by its immense body size, but instead has adopted a fast passage-low digestibility-strategy.

## Acknowledgements

The authors thank the keeping and management personnel of the Zoological Garden of Munich for their support of this study. Dr. Fred Kurt and the "Tierparkfreunde Hellabrunn e.V." facilitated the participation of W.L. at a research project at the Pinawela Elephant Orphanage, Sri Lanka. Prof. W.D. Ratnasooriya of the Zoological Faculty of the University of Colombo kindly allowed W.L. to use his laboratory facilities.

## References

Benedict, F. G. : *The physiology of the elephant*. Carnegie Institution of Washington, Publication No. 474.

Clauss, M. (1998): *Feeding giraffe*. [MSc Thesis]. London: Royal Veterinary College/The Institute of Zoology.

Clemens, E. T.; Maloiy, G. M. O. (1982): The digestive physiology of three East African herbivores: the elephant, rhinoceros and hippopotamus. *J. Zool. Lond.* 198: 141–156.

Demment, M. W.; Van Soest, P. J. (1985): A nutritional explanation for body-size patterns of ruminant and nonruminant herbivores. *Am. Nat.* 125: 641–672.

Foose, T. J. (1982): *Trophic strategies of ruminant versus nonruminant ungulates.* [PhD Thesis]. Chicago: University of Chicago.

Fujikara, T.; Oura, R.; Sekine, J. (1989): Comparative morphological studies on digestion physiology of herbivores: I. Digestibilitiy and particle distribution of digesta and feces of domestic and feral animals. *J. Fac. Agric. Tottori Univ.* 25: 87–93.

Gill, J. (1960): The rate of passage of foodstuffs through the alimentary tract of the Indian elephant in zoo conditions. *Acta Physiol. Polon.* 11: 277–289.

Hackenberger, M. K. (1987): *Diet digestibilities and ingesta transit times of captive Asian and African elephants.* [MS Thesis]. Canada: University of Guelph.

Hackenberger, M. K.; Atkinson, J. L. (1982): Digestibility studies with captive Asian and African elephants. *Am. Assoc. Zool. Parks Aquariums Conf. Proc.*: 129–137.

Hile, M. E.; Hinz, H. F.; Erb, H. N. (1997): Predicting body weight from body measurements in Asian elephants. *J. Zoo. Wildl. Med.* 28: 424–427.

Hintz, H. F.; Loy, R. G. (1966): Effects of pelleting on the nutritive value of horse rations. *J. Anim. Sci.* 25: 1059–1062.

Illius, A. W.; Gordon, I. J. (1992): Modelling the nutritional ecology of ungulate herbivores: evolution of body size and competitive interactions. *Oecologia* 89: 428–434.

Kane, E. A.; Jacobson, W. C.; Moore, L. A. (1950): A comparison of techniques used in digestibility studies with cattle. *J. Nutr.* 41: 583–596.

Kotb, A. R.; Luckey, T. D. (1972): Markers in nutrition. *Nutr. Abstr. Rev.* 42: 813–845.

Lechner-Doll, M.; Becker, G.; von Engelhardt, W. (1992): Vergleichende Aspekte zur Futterpassagezeit bei Equiden. In: *Pferdeheilkunde*. Sonderausgabe: 1. Europäische Konferenz über die Ernährung des Pferdes, pp. 36–38.

Monfort, A.; Monfort, N. (1979): Rendement d'assimilation et bilan énérgitique chez les éléphanteaux d'Afrique. *Mammalia* 43: 543–557.

Napier Bax, P.; Sheldrick, D. L. W. (1963): Some preliminary observations on the food of elephants of the Tsavo National Park (East) of Kenya. *E. Afr. Wildl. J.* 1: 40–53.

Parra, R. (1978): Comparison of foregut and hindgut fermentation in herbivores. In: *The ecology of arboreal folivores* (G. G. Montgomery, ed.). Washington DC: Smithsonian Inst Press, pp. 205–230.

Petry, H.; Rapp, W. (1970): Zur Problematik der Chromoxidbestimmung in Verdauungsversuchen. *Z. Tierphys. Tierern. Futtermittelkd.* 27: 181–189.

Rees, P. A. (1982): Gross assimilation efficiency and food passage time in the African elephant. *Afr. J. Ecol.* 20: 193–198.

Reichard, T. A.; Ullrey, D. E.; Robinson, P. T. (1982): Nutritional implications of dental problems in elephants. In: *Proc 2nd Ann Dr. Scholl Conf. Nutr. Captive Wild. Anim.*, Chicago, pp. 63–67.

Sharpe, S. J.; Robinson, M. F. (1970): Intermittent and continuous faecal markers in short-term metabolic balance studies in young women. *Br. J. Nutr.* 24: 489–500.

Stevens, C. E.; Hume, I. D. (1995): *Comparative physiology of the vertebrate digestive system*. Cambridge: Cambridge Univ. Press.

Tomat, L.; Schumann, B.; Atkinson, J. L.; Valdes, E. V. (1999): Digestibility studies with captive African elephants. In: *First Europ. Zoo. Nutr. Meeting*, Abstract Book, Rotterdam, Netherlands, p. 76.

Thielemans, M. F.; François, E.; Bodart, C.; Thewis, A. (1978): Mesure du transit gastrointestinal chez le porc à l'aide des radiolanthides. Comparaison avec le mouton. *Ann. Biol. Anim. Biochim. Biophys.* 18: 237–247.

Udén, P.; Rounsaville, T.R.; Wiggans, G. R.; Van Soest, P. J. (1982): The measurement of liquid and solid digesta retention in ruminants, equines and rabbits given timothy hay. *Br. J. Nutr.* 48: 329–339.

Ullrey, D. E.; Robinson, P. T.; Whetter, P. A. (1979): Comparative digestibility studies with zoo herbivores. In: *Am. Assoc. Zoo. Vet. Ann. Proc.*, Denver, pp. 120–121a.

Van der Noot, G. W.; Symons, L. D.; Lydman, R. K.; Fonnesbeck, P. V. (1967): Rate of passage of various feedstuffs through the digestive tract of horses. *J. Anim. Sci.* 26: 1309–1311.

Wolter, R.; Durix, A.; Letourneaut, J. C. (1974): Influence du mode de présentation du fourrage sur la vitesse du transit digestif chez le poney. *Ann. Zootech.* 25: 181–188.

*J. Nijboer*[1], *H. van Brug*[2], *M.A. Tryfonidou*[3]
*J.P.T.M. van Leeuwen*[4]

# UV-B and vitamin $D_3$ metabolism in juvenile Komodo dragons (*Varanus komodoensis*)

### *Abstract*

*The aim of this research project was to assess the vitamin D status in juvenile Komodo dragons held in captivity in Rotterdam Zoo. In addition, the effect of interference with UV-B on the serum levels of vitamin D metabolites and on the serum calcium concentrations were investigated in three Komodo dragons. Supplying 450 IU vitamin $D_3$ /kg feed orally did not increase 25-hydroxyvitamin $D_3$ (25(OH)$D_3$), the 24-hydroxylated metabolite of vitamin D (24,25(OH)$_2D_3$), 1,25-dihydroxyvitamin $D_3$ (1,25(OH)$_2D_3$) and calcium levels. In contrast, exposing the Komodo dragons to UV-B altered the levels of vitamin D metabolites. The amount of 25(OH)$D_3$ increased in komodo dragon 1 (K1) (18 to 195 nmol/ml) and in komodo dragon no 2 (K2) (31 to 291 nmol/ml). The amount of 1,25(OH)$_2D_3$ did not change significantly in both komodo dragons (139.5.6 to 235.3 pmol/l). Measurement of 24,25 (OH)$_2D_3$ in K2 showed a dramatically improvement after exposing to UV-B; the amount of 24,25(OH)$_2D_3$ rose (7.5 to 448.1 ng/ml). Komodo dragon 3 (K3) was send to Gran Canaria where it received natural UV-B. The level of 25(OH)$D_3$ improved from 18 to 272 nmol/l. The amount of 1,25(OH)$_2D_3$ did not increase either. In all komodo dragons the calcium level remained stable and within the range 3.18 to 4.44 mmol/l. The present study documents for the first time the levels of three vitamin $D_3$ metabolites and their regulation by UV-B in Komodo dragons. According to literature low levels of 25(OH)$D_3$ have caused bone defects in juvenile Komodo dragons. The current data show a clear effect of UV-B on the 25(OH)$D_3$ levels and a concomitant rise in serum 24,25(OH)$_2D_3$ levels while 1,25(OH)$_2D_3$ levels remained constant. Although we have no data on the bone metabolism in our 3 Komodo dragons it is tempting to speculate in view of the published improvements of bone after UV-B treatment, that 24,25(OH)$_2D_3$ is involved in bone metabolism in Komodo dragons. This would be in line with data obtained in chicken and human showing a positive effect on bone. Measurements of a UV-B radiating lamp show that the amount of UV-B declines rapidly over time. The decay rate also differs from lamp to lamp. If "UV-B" lamps are used for synthesising vitamin $D_3$ through the skin the UV-B radiation should be measured regularly and the lamp should*

[1] Veterinary Department, Rotterdam Zoo, Veterinary Department, Van Aersenlaan 49, 3039 KE Rotterdam, The Netherlands, Tel.: +31 10 4431 441, Fax: +31 10 4431 414, Email: J.Nijboer@Rotterdamzoo.nl (Corresponding author).

[2] Optic Research Group, Technical University Delft.

[3] Department of Clinical Sciences of Companion Animal Medicine, Utrecht University.

[4] Department of Internal Medicine, Erasmus MC, Rotterdam.

*be replaced before the UV-B radiation is too low for synthesising purposes. This study, although preliminary, clearly shows there is a dramatic change in vitamin D metabolites in juvenile komodo dragons using UV-B light, as compared with offering a dietary vitamin D supplement.*

## 1 Introduction

Komodo dragons (*Varanus komodoensis*) are rare animals, which only inhabit the islands of Komodo, Rintja, and the western half of Flores in Indonesia. Reports of animals on smaller islands nearby, including Padar and Gili Montang are probably based on observations of movement of transient animals by swimming to these islands. Komodo dragons live in the tropics on 8° southern latitude where the intensity of sunlight is much higher than in Western Europe. In nature Komodo dragons bask in the morning, from 15 minutes to more than 3 hours (Auffenberg 1981).

Komodo dragons are opportunistic carnivores, at the top of the food chain on the Indonesian islands. It has been suggested that Komodo dragons can survive on these islands as alpha predators because they are ectothermic, therefore they require less food than mammals. As an adaptation to survival during long periods of low prey density, a Komodo dragon can consume up to 80 % of its own body weight in one meal, feeding on live prey as well as carrion. They are capable of taking down deer, wild boars and water buffalos. When necessary they do not feed for months at a time. Young Komodo dragons feed on insects, small birds and mammals and on other reptiles that may be more readily available throughout the year (Walsh 1999).

Komodo dragons are listed on Cites Appendix 1 by IUCN. The wild population is considered to be several thousands of animals. The major threats include habitat alteration, poaching of prey species and tourism.

The total captive population as of November 1998 was 272 animals which consisted of 65 males, 50 females and 157 of unknown sexes in 49 institutions. Indonesian zoos have 160 animals, North America (82), Europe (14) and Asia (excluding Indonesia) and Australia together have 8 animals. Approximately a dozen successful breedings have been recorded worldwide. Zoos in Europe that maintain Komodo dragons are Thoiry in France, Chester in United Kingdom, Lisbon in Portugal, Reptillad on the Canary Islands in Spain, Zoo Berlin in Germany, Pilzen in the Czech Republic and Rotterdam Zoo in the Netherlands.

In captivity an adult Komodo dragon eats 1.5–3.0 kg of rats a week, depending upon the size of the lizard and the time of the year. Adult animals generally receive no supplemented vitamins and minerals. A diet of whole animals combined with access to hot spots up to 40 °C and natural or artificial UV-B light are thought to be adequate to promote healthy growth and development for adult Komodo dragons.

Hatchlings are fed daily for the first eight months and then every third day throughout the next year. In captivity they live on a diet comprising 20 % of whole mice and 80 % of chopped beef or lamb to which a vitamin and mineral supplement is added (Walsh 1999).

### 1.1 Bone problems in (juvenile) Komodo dragons

Allen et al. (1994) reported that nine of the twelve Komodo dragons hatched at the National Zoo in Washington D.C. (USA) had long bone fractures, discovered at about two months of age. Correspondingly the level of 25-hydroxyvitamin $D_3$ (25(OH)$D_3$), one of the intermediaries metabolites in the Vitamin $D_3$ synthesis, was low. After exposing the animals to UV-B over two months the 25(OH)$D_3$ level increased significantly. It was presumed that rapid growing animals have increased requirements for calcium (Ca), phosphorus (P), and vitamin $D_3$ and that non-reproductively active adults may be more tolerant to low levels of Ca, P and/or vitamin $D_3$, or low exposure to UV-B.

In October 1995 Rotterdam Zoo obtained three juvenile Komodo dragons hatched at the National Zoo in Washington D.C. (USA), and known to have received UV-B light to prevent bone problems. Upon arrival in Rotterdam, the young Komodo dragons did not receive UV-B or extra vitamin D initially. Later the decision was made to add vitamin $D_3$ to their diet, and subsequently they were provided with UV-B emitting lamps. One of the juvenile dragons was moved to Gran Canaria in Spain in June 1999.

### 1.2 Vitamin $D_3$ metabolism

Vitamin D represents a group of closely related compounds that possess anti rachitic activity. (Machlin 1990). The major effects of vitamin D are to increase active absorption of the calcium-ion from the proximal intestine and to increase the mineralisation of bones. Rachitis is a deficiency disease of vitamin D, which appears to have been a problem recorded in ancient times; evidence shows that rickets occurred in the Neanderthal man about 50,000 BC. (Machlin 1990). A diagram depicting the synthesis and initial step of metabolism via 24-hydroxylase activity is shown in Figure 1. There are two sources from which vitamin $D_3$ (cholecalciferol) is normally provided: it is produced in the skin and it is taken up via the diet.

In the skin, 7-dehydrocholesterol is photochemically converted by UV-B to provitamin $D_3$ that then isomerizes to vitamin $D_3$. Whether absorbed from the diet via the intestines or produced in the skin, vitamin $D_3$ is bound to vitamin D-binding protein and moves to the liver, where it is hydroxylated at the carbon 25 position by the enzyme 25-hydroxylase to form 25-hydroxyvitamin $D_3$ (25(OH)$D_3$). Finally, in the proximal tubules of the kidney the most biologically active vitamin $D_3$ metabolite, 1,25-dihydroxyvitamin $D_3$ (1,25$(OH)_2D_3$), is formed. A second metabolite of vitamin $D_3$ is produced in the kidney, namely 24,25$(OH)_2D_3$. Generally, 24,25$(OH)_2D_3$ has been considered to be the first step in the degradation pathway of 1,25$(OH)_2D_3$ and 25(OH)$D_3$. However, several human and animal studies have demonstrated a positive contribution of 24,25$(OH)_2D_3$, either alone or in combination with other hormones, to bone metabolism (van Leeuwen et al. 2001). Recent studies in chickens suggest that

24,25$(OH)_2D_3$ together with 1,25$(OH)_2D_3$ treatment improves fracture healing, and that 24,25$(OH)_2D_3$ serum levels are correlated to fracture healing (Kato et al. 1998, Seo et al. 1997).

The synthesis of 1,25$(OH)_2D_3$ is tightly controlled in order to maintain the calcium homeostasis. The major stimulators of 1,25$(OH)_2D_3$ formation are low serum calcium, parathyroid hormone and low serum phosphate levels. Increased serum calcium levels (hypercalcemia) inhibits formation of 1,25$(OH)_2D_3$. Most interestingly, 1,25$(OH)_2D_3$ itself inhibits its own formation but stimulates 24-hydroxylase activity and the formation of 24,25$(OH)_2D_3$ and 1,24,25-$(OH)_3D_3$. Thus the metabolic clearance of 1,25$(OH)_2D_3$ is enhanced. By these regulatory mechanisms toxic effects of hypercalcemia (too much calcium) in the blood is prevented.

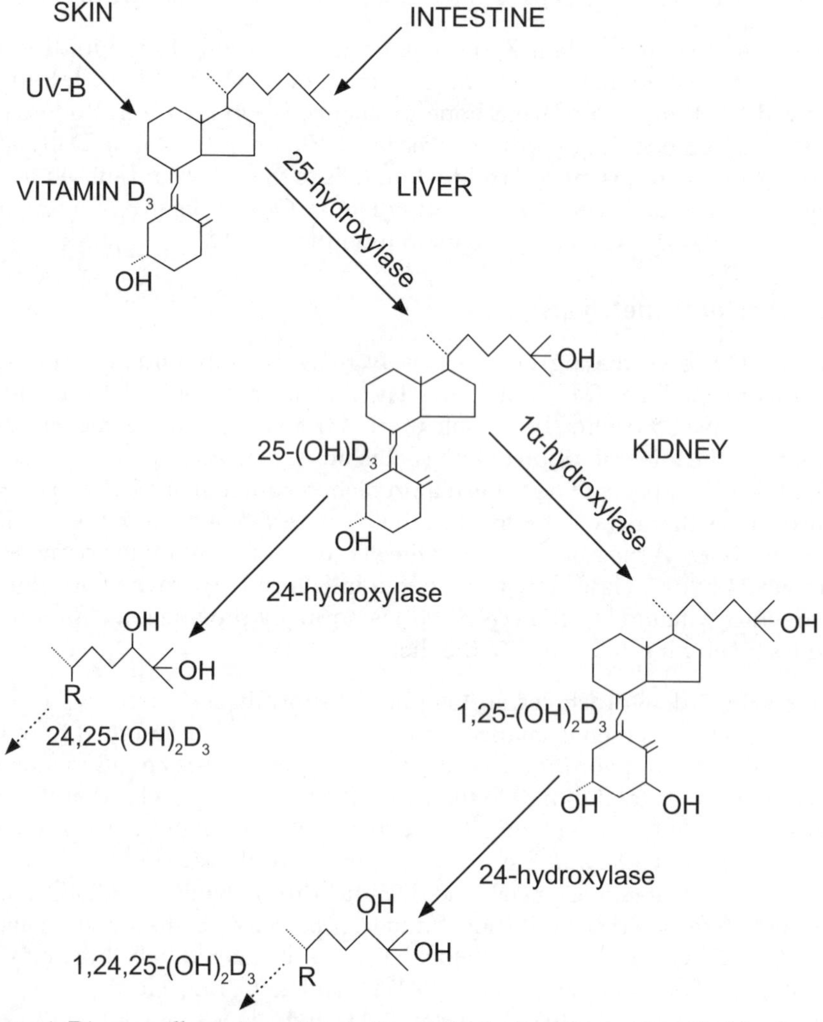


**Figure 1.** Diagram illustrating vitamin $D_3$ synthesis. Details are described in the text above.

### 1.3 UV and UV-B meter

The spectrum of irradiance of wavelengths that reach the earthly atmosphere from the sun is approximately from 100 to 3200 nanometer (nm). Molecules in the atmosphere absorb certain wavelengths, so that the solar spectrum is attenuated when the radiation reaches the surface of earth. Some of the solar radiation is partly absorbed by ozone, oxygen, carbon dioxide and water. It means that life on earth is principally exposed to Ultra Violet (UV), Visible Light and Near Infra Red. The wave length of Near Infra Red is longer than 700 nm. Visible Light has a wavelength from 400 to 700 nm. UV can be divided into: UV-C, with a range from 100–280 nm; UV-B, with a range from 280 to 315 nm; and UV-A, with a length of 315–400 nm. As mentioned before UV-B plays a major role in converting 7-dehydrocholesterol into provitamin $D_3$ in the skin with a maximum conversion at 297 ± 3 nm (Bernard 1995).

Dependent on the degrees latitude and the time of the year, in some places it is not possible for humans to produce provitamin $D_3$ by natural light. In locations 52° North latitude (for example Edmonton, in Canada) no provitamin $D_3$ will be produced from October until the beginning of April (Holick 1997). Berlin, Warschau and Rotterdam in Europe are also situated on the same latitude. Tests in Boston (42° North), have confirmed that no provitamin $D_3$ was produced from November until February. The European cities of Barcelona and Rome also lie on 42° North. Experiments have demonstrated that provitamin $D_3$ is produced throughout the year at the latitude of Los Angeles (34° North), the same latitude as locations in Morocco and Northern Syria. The data is relevant to human provitamin $D_3$ synthesis under these light conditions, but similar considerations can be made about synthesis in reptiles, and Komodo dragons in particular. Normal windows absorb UV-B emissions rather than transmitting them thus if Komodo dragons rely on the availability of UV-B for their provitamin $D_3$ synthesis, it is unlikely they receive enough UV-B light when kept at European latitudes, particularly during winter months.

The aim of the current study was to assess the vitamin $D_3$ status in Komodo dragons held in captivity in the Rotterdam Zoo (at 52° North), and to investigate the efficacy of feeding an oral vitamin supplement versus the use of UV-B lamps. A special meter was designed to measure the intensity of UV-B light emissions from the lamps being used (figure 2).

## 2 Methods

### 2.1 The Komodo dragons

In Rotterdam Zoo, three Komodo dragons (K1, K2 and K3 respectively) were housed according to the suggestions made by the taxon manager (Walsh 1999). All three were housed separately in a cage with a surface area of 10 square meters. All the Komodo dragons were fed once a week. The diet consisted of whole rats and small rabbits and they were fed ad libitum. After 20 months K1 weighed 2.1 kg , K2 2.5 kg and K3 1.5 kg. According to data from the National Zoo, the weight for juvenile dragons at 20 months should be between 1.5 kg and 3.1 kg (Allen et al. 1994).

As mentioned already, the Komodo dragons arrived in Rotterdam Zoo in October 1995. For ethical reasons relating to the care and welfare of these animals it was not possible to consistently blood sample all three Komodo dragons simultaneously. Furthermore, on several occasions samples taken were insufficient for analyses. Thus, the data presented in this paper simply documents physiological responses over time to management changes for this species.

In May 1996 (Month 1) the first blood samples were taken from the tail vein using heparin tubes and immediately stored at –68 ºC until analysis. In February 1997 (Month 9) Carmix®, a vitamin and mineral supplement, was added to the diet contributing 450 IU vitamin $D_3$ per kg food. Blood samples were taken again two months later (Month 11).

Two of the Komodo dragons were exposed to UV-B using Osram Ultra-Vitalux® lightbulbs. The wattage of the lamp is 300 W and it has a service time of 1000 hours. The Osram Ultra-Vitalux® consists of a quartz burner and a tungsten filament which are blended in such a way that, in combination with the special glass bulb and its interior reflector, a certain radiation is emitted. The effect of this radiation is practically the same as the radiation of natural sunlight (Osram Ultra-Vitalux® manual 2001).

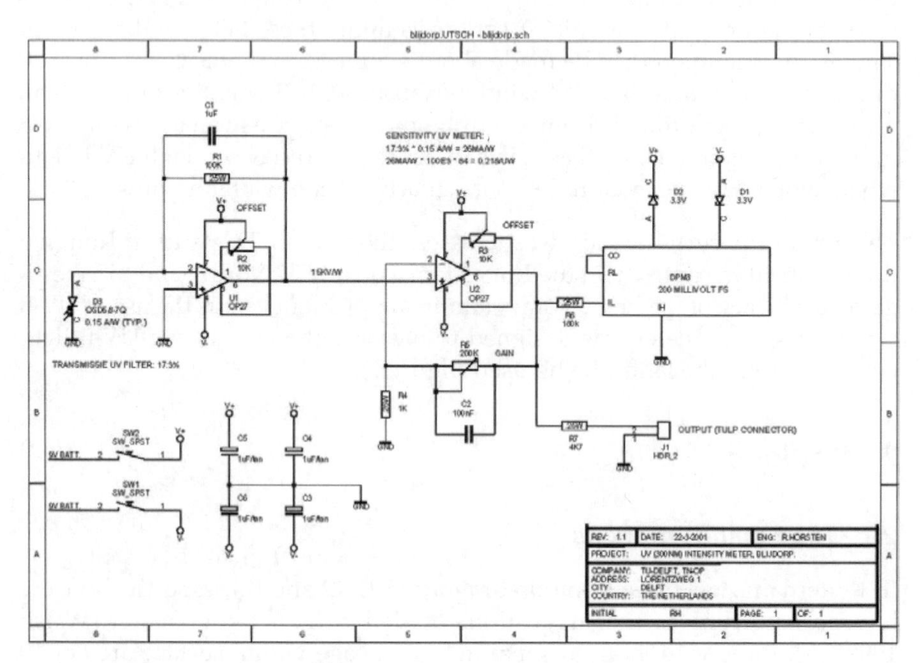


**Figure 2.** Electric schedule of the UV intensity meter.

K1 was exposed to UV-B from Month 13, K2 from Month 21. All lamps were hung between 60–80 cm above the ground surface in the cages in such a way that the Komodo dragons had free access to the radiation of the lamps.

K3 was sent to Gran Canaria (situated 28° North) in Month 25, where it had access to an outdoor facility and was exposed to natural sunlight. A blood sample of that dragon was obtained in Month 33 and analysed in the same way as samples collected in Rotterdam.

## 2.2 Vitamin D analyses

The $25(OH)D_3$ analyses were performed according the description of DiaSorin (Minnesota, USA). The assay consists of a two step procedure. The first procedure involves a rapid extraction of $25(OH)D_3$ and other hydroxylated metabolites from the serum. Following extraction, the treated sample is then assayed using an equilibrium radio immunoassay (RIA) procedure which is based on an antibody with specificity to $25(OH)D_3$. The sensitivity of this assay has shown rates to be at or below 1.5 ng/ml.

The amount of $1,25(OH)_2D_3$ was analysed by the IDS Gamma-B kit by immunoextraction followed by quantitation by $^{125}I$ radio immunoassay. The assay has a calculated sensitivity of 2.1 pg/ml.

Calcium analyses were performed using a colorimetric calcium assay (Sigma Diagnostics). All analyses were performed by the laboratories of the Department of Internal Medicine of the Erasmus MC in Rotterdam, except the analysis of $24,25(OH)_2D_3$ which was performed on the Department of Clinical Sciences of Companion Animal Medicine of the Utrecht University. $24,25(OH)_2D_3$ was quantitatively determined by a modified radio immunoassay (RIA) (DiaSorin, Stillwater, Minnesota, USA). Before processing, labeled standards 24R,25-dihydroxy[26,27-methyl-$_3$H]cholecalciferol (specific activity 15.4 GBq/mg, Amersham Pharmacia Biotech, UK) was added to plasma samples and to the standards of the RIA to determine individual sample recovery. Samples were extracted twice with ethylacetate:cyclohexane (1:1, v/v) and once with methanol:ethylacetate:cyclohexane (4:5:5, v/v) (Bosch 1983) and $24,25(OH)_2D_3$ was separated by solid phase extraction using $NH_2$ cartridges (Bakerbond spe Amino Disposable Extraction Columns, J.T. Baker, Phillipsburg, USA) according to the described method of McGraw and Hug (1990). The standard curve of the stable vitamin $D_3$ metabolite showed good parallel dilution to the standard curve of the RIA. The intra- and inter-assay coefficient for $24,25(OH)_2D_3$ were 10.1 % and 8.5 %, respectively.

## 2.3 Design of the UV-B meter

The intensity or UV-B meter was designed and constructed by the Optic Research Group of the Technical University of Delft in the Netherlands. The UV-B meter is sensitive to a narrow wavelength band around 302.01 nm. The intensity meter consists of a photo diode, placed directly behind an interference filter to ensure that only the desired wavelengths impinge the sensor, and an LCD screen. For situations where it is not possible to read the display, a mechanism is provided to connect a simple multi-meter to the UV-B meter. This enables the measurement of UV-B radiation to take place at greater distances and otherwise impossible angles.

The photo detector from Centronic (code OSD 5.8-Q) was selected for its relatively high sensitivity for UV-B radiation. The interference filter was obtained from Oriel and was tested by the Optic Research Group on transmission besides the desired wavelength range. No leakage was observed, which means that no wavelength other than the desired ones could penetrate the filter. The peak transmission (17.25 %) of the filter was at 302.01 nm. The photons impinging on the photo detector result in a small voltage. This voltage is shown, after amplification, on the small liquid crystal display.

The UV-B meter is not calibrated absolutely and therefore it can only be used for relative measurements. It can be used to monitor UV-B radiation over time and the spatial distribution measurements of UV-B radiation from a single lamp or a number of lamps. The UV-B meter can be used to check when lamps require to be changed, and to get an impression where the UV-B rich spots are in certain areas. It can be used to detect the light intensity differences between different animal facilities. Suitably educated technical staff can easily manufacture the meter and the costs can be limited to approximately 700 Euro.

The UV-B meter measurements are in milliVolts: the data collected by the photo diode at every point is equal to about 5 nW light falling on the surface of the sensor (1 $cm^2$). The meter was calibrated in such a way that the value for a distance of 1 meter is 150. The numeric value of the UV-B meter is 0.218 V/microW, therefore in practical terms, the amount of microW/$cm^2$ is the read out value divided by 218.

In cage no 1 (K2) the UV-B lamp was hung 80 cm above the ground and in cage 2 (K1) for practical reasons, the lamp was 60 cm above the ground. Values presented are the average of two measurements taken during the same day. The UV-B measurements were taken from the ground. Both Komodo dragons had free access to sunbath under the lamps. The lamps were connected to a timer, on for two hours in the morning and two hours in the afternoon, every day. The lamps were changed every six months.

## 3 Results

### 3.1 Vitamin D metabolites

Table 1 and figures 3–5 present all the data on levels of $25(OH)D_3$, $1,25(OH)_2D_3$ and $24,25(OH)_2D$ measured in the blood serum of K1, K2 and K3.

From their arrival from Washington D.C. in October 1995 until May 1997, the Komodo dragons did not receive any UV-B or orally supplemented vitamin $D_3$, aside from what their normal diet (rabbits and rats) would provide. Although they all received sufficient UV-B at the National Zoo (Allen, pers. comm.) to maintain the normal level of $25(OH)D_3$ (150–200 nmol/ml (Gillespie et al. 2000), the amount of $25(OH)D_3$ dropped during the 18 months after arrival

**Table 1.** Levels of $25(OH)D_3$, $1,25(OH)_2D_3$ and $24,25(OH)_2D_3$ in the blood of the Komodo dragons.

| | Komodo dragon (K1) | | Komodo dragon (K2) | | | Komodo dragon (K3) | |
|---|---|---|---|---|---|---|---|
| Month | $25(OH)D_3$ nmol/l | $1,25(OH)_2D_3$ pmol/l | $25(OH)D_3$ nmol/l | $1,25(OH)_2D_3$ pmol/l | $24,25(OH)_2D_3$ ng/ml | $25(OH)D_3$ nmol/l | $1,25(OH)_2D_3$ pmol/l |
| 1 | 18 | 235.3 | 31 | 139.5 | | 18 | 158.2 |
| 11 | 26 | 159.9 | 37 | 201.9 | 7.5 | 33 | 161.3 |
| 18 | 131 | 132.8 | 29 | 188 | | 19 | |
| 20 | | | | | | 17 | 121.6 |
| 26 | 195 | 177.9 | 201 | 143.8 | 294.6 | | |
| 33 | | | | | | 272 | 152.7 |
| 35 | | | 291 | 158.2 | 448.1 | | |

in Rotterdam. This data can be found as Month 1 in the tables and figures. Vitamin D was then added to the diet (Month 9) and for each dragon, vitamin $D_3$ was supplemented at the level of 450 IU per kg food. Analyses of the serum in Month 11 showed no significant changes in the level of $25(OH)D_3$.

In Month 13 UV-B emitting lambs (Osram Ultra-Vitalux®) were installed in the cage of K1. The amount of $25(OH)D_3$ increased (Table 1 and Figure 3). K2 was exposed to UV-B in Month 21 which also resulted in an increase of $25(OH)D_3$ (table 1, figure 4). A similar rise in $25(OH)D_3$ was measured from blood analyses taken after K3 was sent to Gran Canaria, in Month 25 (table 1 and figure 5).

The concentration of $1,25(OH)_2D_3$ levels were determined using the same blood samples. However, neither the 450 IU vitamin D supplemented food nor the UV-B treatment resulted in a consistent change in $1,25(OH)_2D_3$ levels (table 1 and the figures 3–5).

Another important vitamin $D_3$ metabolite is $24,25(OH)_2D_3$. Due to limited amounts of heparin plasma available the $24,25(OH)_2D_3$ levels were only assayed for one dragon (K2). Data were obtained at Months 11, 26 and 35 and concentrations of $24,25(OH)_2D_3$ increased over this time period (table 1 and figure 4). The timing of the increase suggests that it was in response to the UV-B lamps, rather than dietary supplementation.

### 3.2 Calcium

Throughout the UV-B treatment and the move to Gran Canaria serum calcium levels remained stable for all three dragons. The values are shown in table 2.

**Table 2.** Calcium levels in the blood of Komodo dragons (mmol/l).

| *Month* | *K1* | *K2* | *K3* |
|---|---|---|---|
| 11 | 4.16 | 3.84 | 4.48 |
| 18 | 3.18 | | |
| 20 | | | 3.8 |
| 26 | 3.7 | 4.44 | |
| 33 | | | 3.98 |
| 35 | | 3.86 | |

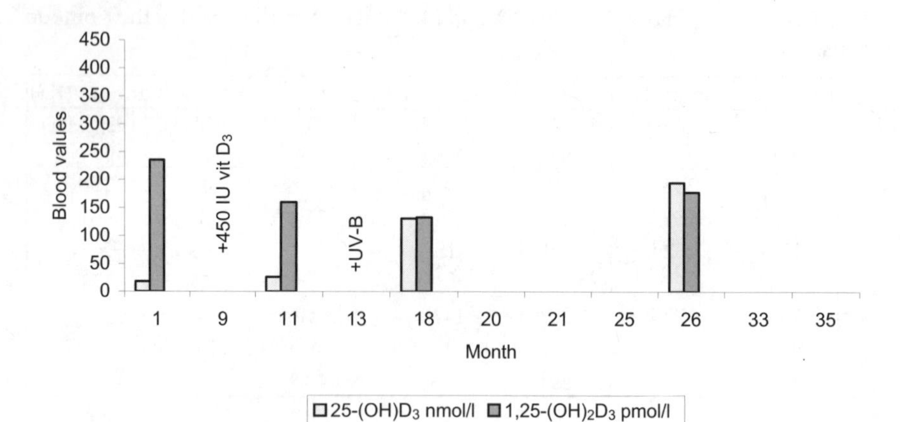


**Figure 3:** Blood values found in komodo dragon no 1 (K1)

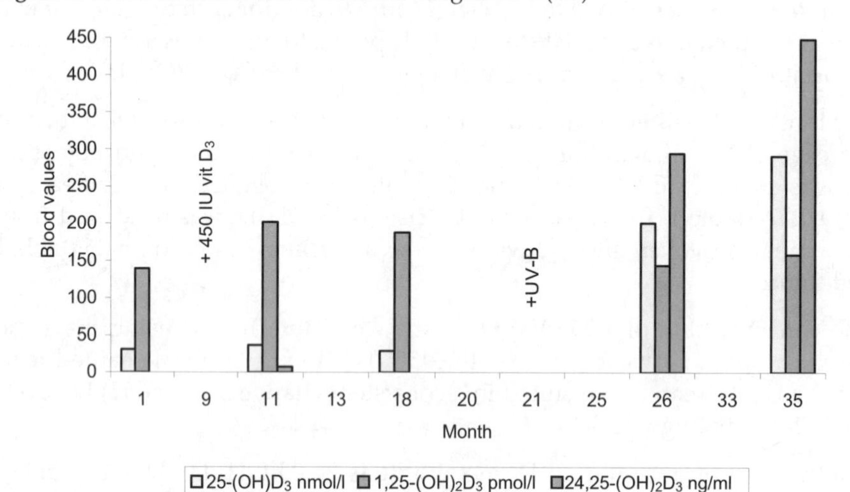


**Figure 4.** Blood values found in komodo dragon no 2 (K2)

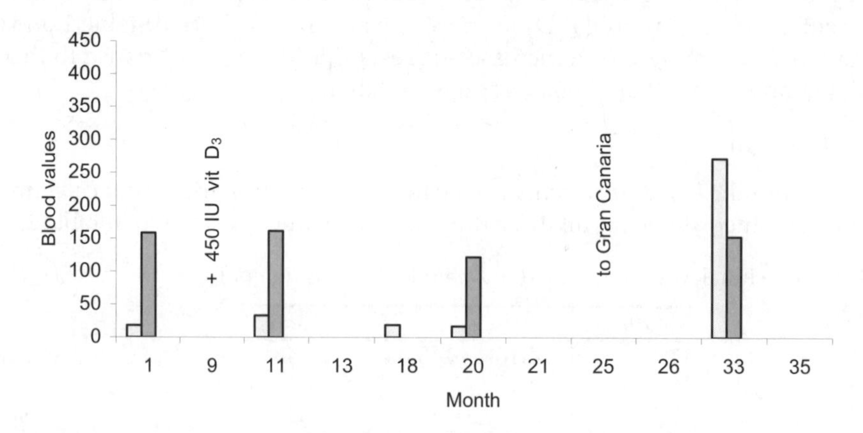


**Figure 5.** Blood values found in komodo dragon no 3 (K3)

### 3.3 Lamp radiation

Table 3 shows the decline over time in UV-B emitted from the lamps used in the Komodo dragon facilities. After it was removed from cage No 2, that particular UV-B lamp was used in enclosures for other reptiles and UV-B measured six months later was reduced to 0.16 UVB/cm$^2$. Similar values were observed after replacing the lamps every six month (van de Koore, pers. comm.).

**Table 3.** Decline in lamp radiation (watts UV-B/cm$^2$) of two lamps hanging in two cages.

| *Month* | *Cage 1* | *Cage 2* |
|---|---|---|
| 19 | 0.72 | |
| 22 | 0.43 | 0.8 |
| 24 | 0.34 | 0.3 |
| 25 | 0.23 | 0.34 |

## 4 Discussion

For practical reasons blood could not be sampled on a systematic basis, therefore the analysed data represents a trend in the changes of the vitamin D metabolites under different circumstances.

The initial values for 25(OH)$D_3$ measured in Month 1 were very low when compared with levels measured in Komodo dragons exposed to UV-B (150 to 200 nmol/L), and most certainly would have caused bone problems. Similar levels were found in cases of clinical lameness and poor density on radiographs, with fractures in several long bones (Gillespie et al. 2000). Supplementing 450 IU vitamin $D_3$ per kg food for two month did not improve the 25(OH)$D_3$ levels, suggesting that juvenile Komodo dragons cannot rely on oral vitamin $D_3$ to satisfy their vitamin D synthesis. Exposing Komodo dragons to artificial or natural light improves the amount of 25(OH)$D_3$ within 5 months to within the 'normal' range (150–200 nmol/l).

No reference data were available to evaluate the levels of 1,25$(OH)_2D_3$ observed, ranging from (121.6 to 235.3 pmol/l). The mean value was 163.9 pmol/l (13 blood samples from 3 komodo dragons). No correlation was found with supplying extra vitamin $D_3$ or exposing the Komodo dragons to UV-B, however the data set is extremely limited.

Although normal values of 24,25$(OH)_2D_3$ are not known it is clear that when Komodo dragons exposed to UV-B the amount of 24,25$(OH)_2D_3$ increases significantly. Due to limited availability of serum, the effect of supplying vitamin $D_3$ orally on 24,25$(OH)_2D_3$ levels could not be determined in this study.

Calcium levels varied from 3.18 to 4.48 mmol/l, with a mean of 3.93 mmol/l (6 samples from 3 animals). Gillespie et al. (2000) found the mean value for 48 Komodo dragons was 3.62 mmol/l with an observed range for measured values of 2.94 to 4.30. Therefore the calcium levels measured in Rotterdam fall within the mean range and variation of this larger data set.

The limited data of the current study shows the effect of UV-B on the 25(OH)$D_3$ levels in Komodo dragons. Although we have no information on the bone density of the dragons in our study, by combining our observations with those made at the National Zoo on increasing serum 25(OH)$D_3$ and the subsequent reduction in bone problems and other clinical symptoms they observed, it is reasonable to suggest that adequate UV-B availability is important for the well being of Komodo dragons. The current study reports for the first time 1,25$(OH)_2D_3$ levels in Komodo dragons. An interesting observation is that throughout the treatment period the levels of serum calcium and the most biologically active vitamin D metabolite (1,25$(OH)_2D_3$) remained stable. From a physiological prespective this makes good sense since calcium is a very important ion whose level needs to be controlled very tightly, because both hypocalcaemia and hypocalcaemia can be life threatening. Given that 1,25$(OH)_2D_3$ is the most important regulator of serum calcium it is important that the level of this hormone is also strictly regulated. If the dramatic increase in 25(OH)$D_3$ levels after UV-B treatment had been followed by a comparable increase in 1,25$(OH)_2D_3$ then the animals would have become hypercalcemic.

Combining Gillespie's data and with values presented in this paper it is intriguing to note that despite similar levels of 1,25$(OH)_2D_3$ in relation to low and high 25(OH)$D_3$ concentrations, clinical problems are observed in Komodo dragons when the concentration of 25(OH)$D_3$ is low (Gillespie et al. 2000). Therefore, it is tempting to speculate that an additional vitamin $D_3$ metabolite might be important to restore the bone defects. A possible candidate is 24,25$(OH)_2D_3$ (van Leeuwen et al. 2001), which we show here to increase in parallel to 25(OH)$D_3$. This is not unique to Komodo dragons, since in humans an increase in serum calcium or 1,25$(OH)_2D_3$ is followed by an increase in 24-hydroxylase activity in order to prevent further formation of 1,25$(OH)_2D_3$ and to stimulate inactivation of 1,25$(OH)_2D_3$ by forming 1,24,25-$(OH)_3D_3$. A possible role for 24,25$(OH)_2D_3$ in this respect is supported by data in humans showing a beneficial effect on bone when 24,25$(OH)_2D_3$ was added to the treatment with 1$\alpha$-(OH)-vitamin $D_3$ (i. e. a precursor of 1,25$(OH)_2D_3$, see figure 1) (Birkenhäger-Frenkel et al. 1995). Moreover, a positive effect of 24,25$(OH)_2D_3$ on fracture healing has been reported (Seo et al. 1997; Kato et al. 1998).

The amount of UV-B emitted from a so-called UV-B lamp declines rapidly. Furthermore not every Osram Ultra-Vitalux® has the same amount of UV-B radiation and the decay rate of radiation also differs for each lamp. The UV-B radiation is highest in the middle of the lamp. When the sensor of the UV-B meter is moved from the centre of the lamp, the radiation declines very fast. Also, the radiation declines rapidly if the lamp is placed higher above the ground (Nijboer 2000, unpublished data). No UV-B radiation values were measured from other UV-B lamps but it is likely that similar observations would be made. Thus, when UV-B lamps are provided for vitamin $D_3$ synthesis via the skin, the amount of UV-B radiation should be measured not just when the lamps are installed, but also during the burning life of the lamp so they are replaced once UV-B emittance declines (which may not be the same as the manufacturer's recommendation).

More research is needed to estimate the minimal UV-B radiation for Komodo dragons to ensure vitamin $D_3$ metabolic synthesis remains within the normal range.

## 5 Conclusions

1. Supplying vitamin $D_3$ orally to juvenile Komodo dragons did not improve serum levels of $25(OH)D_3$ and $1,25(OH)_2D_3$.
2. Exposing juvenile Komodo dragons to UV-B radiation increased the $25(OH)D_3$ and $24,25(OH)_2D_3$ levels but not the amount of $1.25\text{-}(OH)_2D_3$.
3. Exposing juvenile Komodo dragons to UV-B did not change the amount of calcium in the blood.
4. Measuring UV-B radiation of lamps is necessary to obtain a reliable indication of the used UV-B lamps.
5. Adequate UV-B radiation is important for vitamin D synthesis and the well being of Komodo dragons.

## Acknowledgment

C. J. Buurma, Department of Internal Medicine, Erasmus Medical Centre, Rotterdam for technical laboratory support.

## Products mentioned in the text

Carmix®: vitamin mineral supplement, manufactured by Hope Farms, Hoge Rijndijk 14, 3440 AB Woerden, The Netherlands.

Osram Ultra-Vitalux® : Solar lamp, Osram, Germany.

## References

Allen, M. E.; Oftedal, O.; Roiscoe, R.; Walsh, T.; Holick, M. (1994): Update on vitamin D and UV light in basking lizards. *Proceedings American Association of Zoo Veterinarians,* pp. 214–215.

Auffenberg, W. (1981): *The behavioural ecology of the Komodo dragons.* Library of Congress Cataloging in Publication Data. USA.

Bernard, J. B. (1995): *Spectral irradiance of fluorescent lamps and their efficacy for promoting vitamin D synthesis in herbivorous reptiles.* Dissertation Michigan State University. UMI, Ann Arbor. USA.

Birkenhäger-Frenkel, D. H.; Pols, H. A. P.; Zeelenberg, J.; Eijgelsheim, J. J.; Schot, R.; Nigg, A. L.; Weimar, W.; Mulder, P. G.; Birkenhäger, J. C. (1995): Effects of 24R,25-dihydroxyvitamin $D_3$ in combination with the 1αhydroxyvitamin D3 in predialysis renal insufficiency: biochemistry and histomorphometry of cancellous bone. *J. Bone Miner. Res.* 10: 197–204.

Bosch, R.;Visser, W. J.; Thijssen, J. H.; Duursma, S. A. (1983): Synthesis of [10S(19)-3H] dihydrotachysterol from ergocalciferol and preliminary investigations into its metabolic fate in rats. *J. Steroid Biochem.* 18: 441–447.

Gillespie, D.; Frye, F. L.; Stockham, S. L.; Fredeking, T. (2000): Blood values in Wild and Captive Komodo Dragons (*Varanus Komodoesnis*). *Zoo Biology* 19: 495–509.

Holick, M. F. (1997): Photobiology of Vitamin D. In: *Vitamin D* (Feldman, Glorieux and Pike, eds.). Academic Press.

Kato, A.; Seo, E. G.; Einhorn, T. A.; Morita, K.; Bishop, J. E.; Norman, A. W. (1998): Studies on 24R,25-dihyroxivitamin $D_3$: evidence for a non nuclear membrane receptor in the chick tibial fracture-healing of tibial fracture-healing callus. *Bone* 23: 141–146.

Van Leeuwen, J. P. T. M.; van den Bemd, G. J. C. M.; van Driel, M.; Buurman, C. J.; Pols, H. A. P. 2001: 24,25-Dihydroxyvitamin $D_3$ and bone metabolism. *Steroids* 66: 375–380.

Machlin, L. J. (1990): *Handbook of vitamins.* 2nd Edition, Marcel Dekker, Inc. New York. USA.

McGraw, C. A.; Hug, G. (1990): Simultaneous measurement of 25-hydroxy, 24,25-dihydroxy-, and 1,25-dihydroxyvitamin D without use of HPLC. *Med. Lab Sci.* 47: 17–25.

Seo, E. G.; Einhorn, A. W.; Norman, A. W. (1997): 24R,25-dihydroxyvitamin $D_3$: an essential vitamin $D_3$ metalbolite for both normal bone integrity and healing of tibial fracture in chicks. *Endocrinology* 138 (9): 3864–3872.

Walsh, T.; Visser, G. (1999): *Taxon Management Account Komodo Dragon.* National Zoological Park, Washington D.C., U.S.A.

*C. Schwitzer*[1], *W. Kaumanns*[1]

# Foraging patterns of free-ranging and captive primates – implications for captive feeding regimes

### *Abstract*

*In the wild, primates usually spend a large proportion of their active time foraging and feeding. Access to food is influenced by individual factors (e. g. the physiological abilities of the animal), social factors (e. g. dominance hierarchies), and especially by the spatial and seasonal distribution of the food resources.*

*Food resources in the wild may be scarce and widely distributed throughout the animals' home ranges, and certain food types may be available only during limited periods of the year. The amount of food consumed within a certain time period, and the temporal pattern of nutrient and energy intake, are influenced by these distribution patterns. Ideally, feeding primates in captivity should include such a varied food distribution, both spatially and temporally. However, this is often not possible under captive conditions. Spreading out food can only be done within the limits of the animals' enclosure. Moreover, it is rarely feasible to feed more than four times a day, as there is not enough staff available. Also, the "zoo-day" is usually not more than eight hours long (depending on the working times of the keepers).*

*A review of the literature on human feeding behaviour suggests that the temporal pattern of food intake is critical for an optimal (species-specific) functioning of satiation processes. Ideally, optimal feeding schedules should be developed with reference to foraging data from the field. The aim of this paper is to analyse relevant studies and, with regard to certain nutrition-related problems, to work out how optimal feeding and foraging patterns in captive primates could be induced.*

Keywords

*Primates, nutrition, feeding ecology, feeding frequency, energy intake, food intake regulation*

[1] Zoologischer Garten Köln, WG Primatology, Riehler Str. 173, 50735 Köln, Germany. Corresponding author: Dipl.-Biol. Christoph Schwitzer, Zoologischer Garten Köln, Riehler Str. 173, 50735 Köln, Germany, Tel.: 0221-7785143, Fax: 0221-7785111, e-mail: studpri@zoo-koeln.de

## 1 Introduction

Although there have been considerable advances within the field of primate nutrition during the last half-century, nutrition-related problems still exist in many primate species kept in zoos. Not only does this apply to nutritionally highly specialised species such as douc langurs (*Pygathrix nemaeus*; Ruempler, 1991) or bamboo lemurs (*Hapalemur spec.*; Feistner and Mutschler 2000), but also "generalists" such as certain macaque species (e.g. Oxnard, 1989) and lemurs of the *Lemuridae* family (Schwitzer and Kaumanns 2000) are affected. Problems range from malnutrition (not enough of one or more specific nutrients; e.g. Crissey et al. 1998; Crissey and Pribyl 2000; Junge et al. 2000) to toxicity (too much of one particular nutrient; e.g. Spelman et al. 1989) and overnutrition (too much of everything, particularly energy; e.g. West and York 1998). The latter in many cases results in obesity, a condition often seen in lemurs (Pereira and Pond 1995; Terranova and Coffman 1997; Schwitzer and Kaumanns 2001), but also in cercopithecines (Kemnitz 1984; Schwartz et al. 1993; West and York 1998) and apes (Cousins 1972; Goeltenboth 1982; Weisenberg et al. 1991; Mueller and Schildger 1992; Schmidt et al. 2001; Lintzenich and Ward 2001). Obesity in turn can be the cause of problems like reproductive failure or skeletal abnormalities (see Hume 1986, 1995; Pereira and Pond 1995; Terranova and Coffman 1997). Moreover, in zoo animals, problems such as behavioural stereotypies or high frequencies of intra-group aggression can be caused by inappropriate feeding schedules (Wasserman and Cruikshank 1983; Akers and Schildkraut 1985; Gil Burmann and Pelaez 1990; Lam et al. 1991; Lukas 1999).

In their model of the foraging process, Cant and Temerin (1984) regard the problems that a foraging animal has to solve as a combination of the nutritional needs of the animal and the biotic and physical environmental factors determining the circumstances under which needs must be met. The environmental factors were grouped into nine categories (Cant and Temerin 1984): climate, physical structure of the habitat, predators, co-consumers, spatiotemporal distribution of food patches, patch size, arrangement of foods within a patch, physical characteristics of food items, and constituents of food items. In this paper we will focus on the spatiotemporal distribution of primates' food patches and the resulting foraging and feeding patterns. Emphasis is laid on linking these patterns to food intake regulation and, thus, to nutrition-related problems such as obesity. It is intended to demonstrate differences between patterns of primates' nutrient and energy intake in the wild and in captivity and to work out how feeding schedules for captive primates could be optimised.

## 2 Food distribution and feeding patterns in the wild

The nature of many primate environments in the wild is such that food resources are distributed spatially and seasonally in a patchy fashion (Oates 1987). Since food is such a crucial resource, foraging is usually the major determinant of patterns of primate activity (Carlstead 1996). Because the utilisation of food items and the movements of an individual from one resource point (food patch) to another each take a certain amount of time, the spatial distribution of resource points that are utilised is reflected in the time budgets of the animals (Altmann 1979). Although it is theoretically possible that food patches are evenly dispersed, it is more likely that primates must deal with clumped and/or random distributions. The resulting variation in interpatch distances and resource predictability influences search and travel activities (Cant and Temerin 1984).

Regarding the spatial distribution of food, Oates (1987) divides primates into two groups: *foragers*, which exploit small, highly dispersed food patches (insects, certain fruits), and *banqueters*, which feed in patches that are large relative to the animal's needs (leaves). In primates belonging to the latter group, whose diets largely consist of leaves, the foraging time is reduced in favour of prolonged resting bouts that are important for digestion processes. However, folivorous species need longer to actually ingest and chew their food. Red colobus monkeys (*Piliocolobus badius*) in a study by Struhsaker (1980) for instance spent 52 % of the day foraging and feeding, of which 41 % was devoted to feeding alone. Resting made up for 32 % of the day. Primate species belonging to the *forager* group tend to devote much of their daily activity to travelling and foraging. Red-tailed guenons (*Cercopithecus ascanius*) in Struhsaker's study (1980) for example spent 34 % of the day ingesting and chewing food, 17 % travelling on search for food, and 21 % scanning the vegetation (foraging). This adds up to 72 % of the day devoted to feeding and foraging in this species. Table 1 summarises the findings of a number of field studies on different primate species with regard to proportions of activity time spent on foraging, feeding, and resting, as well as feeding frequency and feeding bout duration.

Foraging activity must not only be closely tied to where, but also to when and for how long food patches exist. The patches may appear and disappear or fluctuate in size over short and long time intervals (Cant and Temerin 1984). Where animal prey is consumed for instance, the activity patterns of the prey are a major source of temporal variation in the existence of a patch and the potential gain derived from foraging in it (Cant and Temerin 1984). Regarding plant foods, there exist tree species bearing ripe fruit for only a few hours of the day and then ceasing to be a food patch until the next day (e. g. Howe 1977; cited in Cant and Temerin 1984). For many primate species there are periods when preferred, high-quality food items are scarce and at these times lower-quality items are eaten and harvesting patterns change (Oates 1987). Primates have evolved different behavioural and physiological adaptations to seasonal environments. Heiduck (1998) for example found that masked titi monkeys (*Callicebus personatus melanochir*) adapt their patch residence times to cope with seasonality in food availability. The studied animals increased patch residence time as well as feeding time and reduced the daily distance travelled in the lean season. In a study by Meyers and Wright (1993), golden-crowned sifakas (*Propithecus tattersalli*) decreased their daily path lengths during the dry season, which the authors interpreted to represent a behavioural

**Table 1.** Proportions of activity time [%] of wild primates spent on foraging, feeding, and resting, as well as feeding frequency and feeding bout duration. % f. + f. = % foraging + feeding; feed. bouts = no. of distinct feeding bouts per day; bout length = mean duration of one feeding bout [min.]; - = no data available; *average number of food types eaten per day (actual number of distinct feeding bouts might be higher); **average number of feeding trees utilised per day (actual number of distinct feeding bouts might be higher, e.g. insects are not included in these figures); [1]only diurnal activity records included; nomenclature following Groves (2001).

| Species | % foraging | % feeding | % f. + f. | % resting | feed. bouts | bout lenght | Source |
|---|---|---|---|---|---|---|---|
| *Lemur catta* | – | 25–31 | – | 39–41 | – | – | Sussman, 1977; 1979 |
| *Eulemur rufus* | – | 17–26 | – | 46–57 | – | – | Sussman, 1977; 1979; Overdorff, 1996 |
| *Eulemur rubriventer* | – | 20 | – | 54 | – | – | Overdorff, 1996 |
| *Hapalemur alaotrensis*[1] | – | – | 20–21 | 60–68 | – | – | Mutschler, 1999 |
| *Varecia variegata variegata* | 6 | 16–20 | 22–26 | 55 | 5,8* | – | Britt, 1998; Morland, 1991 |
| *Lepilemur leucopus* | – | 30 | – | 50 | – | – | Nash, 1996 |
| *Indri indri* | – | 37–39 | – | – | 5–12** | – | Pollock, 1977 |
| *Avahi laniger* | – | 22 | – | 60 | – | – | Harcourt, 1991; Ganzhorn et al., 1985 |
| *Propithecus edwardsi* | – | – | – | – | >20 | – | Wright, 1987 |
| *Propithecus verreauxi* | – | 24–33 | – | ~ 35–45 | – | – | Richard, 1977; 1979 |
| *Daubentonia madagascariensis* | – | 14–41 | – | 5–19 | – | – | Andriamasimanana, 1994; Ancrenaz et al., 1994 |
| *Otolemur crassicaudatus* | ~ 20 | ~ 6 | ~ 26 | ~ 10 | – | – | Crompton, 1984 |
| *Galago senegalensis* | 25–77 | 2–11 | 27–88 | ~ 5 | – | – | Crompton, 1984 |
| *Lemur catta* | – | 25–31 | – | 39–41 | – | – | Sussman, 1977; 1979 |
| *Eulemur rufus* | – | 17–26 | – | 46–57 | – | – | Sussman, 1977; 1979; Overdorff, 1996 |
| *Eulemur rubriventer* | – | 20 | – | 54 | – | – | Overdorff, 1996 |
| *Hapalemur alaotrensis*[1] | – | – | 20–21 | 60–68 | – | – | Mutschler, 1999 |
| *Varecia variegata variegata* | 6 | 16–20 | 22–26 | 55 | 5,8* | – | Britt, 1998; Morland, 1991 |
| *Lepilemur leucopus* | – | 30 | – | 50 | – | – | Nash, 1996 |
| *Indri indri* | – | 37–39 | – | – | 5–12** | – | Pollock, 1977 |
| *Avahi laniger* | – | 22 | – | 60 | – | – | Harcourt, 1991; Ganzhorn et al., 1985 |
| *Propithecus edwardsi* | – | – | – | – | >20 | – | Wright, 1987 |
| *Propithecus verreauxi* | – | 24–33 | – | ~ 35–45 | – | – | Richard, 1977; 1979 |
| *Daubentonia madagascariensis* | – | 14–41 | – | 5–19 | – | – | Andriamasimanana, 1994; Ancrenaz et al., 1994 |
| *Otolemur crassicaudatus* | ~ 20 | ~ 6 | ~ 26 | ~ 10 | – | – | Crompton, 1984 |
| *Galago senegalensis* | 25–77 | 2–11 | 27–88 | ~ 5 | – | – | Crompton, 1984 |

| | | | | | | | |
|---|---|---|---|---|---|---|---|
| *Saguinus fuscicollis* | 10–22 | 13–17 | 23–39 | 30–43 | 12** | 5,6 | Garber, 1993 |
| *Saguinus mystax* | 13–21 | 13–25 | 26–46 | 30–40 | 11,5** | 6,7 | Garber, 1993 |
| *Cebus capucinus* | – | – | 28 | 14 | 5–7* | – | Oppenheimer, 1968; Freese, 1977 |
| *Cebus apella* | – | – | 67 | 8 | – | – | Janson, 1975 |
| *Aotus trivirgatus* | – | 53 | – | 22 | – | – | Wright, 1978 |
| *Callicebus torquatus* | – | 26–28 | – | – | 11** | 16 | Kinzey, 1977 |
| *Alouatta palliata* | – | 14–18 | – | ~ 75 | – | – | Smith, 1977 |
| *Ateles belzebuth* | – | 22 | – | 63 | 11–13 | 5–25 | Klein & Klein, 1977 |
| *Brachyteles arachnoides* | – | 18–36 | – | 53–67 | – | – | Young, 1983; Milton, 1984 |
| *Cercopithecus ascanius* | 38 | 34 | 72 | – | – | – | Struhsaker, 1980 |
| *Macaca silenus* | – | 31 | – | 18 | – | – | Singh et al., 2000 |
| *Macaca fascicularis* | – | ~ 14 | – | ~ 40 | 18,3 | 10,5 | Temerin et al., 1984 |
| *Lophocebus albigena johnstoni* | 10 | 33 | 43 | – | – | – | Waser, 1977; 1984 |
| *Theropithecus gelada* | – | 45–80 | – | 2 | – | 1,6 | Dunbar, 1977; Kawai & Iwamoto, 1979; Iwamoto, 1979 |
| *Cercocebus galeritus* | – | – | 49 | – | – | – | Waser, 1984 |
| *Colobus guereza occidentalis* | – | 20 | – | 57 | – | <30 | Oates, 1977; Struhsaker & Oates, 1979 |
| *Piliocolobus badius* | 11 | 41 | 52 | 32 | – | – | Struhsaker, 1980 |
| *Piliocolobus tephrosceles* | – | 45 | – | 35 | – | – | Struhsaker & Oates, 1979 |
| *Procolobus verus* | – | 24 | – | 63 | – | – | Deschner, 1996 |
| *Semnopithecus entellus* | – | 32 | – | – | 10–12* | 16 | Hladik, 1977a; Koenig et al., 1997 |
| *Trachypithecus vetulus philbricki* | – | – | – | – | 6 | 32 | Hladik, 1977a; Koenig et al., 1997 |
| *Trachypithecus johnii* | – | 33 | – | 34 | – | – | Singh et al., 2000 |
| *Hylobates lar* | – | 29 | – | 5 | – | – | Chivers, 1979 |
| *Symphalangus syndactylus* | – | 53 | – | 29 | 12,9* | 26,6 | Chivers, 1977; 1979 |
| *Pongo pygmaeus* | – | 46 | – | 39 | 6,9–7,2 | 36–51 | Rodman, 1977; 1984; Temerin et al., 1984 |
| *Gorilla beringei beringei* | 21 | 25 | 46 | ~ 53 | – | – | Fossey & Harcourt, 1977; Harcourt & Stewart, 1984 |
| *Pan troglodytes* | – | – | 52–62 | 26–38 | 37,8 (14,6–20*) | ~ 10–15 | Wrangham, 1977; Hladik, 1977b; Ghiglieri, 1984; Rodman, 1984 |
| *Pan paniscus* | – | 30 | – | 43 | 10* | – | Kano & Mulavwa, 1984 |

mechanism for energy expenditure minimisation during periods of low resource abundance. Adaptations to temporally varying food availability can be as extreme as in some cheirogaleid lemurs, which hibernate for several months in Madagascar's dry season. During hibernation the animals exploit their fat deposits under the skin and in the tail (Hladik et al. 1980).

The proportion of time spent feeding probably reflects relationships between several factors, including the richness of the food sources, their spatial proximity, the processing time required to utilise them, and the metabolic requirements of the animals. In most cases, the length of distinct feeding bouts will be limited by the number of food items per food patch. Bout length will be further reduced by the presence of other individuals that feed concurrently on the same patch (intra-specifically regulated through dominance hierarchies; see e. g. Pruetz and Isbell 2000), by the failure of the animals to utilise all of the items in a patch, and by activities that interrupt feeding (Altmann 1979). The shorter the single feeding bout is, the higher should be the bout frequency in order to meet energy and nutrient requirements (see table 1). It seems thus reasonable to assume that a primate in the wild usually has to go through a number of distinct feeding bouts of roughly equal energy yield which are distributed over large proportions of its daily activity time (see also Kinzey 1977). This is illustrated schematically in figure 1.

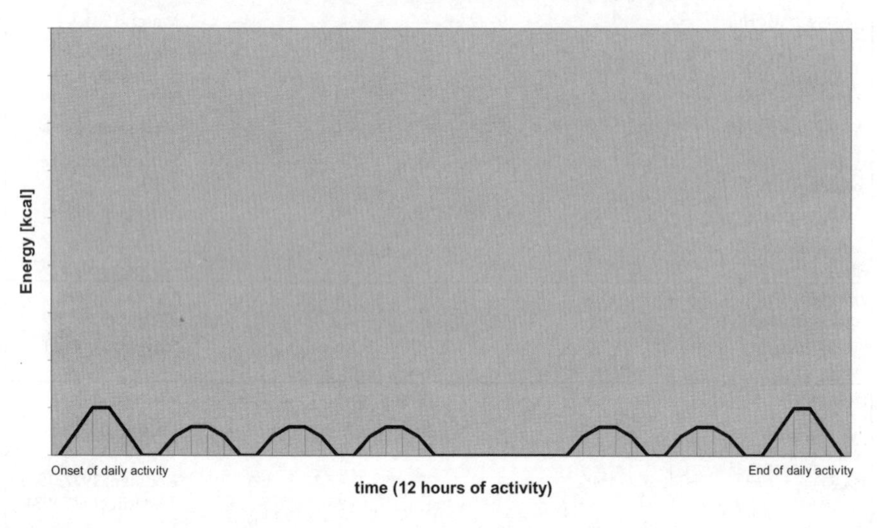


**Figure 1.** Schematic model of the daily energy intake distribution for a primate in the wild. The graph shows the amount of energy [kcal] consumed per ¼ hour within 12 hours of activity (see also Cant and Temerin 1984).

In figure 2 we show how the spatiotemporal food distribution, together with a number of other biotic and abiotic factors which act from outside on the processes of foraging and feeding (e.g. predation, weather conditions, competition), determines the patterns of daily energy and nutrient intake in wild primates.

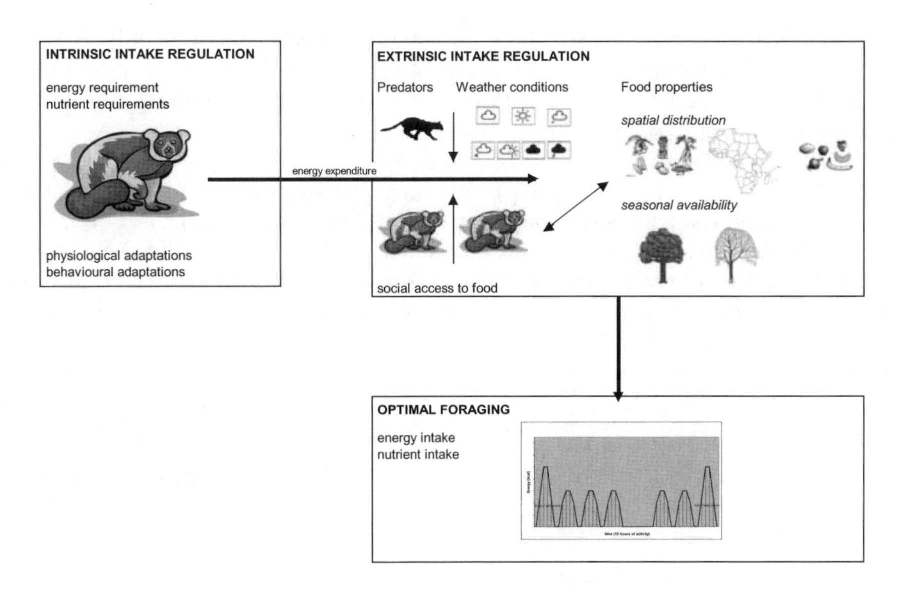


**Figure 2.** The determinants of food intake in wild primates.

## 3 Food distribution and feeding patterns in captivity

In the vast majority of captive situations, animals are fed in one or few (2-4) daily meals (Carlstead, 1996; see e.g. Kerscher & Kaumanns, 1993; Kaumanns et al., 2000; Krebs, 2001). Akers & Schildkraut (1985) for example, having surveyed 206 gorilla feeding schedules from 56 institutions, found that only 21% of the animals were given three or more meals per day, whereas the remaining 79% were fed only once or twice daily. Moreover, no effort is expended by the animals to acquire the food, and it is consumed in a short time (Carlstead, 1996). Thus, under captive conditions, feeding and foraging generally account for a lesser proportion of primates' daily activity than in the wild. Britt (1998) for example found that captive black-and-white ruffed lemurs (*Varecia variegata variegata*) at Chester Zoo spent significantly less time feeding than the wild individuals he studied, with 15% and 22% respectively. In a study by Klumpe (2001), captive douc langurs spent 22% (about two hours) of the observation day with food intake. The langurs in this study spent 84 minutes per day with the intake of leaves alone, whereas the intake of fruits, vegetables, and salad only amounted to less than 40 minutes. The latter foodstuffs, however, made up almost three quarters of their mean total daily energy intake. A summary of the findings of several studies on different primate species in captivity with regard to proportions of activity time spent on foraging, feeding, and resting, as well as feeding frequency and feeding bout duration is presented in table 2.

The conditions in captivity usually do not allow a spatial food distribution which would lead to natural foraging patterns and, thus, to food intake distributed over the animals' daily active time. Instead, food is consumed in two or three feeding sessions (see table 2), each of a short duration only. Even if the amount of time spent on food intake came close to the amount spent in the wild, the individual feeding bouts would most likely still be less numerous and more unevenly distributed over the day.

**Table 2.** Proportions of activity time [%] of captive primates spent on foraging, feeding, and resting, as well as feeding frequency and feeding bout duration. % f. + f. = % foraging + feeding; feed. bouts = no. of distinct feeding bouts per day; bout length = mean duration of one feeding bout [min.]; - = no data available; *semi-captive in large natural enclosure; [1]in 24 hours; [2]number of meals offered; [3]as kept on "old" diet; nomenclature following Groves (2001)

| Species | % foraging | % feeding | % f. + f. | % resting | feed. bouts | bout lenght | Source |
|---|---|---|---|---|---|---|---|
| *Lemur catta** | – | 12 | – | – | – | 5,9 | Ganzhorn, 1986 |
| *Eulemur fulvus** | – | 11 | – | – | – | 17,2 | Ganzhorn, 1986 |
| *Hapalemur griseus* | – | 17–18[1] | – | 52–61[1] | – | – | Lopes Santini, 1992 |
| *Prolemur simus* | – | 17–22[1] | – | 51–61[1] | – | – | Lopes Santini, 1992 |
| *Varecia variegata variegata* | – | 15 | – | – | 2[2] | – | Britt, 1998 |
| *Propithecus coquereli* | – | 14–21 | – | 50–70 | – | – | Pereira et al., 1989 |
| *Propithecus deckenii coronatus* | – | 5–8[1] | – | 72–82[1] | – | – | Lopes Santini, 1992 |
| *Leontopithecus rosalia* | 8,7 | 9 | 17,7 | 20–30 | 1–2[2] | – | Molzen & French, 1989 |
| *Papio cynocephalus* | – | 19 | – | 32 | 1[2] | – | Lambert & Whitham, 2001 |
| *Pygathrix nemaeus* | – | 22 | – | 56 | 6[2] | 13–28 | Klumpe, 2001 |
| *Pongo pygmaeus* | 11 | 10 | 21 | 9 | – | – | Classen, 2001 |
| *Gorilla gorilla gorilla* | – | 8 | – | – | 2–3[2] | – | Akers & Schildkraut, 1985 |
| *Gorilla beringei graueri* | 16 | 22 | 38 | 38 | – | – | Savini et al., 2000[3] |

The problem that much food is being consumed within a short time period is enhanced by a tendency to calculate the quantity of food offered to group-living primates such, that hierarchy-related differences in access to food are concealed to ensure that each group member is able to get an appropriate proportion of a meal (Kaumanns et al. 2000; see also Kerscher and Kaumanns 1993; Gore 1993). Dominant individuals under such conditions may consume inappropriate amounts of preferred, that is energy-rich food.

Other factors which influence access to food and which therefore may lead to temporally more extended food intake patterns, like inter-species competition, predation, or weather conditions do not play a role in the captive environment.

Taking these considerations into account, it is obvious that the food intake patterns of captive primates deviate from those of wild primates. In general, the meal frequency is reduced compared to the frequency observed in the wild. The corresponding energy intake graph therefore should show only few peaks, but because all the energy needed is consumed in such few bouts, some of the peaks should be of considerable height. This is demonstrated schematically in figure 3.

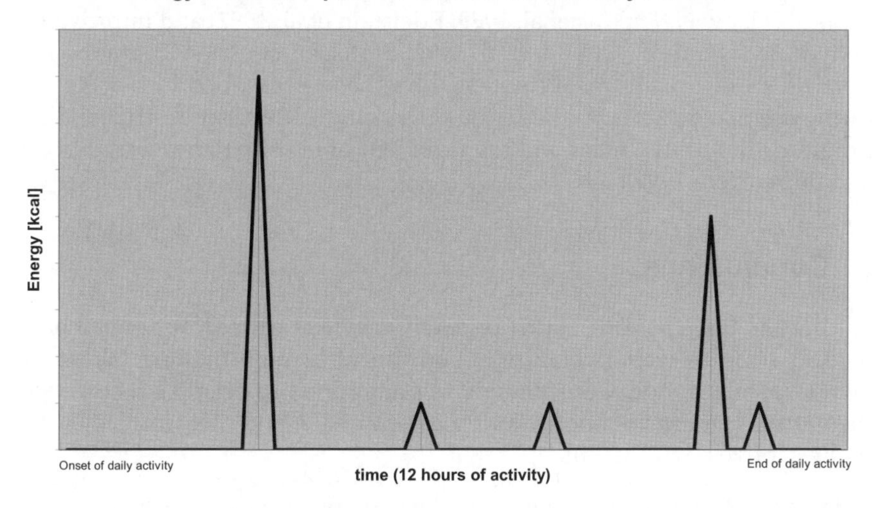


**Figure 3.** Schematic model of the daily energy intake distribution for a captive primate. The graph shows the amount of energy [kcal] consumed per ¼ hour within 12 hours of activity (see also Cant & Temerin, 1984).

## 4 Feeding frequency: an intake regulation mechanism

Under the assumption that there are species-specific adaptive patterns of foraging and food intake, long-term deviations from these patterns as possibly in existence under captive conditions may lead to changes on the level of behaviour and to health problems. The latter, of which obesity is probably the most common problem in captive primates, might be related to impaired food intake regulation mechanisms.

For non-human primates, corresponding studies are not available. There exist however a number of studies on humans and laboratory animals which address this subject. In the study of human obesity, diabetes, and cardiovascular diseases, an increase of meal frequency (= nibbling) was found to have various beneficial effects on the studied subjects, both on humans and laboratory animals. Several studies showed an inverse relationship of meal frequency and obesity (Fabry et al. 1964; Metzner et al. 1977; Edelstein et al. 1992; Kant 1995; Summerbell et al. 1996), although Bellisle et al. (1997) concluded in their review that these studies are extremely vulnerable to methodological errors and highlight the need for considerable caution in interpreting the results. Data from Speechly and Buffenstein (1999) suggest that when the nutrient load was spread into equal amounts and consumed evenly through the day in lean healthy human males, there was an enhanced control of appetite. The same was found in obese male human subjects by Speechly et al. (1999). The authors concluded that this greater control of satiety when consuming smaller multiple meals may possibly be linked to an attenuation in insulin response although clearly both other physical (gastric stretch) and physiological (release of gastric hormones) factors may also be affected by the periodicity of eating. Other studies found that increased meal frequency reduced serum cholesterol levels (Jenkins et al. 1989; Edelstein et al. 1992) and improved carbohydrate tolerance (Jenkins et al. 1992; Bertelsen et al. 1993; Jenkins 1997). Consequently, greater meal frequency has been prescribed in diabetes care, cardiovascular treatment, and in the prescription of energy-restricted dietary programs in the treatment and management of obesity in humans (Speechly and Buffenstein 1999).

## 5 Conclusions

During the last 15 years, much research has been carried out on enhancing feeding time as well as energy expenditure through making the animals "work" for their food. Considerably less attention has been paid, however, to the natural patterns of energy and nutrient intake and their implementation in the captive environment.

Many primate species in captivity are affected by obesity problems. Although the most obvious approach to controlling body weight surely is to offer less energy-dense foods, other measures might be equally important and should be taken into account. Results from studies on human subjects suggest that the temporal distribution of food intake, i. e. the feeding frequency, influences the regulation of energy intake as well as other physiological pathways. This needs to be further studied in non-human primates, especially with reference to the above mentioned overweight problems.

The wide spatiotemporal food distribution which is characteristic for primate habitats in the wild as well as other factors which contribute to a temporally extended food intake cannot be imitated in captivity. On a practical level it is therefore necessary to provide primates in zoos with small amounts of food in several distinct feeding sessions distributed over a large proportion of the day.

## Acknowledgements

We would like to thank the anonymous reviewers for their helpful comments on the manuscript. C. Schwitzer is supported by a post-graduate funding from Konrad-Adenauer-Stiftung e.V.

## References

Akers, J. S.; Schildkraut, D. S. (1985): Regurgitation/reingestion and coprophagy in captive gorillas. *Zoo Biology* 4: 99–109.

Altmann, S. A. (1979): Baboons, space, time, and energy. In: *Primate ecology: Problem-oriented field studies* (R. W. Sussman, ed.). New York: John Wiley and Sons, pp. 243–280.

Ancrenaz, M.; Lackman-Ancrenaz, I.; Mundy, N. (1994): Field observations of aye-ayes (*Daubentonia madagascariensis*) in Madagascar. *Folia Primatol.* 62: 22–36.

Andriamasimanana, M. (1994): Ecoethological study of free-ranging aye-ayes (*Daubentonia madagascariensis*) in Madagascar. *Folia Primatol.* 62: 37–45.

Bellisle, F.; McDevitt, R.; Prentice, A. M. (1997): Meal frequency and energy balance. *British Journal of Nutrition* 77(Suppl. 1): S57–S70.

Bertelsen, J.; Christiansen, C.; Thomsen, C.; Poulsen, P. L.; Vestergaard, S.; Steinov, A.; Rosmussen, L. H.; Rosmussen, O.; Hermansen, K. (1993): Effect of meal frequency on blood glucose, insulin and free fatty acids in NIDDM subjects. *Diabetes Care* 16: 3–7.

Britt, A. (1998): Encouraging natural feeding behaviour in captive-bred black-and-white ruffed lemurs (*Varecia variegata variegata*). *Zoo Biology* 17: 379–392.

Cant, J. G. H.; Temerin, L. A. (1984): A conceptual approach to foraging adaptations in primates. In: *Adaptations for Foraging in Nonhuman Primates: Contributions to an Organismal Biology of Prosimians, Monkeys, and Apes* (P. S. Rodman, J. G. H. Cant, eds.). New York: Columbia University Press, pp. 304–342.

Carlstead, K. (1996): Effects of captivity on the behavior of wild mammals. In: *Wild Mammals in Captivity – Principles and Techniques* (D. G. Kleiman, M. E. Allen, K. V. Thompson, S. Lumpkin, eds.). Chicago and London: The University of Chicago Press, pp. 317–333.

Chamove, A. S.; Anderson, J. R. (1989): Examining environmental enrichment. In: *Housing, care and psychological wellbeing of captive and laboratory primates* (E. F. Segal, ed.). Park Ridge (NJ): Noyes Publications, pp. 183–202.

Chivers, D. J. (1977): The feeding behaviour of siamang (*Symphalangus syndactylus*). In: *Primate Ecology: Studies of feeding and ranging behaviour in lemurs, monkeys and apes* (T. H. Clutton-Brock, ed.). London: Academic Press, pp. 355–382.

Chivers, D. J. (1979): The siamang and the gibbon in the Malay Peninsula. In: *Primate ecology: Problem-oriented field studies* (R. W. Sussman, ed.). New York: John Wiley & Sons, pp. 285–315.

Classen, D. (2001): *Gehegenutzung und soziale Strukturen bei Orang Utans (Pongo pygmaeus) in menschlicher Obhut.* [diploma thesis]. Cologne (Germany): University of Cologne.

Cousins, D. (1972): Body measurements and weights of wild and captive gorillas, *Gorilla gorilla. Zool. Garten* N. F. 41: 261–77.

Crissey, S.; Pribyl, L.; Pruett-Jones, M.; Meehan, T. (1998): Nutritional management of Old World primates with special consideration for vitamin D. *Int. Zoo Yb.* 36: 122–130.

Crissey, S.; Pribyl, L. (2000): A review of nutritional deficiencies and toxicities in captive New World primates. *Int. Zoo Yb.* 37: 355–360.

Crompton, R. H. (1984): Foraging, habitat structure, and locomotion in two species of galago. In: *Adaptations for foraging in nonhuman primates: Contributions to an organismal biology of prosimians, monkeys and apes* (P. S. Rodman, J. G. H. Cant, eds.). New York: Columbia University Press, pp. 73–111.

Deschner, T. (1996): Aspekte des Sozialverhaltens Olivgrüner Stummelaffen *Colobus verus* (Van Beneden 1838) im Tai-Nationalpark / Elfenbeinküste. [diploma thesis]. Hamburg (Germany): University of Hamburg.

Dunbar, R. I. M. (1977): Feeding ecology of gelada baboons: A preliminary report. In: *Primate Ecology: Studies of feeding and ranging behaviour in lemurs, monkeys and apes* (T. H. Clutton-Brock, ed.). London: Academic Press, pp. 251–273.

Edelstein, S. L.; Barrett-Connor, E. L.; Wingard, D. L.; Cohn, B. A. (1992): Increased meal frequency associated with decreased cholesterol concentrations; Rancho Bernardo, CA, 1984–1987. *American Journal of Clinical Nutrition* 55: 664–669.

Fabry, P.; Fodor, J.; Hejl, Z.; Braun, T.; Zvolankova, K. (1964): The frequency of meals – Its relation to overweight, hypercholesterolaemia, and decreased glucose-tolerance. *The Lancet* 2: 614–615.

Feistner, A. T. C.; Mutschler, T. (2000): Feeding fussy folivores: Nutrition of gentle lemurs. In: *Zoo Animal Nutrition* (J. Nijboer, et al., eds.). Fürth (Germany): Filander Verlag, pp. 107–117.

Fossey, D.; Harcourt, A. H. (1977): Feeding ecology of free-ranging mountain gorilla (*Gorilla gorilla beringei*). In: *Primate Ecology: Studies of feeding and ranging behaviour in lemurs, monkeys and apes* (T. H. Clutton-Brock, ed.). London: Academic Press, pp. 415–447.

Freese, C. H. (1977): Food habits of the white-faced capuchins *Cebus capucinus* L. (Primates: Cebidae) in Santa Rosa National Park, Costa Rica. *Brenesia* 10/11: 43–56.

Galdikas, B. M. F.; Teleki, G. (1981): Variations in subsistence activities of female and male pongids: New perspectives on the origins of hominid labor division. *Current Anthropology* 22: 241–255 and 316–320.

Ganzhorn, J. U.; Abraham, J. P.; Razanahoera-Rakotomalala, M. (1985): Some aspects of the natural history and food selection of *Avahi laniger*. *Primates* 26: 452–463.

Ganzhorn, J. U. (1986): Feeding behavior of *Lemur catta* and *Lemur fulvus*. *International Journal of Primatology* 7: 17–30.

Garber, P. A. (1993): Seasonal patterns of diet and ranging in two species of tamarin monkeys: Stability versus variability. *International Journal of Primatology* 14: 145–166.

Ghiglieri, M. P. (1984): Feeding ecology and sociality of chimpanzees in Kibale Forest, Uganda. In: *Adaptations for foraging in nonhuman primates: Contributions to an organismal biology of prosimians, monkeys and apes* (P. S. Rodman, J. G. H. Cant, eds.). New York: Columbia University Press, pp. 161–194.

Gil Burmann, C.; Pelaez, F. (1990): Effect of food distribution on agonistic and feeding behavior of adult males in a colony of baboons. In: *III Congreso Nacional de Etologia*. Leon (Spain): Univ. de Leon, Fac. De Biol., pp. 293–300.

Goeltenboth, R. (1982): Special section: Diseases of zoo animals. Nonhuman primates (apes, monkeys, prosimians). In: *Handbook of Zoo Medicine* (H.-G. Kloes, E. M. Lang, eds.). New York: Van Nostrand Reinhold Company, pp. 46–85.

Gore, M. (1993): Effects of food distribution on foraging competition in rhesus monkeys, *Macaca mulatta*, and hamadryas baboons, *Papio hamadryas*. *Animal Behaviour* 45: 773–786.

Groves, C. P. (2001): *Primate Taxonomy*. Washington (DC): Smithsonian Institution Press.

Harcourt, A. H.; Stewart, K. J. (1984): Gorillas' time feedings: Aspects of methodology, body size, competition and diet. *African Journal of Ecology* 22: 207–215.

Harcourt, C. (1991): Diet and behaviour of a nocturnal lemur, *Avahi laniger*, in the wild. *J. Zool., Lond.* 223: 667–674.

Heiduck, S. (1998): How to cope with seasonality in food availability: Patch use strategies of masked titi monkeys (*Callicebus personatus melanochir*). *Folia Primatologica* 69: 221.

Hladik, C. M. (1977a): A comparative study of the feeding strategies of two sympatric species of leaf monkeys: *Presbytis senex* and *Presbytis entellus*. In: *Primate Ecology: Studies of feeding and ranging behaviour in lemurs, monkeys and apes* (T. H. Clutton-Brock, ed.). London: Academic Press, pp. 323–353.

Hladik, C. M. (1977b): Chimpanzees of Gabon and chimpanzees of Gombe: Some comparative data on the diet. In: *Primate Ecology: Studies of feeding and ranging behaviour in lemurs, monkeys and apes* (T. H. Clutton-Brock, ed.). London: Academic Press, pp. 481–501.

Hladik, C. M.; Charles-Dominique, P.; Petter, J. J. (1980): Feeding strategies of five nocturnal prosimians in the dry forest of the west coast of Madagascar. In: *Nocturnal Malagasy Primates* (P. Charles-Dominique et al., eds.). New York: Academic Press.

Howe, H. F. (1977): Bird activity and seed dispersal of a tropical wet forest tree. *Ecology* 58: 539–550.

Hume, I. D. (1986): Nutrition and feeding of monotremes and marsupials. In: *Zoo and Wild Animal Medicine* (M. E. Fowler, ed.), (2nd ed.). Philadelphia (PA): Sanders, pp. 566–570.

Hume, I. D. (1995): General concepts of nutrition and nutritional ecology. In: *Research and Captive Propagation* (U. Ganslosser, J. K. Hodges, W. Kaumanns, eds.). Fürth (Germany): Filander Verlag, pp. 90–98.

Iwamoto, T. (1979): Feeding ecology. In: *Ecological and Sociological Studies of Gelada Baboons* (M. Kawai, ed.). Basel: S. Karger, pp. 279–330.

Janson, C. H. (1975): *Ecology and population densities of primates in a Peruvian rainforest*. [B.A. thesis]. Princeton (NJ): Princeton University.

Jenkins, D. J. A. (1997): Carbohydrate tolerance and food frequency. *British Journal of Nutrition* 77(Suppl. 1): S71–S81.

Jenkins, D. J. A.; Wolever, T. M. S.; Vuksan, V.; Brighenti, F.; Cunnane, S. C.; Venketeshwer Rao, A.; Jenkins, A. L.; Buckley, G.; Patten, R.; Singer, W.; Corey, P.; Josse, R. G. (1989): Nibbling versus gorging: Metabolic advantages of increased meal frequency. *New England Journal of Medicine* 321: 929–934.

Jenkins, D. J. A.; Ocana, A.; Jenkins, A. L.; Wolever, T. M. S.; Vuksan, V.; Katzman, L.; Hollands, M.; Greenberg, G.; Corey, P.; Patten, R.; Wong, G.; Josse, R. G. (1992): Metabolic advantages of spreading the nutrient load: effects of increased meal frequency in non-insulin-dependent diabetes. *Am. J. Clin. Nutr.* 55: 461–467.

Junge, R. E.; Gannon, F. H.; Porton, I.; McAlister, W. H.; Whyte, M. P. (2000): Management and prevention of vitamin D deficiency rickets in captive-born juvenile chimpanzees (*Pan troglodytes*). *Journal of Zoo and Wildlife Medicine* 31(3): 361–369.

Kano, T.; Mulavwa, M. (1984): Feeding ecology of the pygmy chimpanzees (*Pan paniscus*) of Wamba. In: *The pygmy chimpanzee: Evolutionary biology and behaviour* (R. L. Sussman, ed.). New York: Plenum, pp. 233–274.

Kant, A. K. (1995): Frequency of eating occasions and weight change in NHANES I Epidemiologic Follow-up Study. *International Journal of Obesity* 19: 468–474.

Kaumanns, W.; Hampe, K.; Schwitzer, C.; Stahl, D. (2000b): Primate nutrition – Towards an integrated approach. In: *Zoo Animal Nutrition* (J. Nijboer et al., eds.). Fürth (Germany): Filander Verlag, pp. 91–106.

Kawai, M.; Iwamoto, T. (1979): Nomadism and activities. In: *Ecological and Sociological Studies of Gelada Baboons* (M. Kawai, ed.). Basel: S. Karger, pp. 251–278.

Kemnitz, J. W. (1984): Obesity in macaques: spontaneous and induced. *Adv. Vet. Sci. Comp. Med.* 28: 81–114.

Kerscher, R.; Kaumanns, W. (1993): Nahrungsaufnahmeverhalten bei zwei unterschiedlichen Futterverteilungen untersucht an Brillenlanguren (*Presbytis obscura*) im Zoologischen Garten Wuppertal. *Zool. Garten* N. F. 63: 209–221.

Kinzey, W. G. (1977): Diet and feeding behaviour of *Callicebus torquatus*. In: *Primate Ecology: Studies of feeding and ranging behaviour in lemurs, monkeys and apes* (T. H. Clutton-Brock, ed.). London: Academic Press, pp. 127–151.

Klein, L. L.; Klein, D. B. (1977): Feeding behaviour of the Colombian spider monkey. In: *Primate Ecology: Studies of feeding and ranging behaviour in lemurs, monkeys and apes* (T. H. Clutton-Brock, ed.). London: Academic Press, pp. 153–181.

Klumpe, K. (2001): Nahrungsaufnahme des Kleideraffen (*Pygathrix n. nemaeus*), LINNAEUS 1771 in menschlicher Obhut. [diploma thesis]. Potsdam (Germany): University of Potsdam.

Koenig, A.; Borries, C.; Chalise, M. K.; Winkler, P. (1997): Ecology, nutrition, and timing of reproductive events in an Asian primate, the hanuman langur (*Presbytis entellus*). *J. Zool. Lond.* 243: 215–235.

Krebs, E. (2001): Soziale Beziehungen unter Mantelpavianweibchen (*Papio hamadryas*) unter Berücksichtigung der Konkurrenz. [Diss.]. Göttingen (Germany): Cuvillier Verlag.

Lam, K.; Rupniak, N. M. J.; Iversen, S. D. (1991): Use of a grooming and foraging substrate to reduce cage stereotypies in macaques. *Journal of Medical Primatology* 20: 104–109.

Lambert, J. E.; Whitham, J. C. (2001): Cheek pouch use in *Papio cynocephalus*. *Folia Primatologica* 72: 89–91.

Lintzenich, B.; Ward, A. M. (2001): Weight management strategies in apes. In: *The Apes: Challenges for 21st Century*. Conference Proceedings. Chicago: Brookfield Zoo, pp. 175–176.

Lopes Santini, M. E. (1992) : Comportement alimentaire et « gestion energétique » chez trois espèces de lémuriens folivores, *Hapalemur simus, H. griseus griseus* et *Propithecus verreauxi coronatus*, au Parc Zoologique de Paris. [Diss.]. Paris: Université Paris VII.

Lukas, K. E. (1999): A review of nutritional and motivational factors contributing to the performance of regurgitation and reingestion in captive lowland gorillas (*Gorilla gorilla gorilla*). *Applied Animal Behaviour Science* 63: 237–249.

Metzner, H. L.; Lamphiear, D. E.; Wheeler, N. C.; Larkin, F. A. (1977): The relationship between frequency of eating and adiposity in adult men and women in the Tecumseh Community Health Study. *American Journal of Clinical Nutrition* 30: 712–715.

Meyers, D. M.; Wright, P. C. (1993): Resource tracking: Food availability and *Propithecus* seasonal reproduction. In: *Lemur Social Systems and Their*

*Ecological Basis* (P. M. Kappeler, J. U. Ganzhorn, eds.). New York and London: Plenum Press, pp. 179–192.

Milton, K. (1984): Habitat, diet, and activity patterns of free-ranging woolly spider monkeys (*Brachyteles arachnoides* E. Geoffroy 1806). *Int. J. Primatol.* 5: 491–514.

Molzen, E. M.; French, J. A. (1989): The problem of foraging in captive callitrichid primates: Behavioral time budgets and foraging skills. In: *Housing, care and psychological wellbeing of captive and laboratory primates* (E. F. Segal, ed.). Park Ridge (NJ): Noyes Publications, pp. 89–101.

Morland, H. S. (1991): Social organization and ecology of black and white ruffed lemurs (*Varecia variegata variegata*) in lowland rain forest, Nosy Mangabe, Madagascar. [Diss.]. New Haven: Yale University.

Mueller, K.-H.; Schildger, B.-J. (1992): Empfehlungen für eine artgerechte Ernährung von Flachlandgorillas (*Gorilla g. gorilla*) in menschlicher Obhut auf der Grundlage einer quantitativen Nahrungsanalyse. *Zool. Garten* N. F. 62: 351–363.

Mutschler, T. (1999): Folivory in a small-bodied lemur: The nutrition of the Alaotran gentle lemur (*Hapalemur griseus alaotrensis*). In: *New Directions in Lemur Studies* (Rakotosamimanana et al., eds.). New York: Kluwer Academic/Plenum Publishers, pp. 221–239.

Nash, L. T. (1996): Seasonal changes in time budgets and diet of *Lepilemur leucopus* from southwestern Madagascar. *American Journal of Physical Anthropology* Suppl. 22: 175.

Oates, J. F. (1977): The guereza and ist food. In: *Primate Ecology: Studies of feeding and ranging behaviour in lemurs, monkeys and apes* (T. H. Clutton-Brock, ed.). London: Academic Press, pp. 276–321.

Oates, J. F. (1987): Food distribution and foraging behaviour. In: *Primate Societies* (B. B. Smuts et al., eds.). Chicago and London: The University of Chicago Press, pp. 197–209.

Oppenheimer, J. R. (1968): *Behavior and ecology of the white-faced monkey, Cebus capucinus, on Barro Colorado Island, C.Z.* [Diss.]. Urbana (IL): University of Illinois.

Oxnard, C. (1989): Apparent health, hidden disease: vitamin B12 deficiency and the nervous system. *Laboratory Primate Newsletter* 28: 7–12.

Pereira, M E.; Macedonia, J. M.; Haring, D. M.; Simons, E. L. (1989): Maintenance of primates in captivity for research: The need for naturalistic environments. In: *Housing, care and psychological wellbeing of captive and laboratory primates* (E. F. Segal, ed.). Park Ridge (NJ): Noyes Publications, pp. 40–60.

Pereira, M. E.; Pond, C. M. (1995): Organization of white adipose tissue in Lemuridae. *American Journal of Primatology* 3: 1–13.

Pollock, J. I. (1977): The ecology and sociology of feeding in *Indri indri*. In: *Primate Ecology: Studies of feeding and ranging behaviour in lemurs, monkeys and apes* (T. H. Clutton-Brock, ed.). London: Academic Press, pp. 37–69.

Pruetz, J. D.; Isbell, L. A. (2000): Correlations of food distribution and patch size with agonistic interactions in female vervets (*Chlorocebus aethiops*) and patas monkeys (*Erythrocebus patas*) living in simple habitats. *Behavioral Ecology and Sociobiology* 49: 38–47.

Richard, A. (1977): The feeding behaviour of *Propithecus verreauxi*. In: *Primate Ecology: Studies of feeding and ranging behaviour in lemurs, monkeys and apes* (T. H. Clutton-Brock, ed.). London: Academic Press, pp. 71–96.

Richard, A. (1979): Intra-specific variation in the social organization and ecology of *Propithecus verreauxi*. In: *Primate ecology: Problem-oriented field studies* (R. W. Sussman, ed.). New York: John Wiley & Sons, pp. 23–51.

Rodman, P. S. (1977): Feeding behaviour of orang-utans of the Kutai Nature Reserve, East Kalimantan. In: *Primate Ecology: Studies of feeding and ranging behaviour in lemurs, monkeys and apes* (T. H. Clutton-Brock, ed.). London: Academic Press, pp. 383–413.

Rodman, P. S. (1979): Individual activity profiles and the solitary nature of orangutans. In: *The great apes* (D. A. Hamburg, E. R. McCown, eds.). Menlo Park (CA): Benjamin/Cummings, pp. 234–55.

Ruempler, U. (1991): Haltung und Zucht von Kleideraffen (*Pygathrix nemaeus nemaeus* Linnaeus, 1771) im Kölner Zoo. *Zeitschrift des Kölner Zoo* 34(2): 47–65.

Savini, T.; Leus, K.; Van Elsacker, L. (2000): Effects of dietary changes on the behavior and fecal consistency of three captive eastern lowland gorillas (*Gorilla gorilla graueri*) at the Royal Zoological Society of Antwerp. In: *Zoo Animal Nutrition* (J. Nijboer et al., eds.). Fürth (Germany): Filander Verlag, pp. 139–152.

Schmidt, D. A.; Dempsey, J. L.; Kerley, M. S.; Porton, I. J. (2001): Fiber in ape diets: A review. In: *The Apes: Challenges for 21st Century*. Conference Proceedings. Chicago: Brookfield Zoo, pp. 177–179.

Schwartz, S. M.; Kemnitz, J. W.; Howard Jr., C. F. (1993): Obesity in free-ranging rhesus macaques. *International Journal of Obesity* 17: 1–10.

Schwitzer, C.; Kaumanns, W. (2000): Feeding behaviour in two captive groups of black-and-white ruffed lemurs (*Varecia variegata variegata*), KERR 1792. In: *Zoo Animal Nutrition* (J. Nijboer et al., eds.). Fürth (Germany): Filander Verlag, pp. 119–130.

Schwitzer, C.; Kaumanns, W. (2001): Body weights of captive ruffed lemurs (*Varecia variegata*) in European zoos with reference to the problem of obesity. *Zoo Biology* 20: 261–269.

Singh, M. R.; Singh, M. E.; Kumar, M. A.; Kumara, H. N.; Sharma, A. K.; Sushma, H. S. (2000): Niche separation in sympatric lion-tailed macaque

(*Macaca silenus*) and nilgiri langur (*Presbytis johnii*) in an Indian tropical rain forest. *Primate Report* 58: 83–95.

Smith, C. C. (1977): Feeding behaviour and social organization in howling monkeys. In: *Primate Ecology: Studies of feeding and ranging behaviour in lemurs, monkeys and apes* (T. H. Clutton-Brock, ed.). London: Academic Press, pp. 97–126.

Speechly, D. P.; Buffenstein, R. (1999): Greater appetite control associated with an increased frequency of eating in lean males. *Appetite* 33: 285–297.

Speechly, D. P.; Rogers, G. G.; Buffenstein, R. (1999): Acute appetite reduction associated with an increased frequency of eating in obese males. *International Journal of Obesity* 23: 1151–1159.

Spelman, L. H.; Osborn, K. G.; Anderson, M. P. (1989): Pathogenesis of hemosiderosis in lemurs: role of dietary iron, tannin, and ascorbic acid. *Zoo Biology* 8: 239–251.

Struhsaker, T. T.; Oates, J. F. (1979): Comparison of the behavior and ecology of red colobus and black-and-white colobus monkeys in Uganda: A summary. In: *Primate ecology: Problem-oriented field studies* (R. W. Sussman, ed.). New York: John Wiley & Sons, pp. 165–183.

Struhsaker, T. T. (1980): Comparison of the behaviour and ecology of red colobus and redtail monkeys in the Kibale Forest, Uganda. *Afr. J. Ecol.* 18: 33–51.

Summerbell, C. D.; Moody, R. C.; Shanks, J.; Stock, M. J.; Geissler, C. (1996): Relationship between feeding pattern and body mass index in 220 free-living people in four age groups. *European Journal of Clinical Nutrition* 50: 513–519.

Sussman, R. W. (1977): Feeding behaviour of *Lemur catta* and *Lemur fulvus*. In: *Primate Ecology: Studies of feeding and ranging behaviour in lemurs, monkeys and apes* (T. H. Clutton-Brock, ed.). London: Academic Press, pp. 1–36.

Sussman, R. W. (1979): Ecological distinction in sympatric species of *Lemur*. In: *Primate ecology: Problem-oriented field studies* (R. W. Sussman, ed.). New York: John Wiley & Sons, pp. 53–84.

Temerin, L. A.; Wheatley, B. P.; Rodman, P. S. (1984): Body size and foraging in primates. In: *Adaptations for foraging in nonhuman primates: Contributions to an organismal biology of prosimians, monkeys and apes* (P. S. Rodman, J. G. H. Cant, eds.). New York: Columbia University Press, pp. 217–248.

Terranova, C. J.; Coffman, B. S. (1997): Body weights of wild and captive lemurs. *Zoo Biology* 16: 17–30.

Waser, P. M. (1977): Feeding, ranging and group size in the mangabey *Cercocebus albigena*. In: *Primate Ecology: Studies of feeding and ranging behaviour in lemurs, monkeys and apes* (T. H. Clutton-Brock, ed.). London: Academic Press, pp. 183–222.

Waser, P. M. (1984): Ecological differences and behavioral contrasts between two mangabey species. In: *Adaptations for foraging in nonhuman primates: Contributions to an organismal biology of prosimians, monkeys and apes* (P. S. Rodman, J. G. H. Cant, eds.). New York: Columbia University Press, pp. 195–216.

Wasserman, F. E.; Cruikshank, W. W. (1983): The relationship between time of feeding and aggression in a group of captive hamadryas baboons. *Primates* 24: 432–435.

Weisenberg, E.; Snook, S.; Letcher, J. (1991): Sudden death in an obese orangutan with hypertensive heart disease and a history of stroke. In: *AAZV (Am. Assoc. Zoo Vet.) Annual Conference Proceedings* 1991, p. 172.

West, D. B.; York, B. (1998): Dietary fat, genetic predisposition, and obesity: lessons from animal models. *Am. J. Clin. Nutr.* 67(suppl.): 505S–512S.

Wrangham, R. W. (1977): Feeding behavior of chimpanzees in Gombe National Park, Tanzania. In: *Primate Ecology: Studies of feeding and ranging behavior in lemurs, monkeys and apes* (T. H. Clutton-Brock, ed.). London: Academic Press, pp. 503–538.

Wright, P. C. (1978): Home range, activity pattern, and agonistic encounters of a group of night monkeys (*Aotus trivirgatus*) in Peru. *Folia Primatol.* 29: 43–55.

Wright, P. C. (1987): Diet and ranging patterns of *Propithecus diadema edwardsi* in Madagascar. *American Journal of Physical Anthropology* 72: 271.

Young, A. L. (1983): Preliminary observations on the ecology and behavior of the muriqui and brown howler monkey. [Bachelor's thesis]. Cambridge (MA): Harvard University.

*C. W. Yang, A. S. Li, and J. C. Guo*

# Diet, feed adjustment and parasite control for ungulates at the Taipei Zoo

***Abstract***

*As of September 2001, the Taipei Zoo managed 388 specimens of ungulates from 10 taxonomic families of 43 species. Since 1997, we adjusted the types of feeds and formulations, which began with fresh forage and edible hay. Included were six species of fresh grass, branches, and leaves used as the major food for our ungulates. Increased fibre consumption effectively reduced the undesirable condition of soft excrement, which was often seen with our giraffes. We experimented with five kinds of imported hay between 1997 and 1999, eventually eliminating all but one type exclusively; the domestically-produced Pangola hay (Digitaris decumbens), offered ad libitum. In light of the damp weather in Taipei, especially in wintertime, the hay storehouse is air-conditioned, kept at a constant temperature of 16–18 °C, and a relative humidity < 75 %. Improved hay storage conditions has improved hay quality, and added variety and quantity in forage components has increased consumption of dietary fibre to improve health and fecal consistency in a number of ungulates. Pelleted feeds were adjusted to increase the content of vitamin E from 100 IU/kg to 400 IU/kg dry matter, resulting in improved health and reproduction. Altered feed placement and oral anthelminthics added to manufactured feeds has controlled parasites in hoofstock herds at Taipei Zoo. Hence a variety of feeding management improvements contributes to success of the ungulate feeding program at Taipei Zoo.*

***Keywords***

*Ungulates, feed management, concentrate formulation, parasite control*

## 1 Introduction

Ungulates consume plant material with a moderate to high fibre content. Because they lack the endogenous enzymes necessary for digestion of the fibre components, herbivores rely on anaerobic fermentation of the fibre by symbiotic gastrointestinal microorganisms. One or more segments of the digestive tracts of mammalian herbivores are usually modified to form fermentation chambers that can support a large and active population of bacteria, protozoa, and fungi (Oftedal et. al. 1996).

In herbivores, complex co-evolutionary processes of adaptation have occurred to make use of abundantly available forage resources, and to cope with plant defense systems, and seasonal changes of plant digestibility and availability. African rumi-

[1] Taipei Zoo, 30 Sec. 2 Hsin Kuang Road, Taipei, Taiwan 11628, Republic of China.

nants, for example, are grouped according to three feeding types: the "concentrate selectors", the "intermediate feeders", and the "grass/roughage eaters" (Hoffmann 2000). Giraffe are included in the first group, impala antelope are included in the second group, and the African buffalo is an example of the last.

## 2 The number of ungulates and species in the Taipei Zoo

As of September, 2001, Taipei Zoo managed 388 ungulate specimens from 10 taxonomic families, and 43 species (see table 1).

**Table 1.** Numbers of large herbivorous mammal species kept at the Taipei Zoo (September, 2001).

| Common name | Scientific Name | Number |
|---|---|---|
| Elephants | Elephantidae | |
| Asiatic Elephant | *Elephas maximus* | 4 |
| African Elephant | *Loxodonta africana* | 4 |
| Horses, Zebras, Asses | Equidae | |
| Domestic Donkey | *Equus asinus* | 6 |
| Common Zebra | *E. burchelli* | 17 |
| Domestic Horse | *E. cabellus* | 1 |
| Pony | *E. cabellus* | 3 |
| Grevy's Zebra | *E. grevyi* | 5 |
| Przewalski's Horse | *E. przewalskii* | 22 |
| Hartmann's Mountain Zebra | *E. zebra hartmannae* | 2 |
| Tapirs | Tapiridae | |
| Malayan Tapir | *Tapirus indicus* | 3 |
| Rhinoceroses | Rhinocerotidae | |
| White Rhinoceros | *Ceratotherium simum* | 7 |
| Black Rhinoceros | *Diceros bicornis* | 2 |
| Boars, Pigs | Suidae | |
| Bearded Pig | *Sus barbatus sumatranus* | 2 |
| Formosan Wild Boar | *Sus scrofa taivanus* | 12 |
| Hippopotamuses | Hippopotamidae | |
| Pigmy Hippopotamus | *Hexaprotodon liberiensis* | 5 |
| Hippopotamus | *Hippopotamus amphibious* | 14 |
| Camels, Llamas | Camelidae | |
| Bactrian Camel | *Camelus bactrianus* | 9 |
| Arabian Camel | *Camelus dromedaries* | 2 |
| Llama | *Lama glama* | 11 |
| Deer | Cervidae | |
| Formosan Sika Deer | *Cervus nippon taiouanus* | 22 |
| Pere David's Deer | *Elaphurus davidianus* | 4 |
| Formosan Muntjac | *Muntiacus reevesi micrurus* | 49 |

| | | |
|---|---|---|
| Giraffes | Giraffidae | |
| Reticulated Giraffe | *Giraffa camelopardalis reticulata* | 6 |
| Antelopes, Bisons, Cattles | Bovidae | |
| Addax | *Addax nasomaculatus* | 21 |
| Impala | *Aepyceros melampus* | 10 |
| Bubal Hartebeest | *Alcelaphus buselaphus* | 2 |
| Barbary Sheep | *Ammotragus lervia* | 22 |
| American Bison | *Bison bison* | 6 |
| Domestic Cattle | *Bos taurus* | 3 |
| Asian Water Buffalo | *Bubalus bubalis* | 1 |
| Wild Goat | *Capra aegagrus* | 1 |
| Domestic Goat | *C. hircus* | 24 |
| Yellow-backed Duiker | *Cephalophus silvicultor* | 5 |
| Thomson's Gazelle | *Gazella thomsoni* | 2 |
| Roan Antelope | *Hippotragus equinus* | 1 |
| Formosan Serow | *Naemorhedus swinhoei* | 12 |
| Beisa Oryx | *Oryx beisa* | 19 |
| Scimitar-horned Oryx | *O. dammah* | 2 |
| Gemsbok | *O. gazella* | 1 |
| Nyala | *Tragelaphus angasi* | 7 |
| Bongo | *T. euryceros* | 11 |
| Common Eland | *T. oryx* | 24 |
| Greater Kudu | *T. strepsiceros* | 2 |

## 3 Grass/Forage Supply

Currently, Taipei Zoo feeds fresh forage including napier grass (*Pennisetum purpureum*), mulberry (*Mours austrialis*), paper mulberry (*Broussonetia papyrifera*), indiacharcial trema (*Trema orientalis*), sweet potato (*Ipoema* spp.), and pangola hay (*Digitaris decumbens* S.). In 1997, Taipei Zoo bought 2600 kg of napier grass for daily use, and the remaining fresh forage totaled 60 kg daily. In 2001, volumes increased to 3100 kg of napier grass daily, with half supplied to the elephants. In 2001, mulberry increased to 160 kg, paper mulberry increased to 40 kg, and the indiacharcial increased to 80 kg, all fed on a daily basis, for an approximate (130 %) increase in forage usage (see table 2).

**Table 2.** Ungulate forage types used at the Taipei Zoo in 1997 and 2001.

| Common name | Scientific name | Daily amount | |
|---|---|---|---|
| | | 1997 | 2001 |
| Napier grass | *Pennisetum purpureum* | 2600 kg | 3100 kg |
| Mulberry | *Mours austrialis* | 60 kg | 160 kg |
| Paper Mulberry | *Broussonetia papyrifera* | Few | 40 kg |
| Indiacharcial Trema | *Trema orientalis* | Few | 80 kg |
| Sweet Potato | *Ipomoea batatas* | 7 kg | 7 kg |
| Pangola Hay | *Digitaria deumbens* | No account | 625 kg |

Also during that time frame (1997 to 2000), 5 other types of imported hay were introduced for use in feeding the ungulates along with the local pangola hay: timothy (*Phleum pratensis L.*), Bermuda grass (*Cynodon dactylon*), redtop (*Agrostis alba L.*), oat grass (*Helictotrichon sempervirens*) and rye grass (*Lolium maltiflorum L.*). These five different species of hays were imported to take advantage of five different harvesting seasons, as well as differing protein and fibre content of each species.

**Table 3.** The nutrition composition of ungulate feeds.

| feed \ nutrients | Energy Kcal/kg | DM % | CP % | EE % | CF % | Ash % | Ca mg/100g | P mg/100g |
|---|---|---|---|---|---|---|---|---|
| Napier grass | 490 | 15.6 | 1.6 | 0.6 | 5.1 | 1.8 | 3 | 7 |
| Mulberry | 822 | 25.6 | 6.1 | 1.2 | 3.7 | 2.6 | ND | ND |
| Paper Mulberry | 692 | 23.3 | 4.4 | 1.4 | 3.4 | 4.3 | ND | ND |
| Indiacharcial Trema | 711 | 23.6 | 4.5 | 1.2 | 4.3 | 3.0 | ND | ND |
| Pangola Hay | 2797 | 93.1 | 8.5 | 4.0 | 29.6 | 7.2 | ND | ND |

ND: no data

When the different species of hays were introduced, some animals experienced problems such as diarrhea, and soft feces, and refused to eat the different hay (Toddes 2001). After March, 2000, the use of imported hay was discontinued, leaving the pangola hay as the sole hay used at the Taipei Zoo. Because of the weather in Taipei is humid in summer and rainy in winter, the hay was difficult to keep from molding, so a temperature-controlled barn was built where the hay could be kept at a constant temperature of 16 to 18°. Two dehumidifiers are kept on all day to control the relative humidity $< 75\%$, and the mold problem has disappeared.

## 4 Pellet Adjustments and vitamin E added into the diet.

Hay and fresh forage comprise the main food for ungulates in captivity at the Taipei zoo. A soybean-and corn-based pellet, which provides more protein, energy, minerals, and vitamins, is also given to these ungulates. These pellets improve the nutrition capabilities of the fresh forage.

The formula for pelleted feeds usually consists of reasonably priced ingredients that are available locally. These feeds can include ingredients like wheat, ground corn, or other grains, soybean or corn oil, soybean meal, alfalfa meal, fibre sources like soybean hulls, ground corncobs, wheat bran, calcium supplements, trace mineral premix, and vitamin premix (Oftedal et al. 1996). A variety of pellets are utilized:

**Table 4.** Concentrates fed to the ungulates at the Taipei Zoo in 2001.

| Concentrate | Amount used daily |
|---|---|
| 12 % CP pellets | 360 kg |
| 18 % CP pellets | 90 kg |
| Alfalfa pellets + cubes | 230 kg |
| Elephant pellets | 83 kg |
| Oats | 60 kg |
| ADF16 pellets | 10 kg |
| Pig feed | 2 kg |

In January 1998, pellet formulations were reviewed and adjusted to improve nutrient balance. The main ingredients (90 %) were imported (American) corn, wheat, wheat bran, soybean meal, and alfalfa meal. Coconut meal, molasses, dibasic calcium phosphate, salt, and yeast made up the other 10 %.

Although NRC (1985) requirements for vitamin E in livestock suggest feed levels of 15–60 IU/kg dry matter for young calves (beef cattle), 15–20 mg/kg dry matter (growing lambs, NRC 1984), and 50 mg/kg in adult horses, 80–100 mg/kg for foals and reproducing females (NRC 1989), research from Dierenfeld and Traber (1992) suggests that dietary concentrations of 150 to 200 IU/kg dry matter may be more appropriate for zoo ungulates. Thus in January 1998, vitamin E content in 12 % CP pellets was increased from 100 IU/kg to 400 IU/kg.

**Table 5.** The nutrition composition of ungulate feeds.

| feed \ nutrients | Energy Kcal/kg | DM % | CP % | EE % | CF % | Ash % | Ca mg/100g | P mg/100g |
|---|---|---|---|---|---|---|---|---|
| 12% CP pellets | 3291 | 89.1 | 13.3 | 3.1 | 4.8 | 5.9 | 950 | 610 |
| Alfalfa pellets | 2486 | 89.8 | 18.1 | 2.6 | 21.7 | 9.2 | 1350 | 230 |
| Oats | 3500 | 87.0 | 8.5 | 1.8 | 0.7 | 0.8 | 20 | 108 |
| ADF16 | 2870 | 89.0 | 17.0 | 3.0 | 15.0 | 2.5 | 810 | 680 |

Summary of ungulate pellet adjustments made for collection animals at the Taipei Zoo:

1. The ingredients of the pellets were altered to include proteins from plants and grains only, animal proteins were removed, and vitamin E was adjusted from 100 IU/kg to 400 IU/kg.

2. Low protein pellets were used in the parasite control program. ADF 16 was imported for the giraffes.

3. Alfalfa cubes were introduced for use with the large ungulates.

# 5 Examples of Successful Implementation of Changes

## 5.1 Diet adjustment of the Formosa serow

An example of success of this program can be illustrated by responses of the Formosan Serow, with diet adjustments initiated in 1997. At that time the nutrition problems of feeding the serow was as follows:

1. Newborns were always weak and had diarrhea problems; winter deaths were numerous as animals could not survive the cold temperatures. From 1990 to 1997, there were no serow newborns on record.

2. Diets contained only forages, with no protein or energy concentrates.

3. Parasite re-infection problems were serious with the serow, causing soft excrement and diarrhea problems that couldn't be solved.

**Table 6.** Serow diet adjustment from 1997 to present.

| Food (g) | 1997 | 1998 to present |
|---|---|---|
| Mulberry | 4000 | 4000 |
| Paper Mulberry | 500 | 1000 |
| Indiacharcial Trema | 500 | 500 |
| Carrot | 500 | 500 |
| 12% CP pellets | — | 100 |
| Sweet potato | — | 300 |
| Vitamin mineral pre mix | 1 drop weekly | 2–3 times 5g per week |
| Vitamin E (50%) | 1 drop weekly | 2–3 times 5g per week |
| Min Rocks | *Ad libitum* | *Ad libitum* |

**Table 7.** Nutrient content before and after adjustment per animal.

| Nutrients | 1997 | 1998 to present |
|---|---|---|
| Energy Kcal (per kg DM) | 4159 | 5453 |
| DM (g) | 1298 | 1585 |
| CP (g) | 294 | 347.5 |
| EE (g) | 63.5 | 77.4 |
| Carbohydrates (g) | 605 | 742 |
| CF (g) | 191 | 224 |
| Ash (g) | 145 | 175 |
| Ca (mg) (addition) | | 2218 |
| P (mg) (addition) | | 1573 |

Summary of serow diet adjustments from 1998 to present.

1. By adding sweet potato, and low protein pellets daily the nutritional value of the feed was increased by 1294 Kcal, CP 43.5 g, Ca 2 g.

2. Vitamin E in the low protein pellets was increased from 100 IU/kg to 400 IU/kg. increasing vitamin E (50 %) 2–3 times a week, 5 g every time.

3. Forages were also presented on a tube instead of putting it on the ground; hence parasite re-infection rates were reduced greatly. Also, by putting the concentrated feed on an aluminum plate, the re-infection problem was brought under control.

From 1998 to 2001, the serow population more than doubled (increased from 5 animals to 12); the survival rate was attributed to the new feeding method.

### 5.2 Diet adjustment of the giraffe (Giraffa camelopardalis reticulata)

In the wild, giraffes eat leaves and browse as their main food (Wilkemeyer 2001), and may benefit both behaviorally and nutritionally from increased intake of green forages in captivity. In 1997 and 1998, 11 different types of fruits and vegetables were used for feeding the giraffes at Taipei Zoo. These foods contained high amounts of sugar and water, but had lower contents of fibre so the giraffe often displayed very soft excrement. From June 1998, to March 2000, there were 7 giraffe deaths in Taipei Zoo; in 5 of 7 deaths, pathologies were associated with digestive tract problems and parasite infections, and the other two had at least parasite infections (see table 8)

**Table 8.** The summary of the diagnosis of giraffe deaths at Taipei Zoo 1998–2000.

| Date of death | Age | Sex | Diagnosis |
|---|---|---|---|
| 2000/2/18 | 3 yrs | F | Parasite & lymph node infection |
| 2000/2/3 | 4 yrs | F | Bacterial enteritis |
| 1999/12/14 | 17 yrs | F | Nutrition deficiency |
| 1999/5/29 | 9 yrs | F | Ovarian tumor |
| 1999/2/28 | 1 yrs | F | Bloat, parasites |
| 1999/1/10 | 6 yrs | F | Rumen acidosis |
| 1998/6/25 | 0.5 yrs | M | Stress to White muscle disease |

In 1999, produce (fruits and vegetables) was decreased in the diet and more leaves and browse were added, and in 2000, all fruits and vegetables were discontinued as foods. Paper Mulberry, Indiacharcial Trema, and hay replaced them as the main foods. Fecal quality improved, as did overall nutritional balance (table 9).

**Table 9.** Giraffe diet adjustment at the Taipei Zoo.

| Food | 1997/1998 | 1999 to present |
|---|---|---|
| Papaya | 0.9 kg | — |
| Carrot | 1.2 kg | — |
| Sweet potato | 0.9 kg | — |
| Corn | 1 kg | — |
| Onion | 0.6 kg | — |
| Green onion | 0.3 kg | — |
| Tomato | 0.4 kg | |
| Celery | 0.5 kg | — |
| Stem vegetable | 0.5 kg | — |
| Lettuce | 1.1 kg | — |
| String beans | 1.1 kg | — |
| Oat | 0.4 kg | — |
| Mulberry | 1 kg | 2 kg |
| Paper Mulberry | 0.7 kg | 2.7 kg |
| Indiacharcial Trema | — | 2 kg |
| 18 % CP pellets | 3.3 kg | — |
| 12 % CP pellets | — | 3.6 kg |
| ADF16 pellets | — | 1 kg |
| Alfalfa pellets | — | 1.8 kg |
| Totally | 13.5 kg | 13.1 kg |
| Hay | Ad libitum | Ad libitum |
| Vitamin mineral per mix | 1 drop weekly | 2 3 times/weekly10 g |
| Vitamin E(50%) | 1 drop weekly | 2 3 times/weekly10 g |
| Mineral Rock | Ad libitum | Ad libitum |

**Table 10.** Nutrient content before and after adjustment per animal.

| Nutrients | 1997 | 1998 to present |
|---|---|---|
| Amount of account kg | 13.5 | 13.1 |
| Energy Kcal (per kg DM) | 15140 | 21268 |
| DM (g) | 4201 | 6761 |
| CP (g) | 594 | 1303 |
| EE (g) | 95.7 | 271 |
| Carbohydrates (g) | 1848 | 3634.6 |
| CF (g) | 556 | 965 |
| Ash (g) | 217.8 | 686.7 |

Summary of giraffe diet adjustment:

1. Simplification of the diet and discontinuation of all vegetables, fruits, and oats. Increase of fresh leaves and browse supplied.
2. Increase the vitamin E content from 100IU/kg to 400IU/kg.

Add anti parasite drops to pellets instead of using powder. In this manner the serious parasite problem was brought under control.

## 6 Parasite control program

Because of the group feedings of all ungulates at the Taipei Zoo, the humidity and heat, the re-infection cycle of parasite infection was a serious problem. For example, the giraffe deaths were due mainly to parasite infections. In the past, powder was used in the feeds for parasite control, but due to the fact that it was bitter and hard to swallow, and the mixture was not good, powder was discontinued. Beginning in May of 2000, Taipei Zoo started adding anthelmintic (Flubendazole 5 mg/kg body weight) in the compound pellets for parasite control. Numerous *Ascaris* spp. were purged from our Mongolian wild horses and zebras only one day after administration. The same method (Ivemectin 0.2 mg/kg body weight) was used in October, 2000, to purge nematodes, with good results.

Now, and in the future (every 3 months), as part of our parasite control, we examine the feces of these animals regularly. Results of the oral anthelminthic administration have been dramatic (see table 12 through 14).

**Table 11.** Time table of adding anthelmintic in the feed pellets.

| Dates | Drug and dosage |
|---|---|
| 2000/5 | Flubendazole 5 mg/kg BW |
| 2000/10 | Ivermectin 0.2 mg/kg BW<br>Cocci-ASSE 2,000 ppm |
| 2001/2 | Ivermectin 0.2 mg/kg BW |
| 2001/4 | Ivermectin 0.2 mg/kg BW |
| 2001/8 | Ivermectin 0.2 mg/kg BW |

**Table 12.** Result of fecal parasite examinations in native ungulates at the Taipei Zoo.

| Species | date | result | date | result | date | result | Date | result | Date | result |
|---|---|---|---|---|---|---|---|---|---|---|
| Formosan Serow | 2000/5 | N | 2000/10 | nematodes, whip worm | 2000/11 | coccidian, nematodes | 2000/12 | N | 2001/7 | N |
| Formosan Munjac | 2000/3 | N | 2000/5 | coccidian, nematodes | 2000/6 | nematodes | 2000/12 | N | 2001/7 | N |
| Formosan Sika deer | 2000/6 | N | 2001/7 | N | — | — | — | — | — | — |
| Formosan Wild Pig | 2000/3 | ascarid | 2000/6 | coccidia | 2001/7 | coccidia | — | — | — | — |

N: none found

**Table 13.** Results of fecal parasite examinations of desert ungulates at the Taipei Zoo.

| | Dates | result | Dates | result | dates | result | date | result | date | result | date | result |
|---|---|---|---|---|---|---|---|---|---|---|---|---|
| Addax | 2000/5 | Nematodes, coccidia | 2000/7 | N | 2000/9 | nema-todes | 2000/12 | N | 2001/7 | Whip worm, Nematodes, hook worm | 2001/11 | N |
| Scimitar Oryx | 2000/5 | nematodes | 2000/7 | N | 2000/9 | nema-todes | 2001/7 | nematodes | 2001/11 | N | — | — |
| Arabian Oryx | 2000/5 | nematodes | 2000/7 | N | 2000/9 | nema-todes | 2001/7 | nematodes | 2001/11 | N | — | — |
| Bactrian Camel | 2000/5 | nematodes | 2000/9 | Whip worm | 2001/2 | N | 2001/3 | N | — | — | — | — |
| Arabian Camel | 2000/5 | Whip worm, nematodes | 2000/7 | Whip worm | 2000/8 | nema-todes | 2000/10 | Whip worm, nematodes | 2000/11 | nematodes | — | — |
| | 2000/12 | N | 2001/1 | nematodes | 2001/2 | N | — | — | — | — | — | — |

N: none found

**Table 14.** Results of fecal parasite examinations on African ungulates at the Taipei Zoo following feed administration of anthelminthics.

| Species | Exam dates | Results |
|---|---|---|
| Reticulated Giraffe | 2001/2/15, 5/24, 7/22 | Nematodes |
| Common Eland | 2001/7/21 | Hook worm |
| Thomson's Gazelle | 2001/7/21 | N |
| Impala | 2001/7/21 | N |
| African Elephant | 2001/7/19 | N |
| Common Zebra | 2001/7/24 | N |
| Grevy's Zebra | 2001/7/19 | N |
| Hartmann s Mountain Zebra | 2001/7/20 | Nematodes |
| Black Rhinoceros | 2001/7/19 | N |
| Pigmy Hippopotamus | 2001/7/19 | N |
| Hippopotamus | 2001/7/19 | N |
| Nyala | 2001/7/24 | N |
| Greater Kudu | 2001/7/24 | N |
| Bubal Hartebeest | 2001/7/20 | N |
| Roan Antelope | 2001/7/22 | N |
| Gemsbok | 2001/7/20 | N |
| Beisa Oryx | 2001/7/24 | N |
| Barbary Sheep | 2001/7/19 | N |

N: none found

## 7 Conclusions

From 1997 Taipei Zoo adjusted the ungulate food supply, depending on the animals' food in the wild, and their digestive process. First of all they were given fresh Napier grass, Pangola hay, Paper Mulberry, Mulberry, and India-charcial Trema, as their main food. Because the climate in Taiwan is humid the hay storage must be kept in a dry storage to prevent mold. This was done by building a temperature and climate controlled building. The storage of hay was maintained at a constant temperature. Pelleted concentrates were added to suit particular needs. The vitamin E content in the 12 % CP pellet complete feeds was increased from 100 IU/kg to 400 IU/kg. Feed formulations were also maintained carefully for the diet change in the ungulates feeding. Since all the ungulates are fed together in group feedings, and the climate is humid and hot, the parasite control program was the other important point here. We also added and keep adding suitable doses of anthelminthics in the feed pellets to address the specific needs of certain species.

## Acknowledgment

Many thanks to Ellen S. Dierenfeld for her interest and help on nutritional information and comments. Thanks to Mary E. Allen for her helpful comments on the diet of giraffes.

## Reference

Dierenfeld, E. S.; Traber, M. G. (1992): Vitamin E status of exotic animals compared with livestock and domestics. In: *Vitamin E in health and disease* (L. Packer, J. Fuchs, eds.). Marcel Dekker, Inc., pp. 345 370.

Hofmann, R.R. (2000): The structure of digestive systems in the feeding of mammals: a comparative approach. In: *Zoo Animal Nutrition* (J. Nijboer et al., eds.). Fürth: Filander, pp. 163–181.

National Research Council (1884): *Nutrient requirements of sheep*. Washington, DC: National Academy Press.

National Research Council (1885): *Nutrient requirements of beef cattle*. Washington, DC: National Academy Press.

National Research Council, (1889): *Nutrient requirements of horses*. Washington, DC: National Academy Press.

Oftedal, O. T.; Baer, D. J.; Allen, M. E. (1996): The feeding and nutrition of herbivores. In: *Wild animals in captivity* (D. G. Kleiman, M. E. Allen, K. V. Thompson, S. Lumpkin, eds.). The University of Chicago Press, pp. 129–138.

Toddes, B. (2001): *Purchasing forage for a diverse group of exotic animals beyond the nutrition analysis*. AZA Nutrition Advisory Group, Fourth Conference on Zoo and Wildlife Nutrition, Orlando.

Wilkemeyer, C. A.; Carpenter, J. R. (2001): *Nutrient composition of selected tropical browse species fed to zoo animal in Hawaii*. AZA Nutrition Advisory Group, Fourth Conference on Zoo and Wildlife Nutrition, Orlando.